W9-AFZ-149

SMALL ARMS

FROM THE CIVIL WAR TO THE PRESENT DAY

SMALL ARMS

FROM THE CIVIL WAR TO THE PRESENT DAY

MARTIN J. DOUGHERTY

BARNES
& NOBLE
BOOKS
NEW YORK

This edition published by Barnes & Noble, Inc.,
by arrangement with Amber Books Ltd
2005 Barnes & Noble Books

M 10 9 8 7 6 5 4 3 2 1

ISBN: 0-7607-6329-1

ARTWORK CREDITS: All artworks **Aerospace/Art-tech** except: **Amber Books**: 28, 99, **John Batchelor**: 10, 11, 23, 31 (both), 33 (b), 34, 38 (b), 44, 45 (t), 47 (r), 49, 52 (t), 56, 57, 61, 64, 78, 83, 84, 109, 117 (b), 118, 119, 120 (t), 122, 123 (both), 124, 125, 130 (both), 146, 148, 150, 152, 154 (both),157, 158, 159, 161, 163, 166 (t), 170 (t), 171, 183, 205, 206, **DeAgostini**: 43 (l), 87 (b), 90, 94, 96, 97, 98, 100, 102 (both), 106, 107, 108, 111 (both), 117 (t), 126, 127, 131 (r), 142, 153, 156, 165, 168, 178, 180 (t), 181, 182, 188 (both), 168, 198 (t), 201, 202, 203 (r), **Salmander**: 12, 73, 74, 75, 76, 85

PICTURE CREDITS: All pictures **Aerospace/Art-tech** except: **Amber Books**: 114, **Corbis**: 8, 9, 11, 28, 29, 30 (r),32, 67, 71, 72 (t,) 74, 76, 89, 113, 138,147, 174, 177, 187, 191, **Heckler & Koch US**: 92, 105 (l), **Mary Evans Picture Library**: 35, **Military Picture Library**: 195, 196, **Popperfoto**: 30 (l), **Private Collection**: 19, **TRH**: 13, 40 (US Army), 48, 55, 66, 72 (b), 78, 81, 86, 90, 90 (Dept of Defense), 97 US Dept of Defence, 107, 122 (Royal Marines), 112, 116, 133 (both), 162, 173, 179 (l), 192, 194, 197, 198, 200, 207 (r), 213, 214, 215 (both), 216, 217, 219, **Ukraine State Archive**: 125, 128, 149, 157, 161, **US Dept of Defence**: 6, 17, 18, 25, 199, 205

Produced by
Amber Books Ltd

Printed in Singapore

CONTENTS

WINTER

INTRODUCTION

Throughout history, the infantryman has depended on his personal weapon in combat; the development of gunpowder and the subsequent dominance of the firearm did little to change this fundamental fact. The past 150 years have witnessed the development of a range of outstanding, and in some cases highly specialized, small arms – from automatic pistols through to machine guns and handheld rocket launchers – that have changed the face of modern combat.

The use of tools has allowed humans to dominate this planet. Tools permit environments to be shaped and threats to be survived by creatures who are really rather puny compared to the natural and animal hazards they face. At a significant disadvantage when faced by ferocious predators, early humans learned to make specialized tools – weapons – to assist them in the hunt and fend off rival creatures. But while the very first arms race may have been between early man and beast, competition between groups of humans ensured ever more effective weapons were necessary for survival and success. As stone gave way to bronze and eventually to steel, the tools of attack and defence grew ever more sophisticated.

Left: A joint force of US and Iraqi personnel on patrol in 2004. Despite the high-tech weaponry available to Coalition forces it is the infantry squad, armed with rifles and light support weapons, that must exert control over the region.

The first weapons

Some vital truths soon emerged. Firtly, it is much better to be able to inflict damage on a threatening creature or person from beyond the range of its fangs or tusks. For this reason the first projectile weapons were invented: hurled rocks, axes and boomerangs, thrown spears and javelins, and bolts and arrows shot by tension in a bowstave or crossbow prod. Secondly, it was obvious that effective weapons must be easy to use and reliable. Complex or unreliable systems were likely to get the user gored or speared before he could react.

Other considerations may also be important, such as concealability or ease of carry and deployment, and there are times when the intimidation factor of a weapon is important. However well-armed and capable the user may be, under most circumstances it is better to have suspects or assailants run off or surrender than to blast holes in them – with all the moral and legal issues that raises.

These, then, are the hallmarks of a great small arm – reliability, ease of use and effectiveness, coupled perhaps with ease of carry and a menacing and businesslike appearance.

Gunpowder

The advent of gunpowder and the subsequent dominance of firearms did not change these factors. Small arms – originally the term referred to gunpowder weapons smaller than cannon – began as clumsy affairs of somewhat dubious effectiveness. It was quicker and easier to train a soldier to use a firearm than a bow, but the weapons available were simply not very good.

The answer was to make them better, and so a succession of weapons emerged offering constant refinements and innovations. Some were poor, some were quite good – and some were truly great. It is these great small arms that we will study in this book; how they worked and what made them

Left: Charge for the guns! Flanked by cannon and under fire from the batteries that were its target, only the iron discipline and tremendous fighting spirit of the Light Brigade allowed it to reach its objective. Although successful in sabring the Russian gunners, the Brigade was effectively ruined as a fighting force.

better than their contemporaries. We will chart the progress over the past one-and-a-half centuries in terms of the finest small arms of the time. We shall consider weapons that, despite their limitations, nevertheless managed to enter widespread use. There are also a few ideas that, while fascinating in their own right, have justly earned their place on the back burner. The quest for better weapons continues today and likely will never end.

This volume charts that quest from the percussion cap firearms and powder charges of the American Civil War to today's high-tech, precision engineered masterpieces. Any tool is only as good (and as well-intentioned) as its user. Small arms have received much bad press over the years, and it is often forgotten that a weapon can be used to protect innocents, to deter aggression, and to defend vital interests just as easily as it can be used to facilitate crime or stupidity. When a car pulls up and armed men jump out, our reaction depends very much upon whether they are armed robbers or law enforcers responding to a call for help.

No matter how great a weapon may be, it is an inert object with no will of its own. It is the user who is responsible for what is done with it, and how well. The great small arms featured in this book will be judged on their merit as tools, not by what might have been done with them, whether honourably or not. It is for us to decide what we will do with them, and to take responsibility for what happens.

The ascent of firearms

The value of missile weaponry on the battlefield was well established by the time the first 'hand cannon' appeared. Javelinmen, slingers and archers – and later crossbowmen – were a vital part of warfare. Their ability to strike from a distance was an essential element of siege warfare and could be crucial on the battlefield.

The first 'hand guns' were deployed towards the end of the Middle Ages. These were little more than a pot on a handle, from which a projectile could be hurled with little accuracy or range. Early firearms were not very effective – indeed they were outperformed by almost every other form of missile weapon – yet their use persisted and in time they came to replace other projectile weapons.

Right: Less than a century after Balaclava and the face of warfare has changed beyond recognition. This 1927 photograph of the US National Guard illustrates the range of equipment available to the modern infantryman: rifles, mortars, grenades and machine guns, backed up by a tank and its nemesis, an anti-tank gun.

The reason for this rise to dominance is one of simple progression. As each advance in weaponry replaced the last – from sling to bow to crossbow – the factor that decided its eventual adoption was not whether it was more effective, but whether it was easier and faster to master than the preceding weapon. When early firearms first made their presence felt there was still rivalry for supremacy between longbows and crossbows. There were arguments in favour of both, but the advent of effective gunpowder weapons changed everything; both bow and crossbow passed out of common use.

As firearms became generally accepted, ways were found to make them easier to carry and use, mainly by making them smaller and lighter, and by creating new means to initiate firing. These weapons, firing a heavy lead bullet from a smooth bore, were the ancestors of today's small arms.

The decline of armour

These early small arms had various names, such as musket and arquebus, and underwent a steady evolution. They were heavy and awkward (early musketeers required a rest to support their weapon), but their usefulness was well established. Armour able to stop a musket ball was heavy and incredibly expensive at a time when tactics emphasized mobility, and strategy dictated the use of larger armies of cheap troops rather than the earlier small forces of armoured cavalry.

The dominance of the knight was killed by economics, not by musketballs, since for a certain amount of cash it was generally more effective to field a number of musketeers, pikemen and light cavalry than its equivalent value in knights.

Armoured cavalry remained a feature of warfare for many years, but their full platemail gradually gave way to cheaper half-armour and then to the back-and-breastplate and helmet of the cuirassier. The last gallant charges of the French heavy cavalry in 1914 were finally swept away by machine guns, barbed wire and rapid rifle fire of entrenched infantry.

The musket, then, was not the cause of the knight's demise but merely a harbinger of doom. Despite their clumsiness, early muskets were effective enough: the King's Musketeers, an élite unit that served as the French king's bodyguard, fought primarily with matchlock muskets.

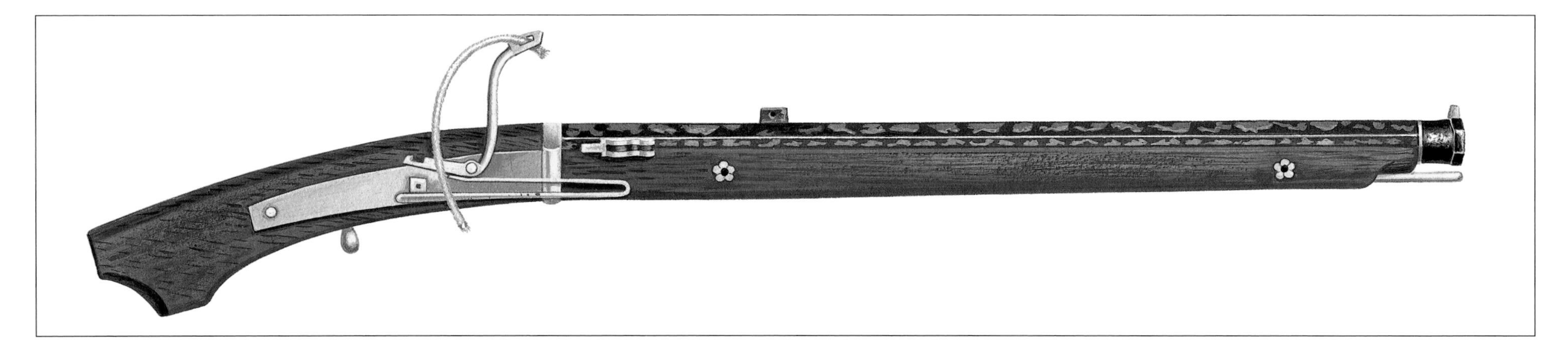

Matchlocks

The invention of the matchlock made the firearm viable and muskets were fielded in ever-increasing numbers over the course of the sixteenth century. A length of burning slow-match was held over a priming pan on the musket. This was filled with fine gunpowder. Pulling the trigger brought the slow-match into contact with this priming powder, igniting it. The resulting flame passed through the 'touch-hole' and into the main charge in the weapon's breech. Assuming the powder did not simply 'flash in the pan', but actually ignited the main charge, an instant later the bullet would be on its way with a roar and a huge cloud of dirty grey smoke.

The musket gave a common footsoldier the power to bring down even the best swordsman without ever coming to grips. The implications of this for the existing social order in Japan were so horrifying that, despite using musket-armed troops quite effectively in a number of internal conflicts, the Shogunate took drastic steps to get rid of these weapons. This was possible in an island nation prepared to cut itself off from the rest of the world. In Europe, however, any such refusal to embrace the future of military technology would be national suicide.

Thus the arms race continued. Matchlocks were replaced by fire-lock mechanisms, thus named because they 'created' fire by striking a piece of flint or pyrites against steel. Early versions used a wheel-lock, a clockwork-like mechanism, but the more efficient flintlock soon followed and became standard until the introduction of the percussion cap well over a century later.

Black powder

Black powder, or gunpowder, was probably invented in China before AD 1000. It consists of saltpetre, sulphur and charcoal and is defined as a 'low explosive'. Black powder burns relatively slowly and unevenly; recoil is a shove rather than a sharp blow.

Nitrocellulose-based propellants were used to create the first 'smokeless powder' in the late 1800s. These were soon superceded by pre-packaged propellants, such as cordite and guncotton. Modern propellants burn much faster than black powder and expel the projectile with a 'kick' rather than a 'shove'.

Above: An early matchlock musket. Slow to load, short-ranged and unreliable, the matchlock nevertheless revolutionized warfare as the first effective infantry gunpowder weapon.

Firepower on the battlefield

The adoption of firearms for mass armies, and the introduction of light cannon that could function usefully on the battlefield, made firepower the decisive factor in the wars of the period. In truth, contemporary firearms were not very effective. Without any real means to aim (and in any case lacking the accuracy to hit what was aimed at beyond a hundred yards or so), they were generally used in massed volleys aimed at a similar mass of enemy troops rather than at individuals. The muskets of the seventeenth century to the early nineteenth were in reality less effective than longbows in every respect, but the ease with which hastily raised troops could be trained to use them made the musket the battlefield weapon of choice.

One of the tactical innovations introduced by King Gustavus II Adolphus of Sweden during the Thirty Years War was the first support weapon.

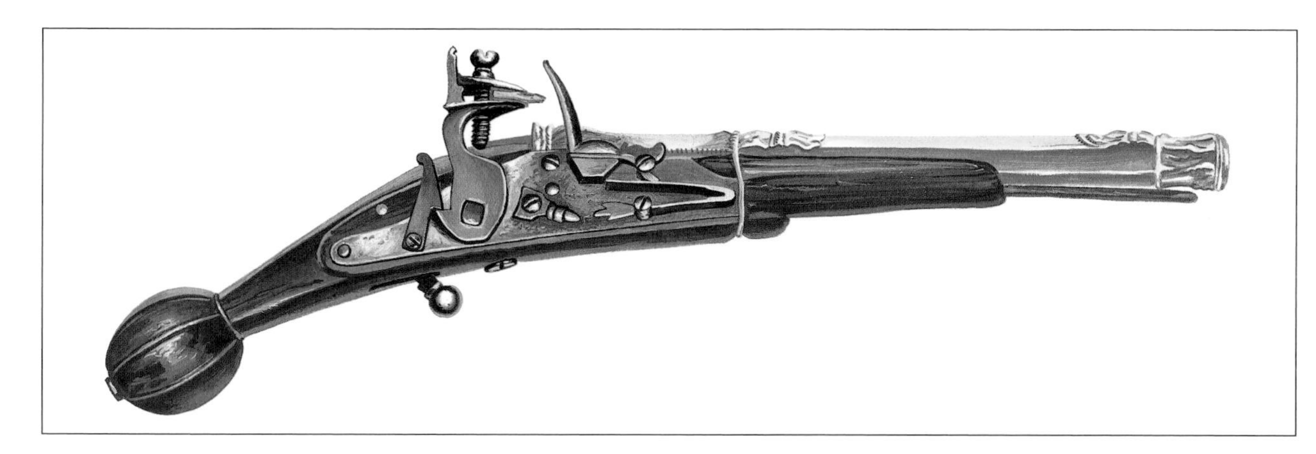

Left: A flintlock pistol. Virtually useless beyond sword range, the flintlock pistol was nevertheless a useful status symbol for officers and a handy weapon for self-defence. Swordsmanship took years to learn but anyone could point a handgun and press the trigger.

Below: American War of Independence re-enactors vanish in the smoke from their muskets. In a protracted firefight troops – especially those clad in off-white or grey – became virtually invisible in their own smokescreen. The only solution was to 'pour it in' and hope for the best.

Most modern infantry formations include one or more light machine guns or grenade launchers to augment the firepower of the unit's rifles. Gustavus Adolphus's support weapon of choice was a fairly small cannon on a light and mobile mount. Like today's support weapons, these cannon used the same technology as the small arms they supported, but were larger, heavier and more deadly.

Personal defence

At this time firearms became practical for personal defence. A flintlock pistol could be carried loaded but uncocked and made an excellent deterrent as well as a reasonable weapon. Pistols were horribly inaccurate and in truth were effective at about only the same range as a sword, but nevertheless they were felt to be useful weapons for cavalry, officers and special troops, such as colour guards. Their main role, just as today, was as a sidearm for personal defence when all else had failed. With only one shot available, a pistol could be a liability, so some came with miniature bayonets or (more practically) a brass-weighted butt for use as a remarkably effective club.

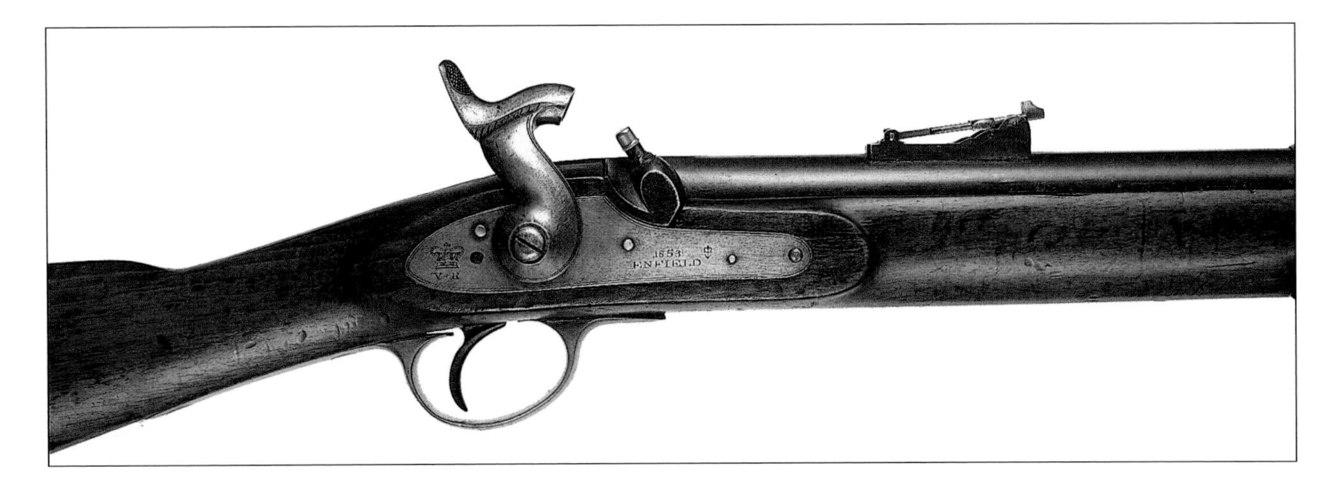

Left: A percussion rifle-musket. Although still muzzle-loaded with black powder and a ball or bullet, percussion weapons were a vast improvement on flintlocks. Placing a cap on the nipple to be struck by the hammer was faster than priming the pan, and firing was far more reliable.

The triumph of the flintlock

Flintlock firearms had reached the pinnacle of their development by the end of the eighteenth century. The standard infantry musket was an effective weapon on the battlefield, and a sharpshooter stood a reasonable chance of hitting his target at 100 metres (330 feet). Rifled weapons – not 'rifles' as we know them today but flintlock weapons with a rifled barrel – were available to equip sportsmen and specialist troops. Great havoc was wrought in the American War of Independence with Kentucky Long Rifles and in the Peninsular War with the Baker Rifle. These weapons were slow to load and gave away their position with a huge cloud of smoke, but they placed controlled killing power in the hands of a skilled user.

Percussion caps and cartridges

The invention of the percussion cap in the nineteenth century can be considered the birth of truly modern firearms. Introduced from about 1820, percussion caps contain a chemical compound called fulminate that explodes on impact. Rather than initiate firing with a flint or other unreliable mechanism, a percussion cap would detonate when struck sharply. Replacing the flint with a 'hammer' meant that there were fewer parts to go wrong and firing was more reliable, especially in wet conditions.

Most weapons in the mid-nineteenth century still used a separate ball or bullet, powder charge and percussion cap (most of the small arms deployed in the American Civil War were 'Rifle-Muskets' of this type), but all-in-one cartridges with the cap (known as a primer when it came as part of the cartridge casing) embedded in the rear of the cartridge case became available. The ammunition in common use today is not very different from this kind of round.

Percussion caps and all-in-one cartridges created exciting new possibilities. Breech-loading weapons, which could be reloaded lying down, were now possible. Given that military small arms were now accurate out to about 500 metres (1640 feet), this offered some important advantages over troops armed with more traditional weapons. Single-shot firearms offered a greatly increased rate of fire over musket-type weapons – but the true innovation was the repeating weapon.

Repeaters

By the middle of the nineteenth century practical repeating firearms were available and indeed were becoming fairly common. For personal defence, a good revolver offered sufficient firepower to deal with most close-range threats. In mass combat, early repeating rifles and carbines, manually reloaded from an internal magazine using a bolt or lever action, allowed very rapid fire. Close support weapons in the form of early Maxim and Gatling machine guns augmented infantry firepower.

Although combat troops carried bayonets for close action (and still do), and cavalry still considered the sword to be the weapon of decision, the reality by 1860 was that firearms dominated the battlefield. The gun was entering its golden age, and whoever had the best ones could dominate any situation.

Fouling

Black powder weapons were very prone to fouling – becoming clogged with residue from burning gunpowder. This residue also contains potassium salts, which suck moisture out of the air and causes dampness inside the bore, leading to rust. Modern propellants cause less fouling, although residue can still build up after sustained firing

Right: Rifled weapons were used successfully in the American War of Independence, mainly by members of irregular or 'special' units, such as this buckskin-clad sharpshooter from Morgan's Riflemen. Regular 'Line' troops continued to use smoothbore muskets for many years.

Principles of operation

Modern small arms all work in more or less the same way. Ammunition is self-contained and is initiated by a sharp blow on a small initiating charge (the primer), which ignites the larger propellant charge in the cartridge itself.

The propellant does not explode, but rather deflagrates, a process halfway between burning and explosion. Deflagration creates a large amount of gas in the confined space of the weapon's firing chamber, consequently causing high pressure. The firing chamber is sealed in most directions, but the gas pressure can find release by pushing a non-fixed plug out of the chamber. That plug is of course the bullet, which in the case of all rifled weapons is a tight enough fit in the barrel that gas cannot escape around it. The bullet is pushed up the barrel, and induced to spin by grooves (known as rifling) in the barrel lining.

The greater the gas pressure in the chamber, the higher velocity at which the round emerges. The length of the weapon's barrel is also a factor in muzzle velocity, since a long barrel means more time spent being pushed by the expanding gases.

Once the bullet has cleared the barrel the hot gas can escape, creating the characteristic muzzle flash. It is estimated that as much as 40 per cent of the energy produced during firing is lost in the muzzle discharge. In the case of very powerful weapons with short barrels, the blast can be quite spectacular, which may give away the firer's position.

Left: The muzzle flash from this SA80 assault rifle is clearly visible against the darkened sky. The short length of the SA80 is an advantage in urban or mechanized warfare; the shorter a weapon's barrel, however, the more noticeable the muzzle flash will be.

Muzzle flash

Even modern weapons produce a noticeable 'muzzle flash' and local disturbance caused by propellant gases escaping the muzzle. This may give away the firer's position, especially at night.

A 'flash hider' is an extension to the barrel, but with a greater diameter, that allows the flash to dissipate a little before escaping.

Recoil and loading

For every action there is an equal and opposite reaction. The bullet is accelerated in one direction and the weapon in the opposite. Due to the vastly greater mass of the weapon, it will not move fast or far, but recoil can be a factor for many weapon users. A powerful handgun will be rather unpleasant to fire for some people, while a fully automatic weapon may jump around alarmingly. The reason a weapon tends to lift its muzzle upwards (and sometimes to the side) is due to the mechanics of how it is held or mounted, its balance point and other factors. Good weapon design can reduce 'felt' recoil while some otherwise excellent weapons are rendered almost unusable by their recoil characteristics.

In many cases, the weapon's recoil can be turned to advantage, sending the bolt, slide or even barrel back to open the breech, eject the spent cartridge and chamber a new round. Auto-loading and fully automatic weapons use a variety of mechanisms to achieve the same end – getting another round into the chamber and ready to fire.

It is actually easier to make a fully-automatic weapon than a self-loader. In the latter, an interrupter holds the hammer or firing pin in the cocked position as the reloading cycle completes itself, requiring that the trigger be released and pulled again to fire the new round.

Without such an interrupter device, the weapon will fire again as soon as reloading is complete, and go on firing until the trigger is released or ammunition is no longer available.

A similar capability exists in some manual repeating weapons, for example shotguns fitted with 'slam-fire' capability. If the user holds down the trigger and works the pump, the weapon will discharge as soon as the new round is in position. Some early revolvers worked in a similar fashion, allowing the user to hold the trigger and 'fan' the hammer back with the other hand for rapid, if rather less than accurate, fire.

Firearms in combat

The purpose of all weapons is the same – to disable, damage or destroy people and objects. In the case of most small arms, their relative worth is determined by their ability to bring down a living target, usually a human one.

To the typical firearms user, lethality is, strangely enough, not the key issue. It does not matter very much whether the target dies immediately, later or not at all, so long as he rapidly ceases to present a threat. With the exception of assassins and perhaps troops engaged in a bitter attritional struggle, most users either do not care if the target dies or would actually prefer that he did not.

There are many reasons for this. Morally, there is less guilt about injuring as opposed to killing someone. Legally, the implications of a mistaken or 'excessive force' shooting are much less severe if the victim survives. Logistically, a wounded soldier absorbs more manpower in the form of evacuation, first aid, surgery and aftercare than a corpse.

Stopping power

What is critically important is the ability of a weapon to render a target immediately harmless. This is the 'stopping power' so desired by firearms users. A bullet, travelling fast, has an immense amount of kinetic energy (energy of movement), which is a function of mass and velocity. Kinetic energy depends directly upon mass but upon the square of velocity, so while doubling the mass of a bullet will double its kinetic energy, doubling velocity gives it four times the energy.

On the face of it, the ideal weapon would seem to be one that shoots a speck of dust at nearly the speed of light, but in practice the matter is more complex. Stopping power is all about dumping energy into the target, not just having it. A bullet that tears right through the target and keeps going at some speed retains much of its energy. Not only is this hazardous for anyone downrange from the target but it is also highly inefficient.

This concept has been demonstrated on a practical basis by many big game hunters who chose to carry small-calibre, high-velocity rifles rather than the traditional big-bore big game rifles. Their victims were more likely to be enraged than disabled. More than a few hunters shot an elephant that subsequently died from internal trauma – but only after goring and trampling the intrepid hunter. A bullet that stops in the target not only poses no threat to anyone else, but also dumps all of its kinetic energy, resulting in massive shock and tissue damage, and delivering a physical blow that may well knock the target down.

There are several ways to increase the stopping power of ammunition. Some, such as using explosive bullets, are prohibited by various conventions (technically, strafing personnel targets with an aircraft's guns, loaded with explosive ammunition for air-to-air combat, is a violation of the Geneva and Hague Conventions) and may be less than practical for technical reasons. Legal and effective methods of increasing stopping power include giving rounds a hollow or soft tip to cause expansion in the target, making them slightly unstable so that they 'tumble' after hitting the flesh of the target and simply making the round large and fat rather than needle-like. Technical innovations such as the Glaser Safety Round also increase stopping power while having other benefits, including a lower propensity to ricochet.

Right: A Lebanese soldier fires his M16 assault rifle at Druze militiamen during 1983. Note the spent 5.56mm cartridges in midair. The M16's straight-through design helps absorb recoil and makes it highly controllable under rapid or full-automatic fire.

Left: A US patrol in Vietnam. Firefights in the jungle tended to be brutal close-range affairs. Lightweight assault rifles are ideal for this kind of maximum-intensity fighting against an enemy that can be spotted at best fleetingly. Automatic fire may suppress hostiles even if hits are not made.

Non-lethal options

Any small arm round can be lethal if it strikes a vital organ, and wound shock or bleeding can kill the target even if the original injury is not life threatening. The surest way to disable a target is to deliver massive amounts of trauma in the form of kinetic energy to a vital location – the more powerful the round, the more likely this is in most cases. A person can be quite satisfactorily disabled, however, by ammunition designed not to be lethal. 'Beanbag' rounds fired from a shotgun do not penetrate and will only kill under very unusual circumstances, but they are quite effective in 'stopping' the target, albeit temporarily and only at short range.

As already noted, it does not always matter so much to the user of a weapon whether the target is dead, dying or merely disabled. The important thing is that he is no longer a threat. The typical shooter requires an immediate result rather than a fatality in a couple of minutes.

Tactical shooting

For the personal defence shooter, any use of a weapon is likely to be at very close range and short notice. Particularly when using a handgun for self-defence, combat is a matter of 'deploy-point-shoot', usually without using sights. Hitting the target is a matter of hand-eye coordination. A good grip on the weapon is vital, and a good stance certainly helps, if the round is to go where the eye and brain are telling it to. Personal defence shooting often takes place in a very short time frame and in a context where taking cover may not be effective. By the time the shooter has looked around for suitable cover, his assailant may have fired several times or reached close quarters. Thus personal defence is a matter – usually – of putting sufficient rounds into the target to disable him, and doing it quickly.

When protracted gunfights do sometimes occur, factors like ease of reloading and size of magazine capacity become critical. This is more likely to involve law enforcement personnel than civilian self defence shooters. When it does happen, a small-scale gunfight begins to resemble a battlefield situation in some ways.

Soldiers on the battlefield are generally armed with rifles that can hit what they are aimed at out

Cartridges

A cartridge was originally a paper package or even a pot containing a musket ball and sufficient powder for one shot. Modern cartridges also contain everything needed for a shot – bullet, propellant and primer.

A modern cartridge has a brass case to enclose the propellant and to hold the components in place. Once the bullet is sent on its way the 'spent brass' is ejected from the chamber to allow a new round to be loaded.

Right: US Marines on a MOUT (Military Operations in Urban Terrain) exercise. The support gunner is armed with a box-fed FN Minimi light machine gun using the same 5.56mm ammunition as his squad mate's Colt Commando carbine. Note the spare ammunition belt.

to 1500 metres (4921 feet) or more. However, most people (even highly trained soldiers) cannot hit a target at that range without expending enormous amounts of ammunition. More commonly, combat takes place at much shorter ranges, generally less than 300 metres (984 feet), while in urban terrain it may often be at 'civilian gunfight' ranges.

No matter who is involved, once a gunfight has gone beyond the close-range, self-defence situation it becomes a rather different matter. Armed combat is about the use of cover and concealment, and of fire and movement.

Cover is defined as something that will prevent an incoming bullet from striking its target. Hard cover such as walls and some parts of a car will grant a shooter partial immunity to hostile fire – only the body parts he must expose to shoot can be hit. Concealment, on the other hand, makes it difficult to see a shooter and thus to target him, but will not stop a bullet. Bushes, fences and even cardboard boxes can be used to gain a tactical advantage from concealment, but stray fire still represents a major hazard.

Battle range

Only a madman stands around in the open blazing away once a protracted gunfight has started. Within seconds everyone involved will be in cover, concealed, or at the very least trying to make themselves a difficult target by crouching, lying on the ground or running towards cover.

This is where the 'battle range' of weapons, among other things, becomes very important. All weapons have an accurate (or effective) range, but there is simply no way the average user can hit anything at this range amid the stress and chaos of gunplay. Battle range is a measure of the distance at which a shooter has a reasonable chance of hitting his target. As a rule, the battle range of a weapon is proportional to its effective range. The upshot of this is that an average shooter has a decent chance of hitting a target at 30 metres (98.5 feet) with a rifle or carbine, but virtually none with a handgun.

With everyone moving or under cover and only small, fleeting targets to aim at, the skill of the people involved is a decisive factor, along with the physical capabilities of the weapons they possess. This assumes that everyone stays put and tries to eliminate the opposition by shooting at them. The alternative is to manoeuvre for a better position.

Fire and manoeuvre

Manoeuvre is dangerous since it exposes the moving person to enemy fire. Most trained firearms wielders use fire and manoeuvre tactics, with some of the unit members directing fire to suppress opposition, while others move to a better position from which to shoot or make a close assault.

The principles of fire and manoeuvre are the same whether the attack is being made by an army platoon using suppressive fire from machine guns, or by a police officer covered by his partner's handgun. The aim is to keep the enemy defensive (or disable them) while others move up.

Weapon characteristics are important here, too. It is not possible to suppress an enemy without making him feel endangered enough to duck into cover. This requires the expenditure of a fair amount of ammunition – or the threat of it – and calls for high-capacity weapons.

Sometimes manoeuvre may allow a clear shot at the target, for example by flanking his cover, in which case accuracy is again vital. On other occasions it may be necessary to make a 'close assault' on the enemy position. For this a short, easy to wield weapon is useful: ideally one with good stopping power. Shotguns and submachine guns are effective in this role, which is why they are frequently used by forces such as hostage-rescue units, who may need to storm buildings and other positions. It may of course be possible to get into a firing position and demand the surrender of the hostiles. In this case again the appearance of the weapon is critical, since the target must perceive sufficient threat to make him choose to surrender.

Left: A US Marine armed with M16 rifle and M203 grenade launcher gives cover as his squad mates advance during a training exercise in 2004. Urban warfare is increasingly the norm, and training must keep pace if military forces are to remain effective.

Right: Australian hostage-rescue personnel of the Tactical Assault Group (TAG), armed with submachine guns and handguns. The SMG is an ideal weapon for urban combat, combining firepower with small size. Equipment of this sort is common to special units worldwide.

Accuracy and snipers

While most weapons users, from civilians through law enforcers to infantry soldiers, need a weapon that is both easy to use and carry, and also effective at the ranges likely to be encountered, some personnel can afford to carry a rather more specialized weapon. One example is the sniper.

Snipers, by definition, shoot from concealment and ideally at an unsuspecting target. While they may have to travel some distance overland to reach a firing point or to evade pursuit, they generally engage in little tactical movement, so can carry large, heavy or relatively fragile weapons.

Accuracy is vital in a sniping weapon, of course, as is lethality. There will not usually be a chance for a second shot. This is especially true of police and hostage-rescue snipers, who must take whatever opportunity they get, however fleeting. Failure will mean needless deaths among innocents or law-enforcement colleagues. Police snipers can afford to use quite temperamental and fragile weapons, since they do not travel far from vehicles and can constantly maintain their weapons. Military snipers, however, require weapons that will function even under difficult conditions, such as after being carried cross-country through snow or desert.

Snipers are sometimes called upon to destroy equipment and machinery. During World War I snipers were issued with armour-piercing ammunition to enable them to disable machine guns by shooting into the breech – quite a feat across trench lines, in the dark and the rain, and possibly while all manner of commotion was going on nearby. A good weapon is vital under such circumstances and a great one is highly desirable. However, the characteristics of the person shooting the gun are just as important.

Great small arms

This is true for all weapons; a great gun will not turn a mediocre shooter into a marksman. What it will do is allow him to function to the very best of his ability. More importantly, the right weapon grants its user all manner of tactical advantages: concealment, deployment, reliability and stopping power. Most gunfights are won by the first person to get a shot on target. The finest sniper rifle may not be the best weapon against a knifeman charging from three metres' range. Similarly, the world's best combat shotgun is almost entirely useless against a rifleman 200 metres (656 feet) away.

Thus there is no single 'best weapon in the world': each has its own applications and weaknesses. It is up to the user to choose the right weapon for the job and to apply it in an effective manner.

HANDGUNS

One of the commonest uses for a weapon is as a 'sidearm' – a light, easy to carry weapon for personal defence. Sidearms must combine a reasonable effectiveness (at least at close range) with compactness and lightness. To be any use, a sidearm must be carried all the time, so one that is heavy, gets in the way or catches on things is unsuitable.

The medieval knight's symbol of status was his sword, but against a heavily armoured opponent it was at best of marginal use. Thus the sword was carried as a sidearm and a heavier weapon – a lance, mace, axe or gigantic two-handed sword, for example – was taken to the field of combat. If the 'battle' weapon were lost, or if the knight were surprised and unable to obtain a better weapon, the sword would have to serve.

So it is today with firearms. No one would choose to go into battle armed with only a handgun; combat troops carry rifles, machine guns and grenade launchers. For those who do not expect to need to defend themselves in the immediate future, however, a handgun is an excellent choice – it is usually small, lightweight and easy to carry or conceal. In many combat situations – in tight spaces or when both hands are required for other purposes – a more unwieldy weapon might be inconvenient. A pistol or revolver also makes a useful backup in case a 'battle' weapon malfunctions, runs out of ammunition or is lost.

Left: Handguns find many uses within the military, mainly as weapons for security personnel or other non-infantry troops. This 9mm Browning BDA9 makes a fine sidearm, but is no substitute for an assault rifle under most circumstances.

Thus while security and police personnel may carry handguns while on duty to defend themselves or their charge, if combat is deemed likely they will arm themselves with more appropriate weapons such as shotguns, rifles or submachine guns.

Handgun advantages

Despite all its limitations in terms of range, accuracy and hitting power, the handgun is a fine weapon and probably the best choice for personal defence, since it can be deployed quickly in a conflict situation. Concealment is also a factor – few other weapons can be carried concealed but still readily available. Even when carried openly, a holstered handgun is more socially acceptable than a rifle or shotgun slung on the back or cradled in the arms. This is important for security and law-enforcement personnel, as well as for military guards who must deal with civilians.

Handguns, simply defined, are small firearms capable of being used with one hand (although a two-handed grip may be desirable for accuracy) and using a short and relatively large calibre round. Handguns come in three basic types: revolvers, self-loaders and derringers. As a rule, while most handguns have sights, they tend to be used at ranges where hand-to-eye co-ordination is more important than careful aim. For this reason some weapons have no sights. Eliminating the protruding sights means a concealed weapon is less likely to snag on clothing.

One important factor in handgun design is 'pointability': the ability of a user to know instinctively where the weapon is aimed from the feel of the weapon in his hand. In a self-defence situation the ability to look at the target, point the weapon and hit what is aimed at is probably the most important factor – with the ability to 'stop' the target immediately coming in a close second.

Above: Handguns can be a practical option for users who need to keep their hands free to perform other tasks. This police SWAT (Special Weapons And Tactics) officer is ready to use his weapon even as he carries a child to safety.

Revolvers

Revolvers are simple, rugged and easy to use. A number of rounds (usually, but not always, six) are held in separate chambers of the central 'cylinder' and rotated one by one into position to fire. Although a few experimental weapons have used recoil force to rotate the cylinder, most weapons are manually operated by either pulling back the hammer to its cocked position or by trigger action.

Modes of operation

Revolvers can be fired using 'double-action' or 'single-action'. Many are capable of both modes of operation. A single-action only revolver, or one that has been manually cocked by pulling back the hammer, requires only a slight pressure on the trigger to fire. This allows greater accuracy but increases the chances of an unintentional discharge. Early revolvers were single-action only and had to be manually recocked before firing again.

Double-action allows the weapon to be fired from a safe, 'hammer-down' position without being manually cocked. Pulling the trigger rotates the cylinder and moves the hammer back to cocked position. Further trigger pressure then allows the hammer to fall, initiating the round. It is thus possible to conduct rapid fire using a double-action revolver, though the extra movement and need for greater trigger pressure reduces accuracy a little. This may be significant when taking an aimed shot on the range or in a long-distance firefight.

Revolver safety mechanisms

Some modern revolvers are constructed as double-action only weapons. This can be important in today's tortuous legal climate, since a wily lawyer may try to claim that a self-defence shooting was in fact a negligent discharge – having cocked the weapon, the user panicked and fired when he neither needed nor intended to. This creates the strange situation in which a justified shooter is forced to prove that he really did mean to fire. A double-action only weapon is much harder to discharge accidentally, so may offer advantages in such a situation, or where the weapon is intended to be used by untrained shooters who might cock the weapon then accidentally discharge it.

Revolvers, as a rule, do not have safety catches, but are very safe to use. One persistent myth maintains that a revolver is safer than a semi-automatic since the weapon can be carried with an empty chamber under the hammer, preventing an accidental discharge. This is a half-truth. Since before the beginning of the twentieth century, revolvers have had an interrupter plate between the hammer and firing pin, which is only withdrawn when the trigger is properly operated: the rest of the time the hammer cannot initiate firing, no matter what it is struck with. Besides, semi-automatics are also designed not to go off at random if the hammer catches on something.

The practice of carrying a revolver with an empty chamber is real enough. Instead of this being the chamber that will first fall under the hammer, some users choose instead the next one to be rotated there when the weapon is cocked. This means that the first time the user attempts to fire his weapon the hammer falls on an empty chamber. Not only does this prevent a clumsy user from shooting himself in the foot while drawing

Primers and propellant

Most modern cartridges use a centre-fire system, where the primer is centrally placed. The primer contains 'fulminate', a fairly unstable explosive that will explode when struck by the firing pin. This in turn sets off the propellant in the body of the cartridge.

Some small-bore weapons use the rimfire system, whereby the fulminate is moulded into the rear rim of the cartridge. It is initiated by being struck by a hammer, again initiating the main propellant charge.

Above: The tip-down design of the Webley-Fosbery revolver allowed quick reloading with a special ammunition clip. The zig-zag grooves on the cylinder are part of a recoil-operated system that rotated the cylinder and recocked the weapon after each shot.

his weapon, but the revolver's owner also knows that, if the weapon is ever used against him, the assailant's first attempted shot will fail, providing an opportunity to react.

Revolver reloading

Revolvers are reloaded by manually refilling the cylinder with fresh rounds. Some early weapons required the weapon to be brought to a half-cocked position, allowing the cylinder to be freely rotated. Rounds were removed through a loading gate and new ones inserted one by one. This method is not only slow but is possibly the origin of the phrase 'going off at half-cock'. (Although this saying may also have originated with flintlock weapons, it is certainly indicative of a situation to be avoided.)

Most modern revolvers have a cylinder that can be swung out for reloading. All the rounds are pushed out at once by the ejector rod and new ones can be inserted singly or as a group of six using a speedloader or similar device. Other means to speed up reloading have been tried, such as detachable cylinders. These allow a weapon to be reloaded quickly, much in the manner of a semi-automatic pistol, by removing the fired rounds still in their housing and replacing the whole unit with a new cylinder filled with fresh rounds.

By definition, a revolver must have a small space between cylinder and barrel to allow it to rotate. Some of the muzzle gases can escape through this gap, reducing the power of the cartridge slightly and incidentally making it very difficult to fit an effective silencer to the weapon.

On the plus side, however, because a revolver is a manual repeater that does not need a cartridge to fire in order to load the next round, in the event that a round is a 'dud', the user can simply pull the trigger again (in the case of a double-action weapon) or recock the pistol manually to bring the next (and, it is to be hoped, functional) round into place. Ejection failures that can render a semi-automatic unusable are almost unknown with revolvers: if a round somehow becomes wedged in the cylinder, the other chambers should remain perfectly workable.

Revolver calibres

The 'industry standard' revolver calibre is .38 (i.e. the barrel is 0.38in/9.65mm in diameter). This calibre is something of an anomaly, since weapon calibres are normally measured in terms of the bullet, not the weapon's bore: a .38 calibre corresponds to a .357in diameter bullet, and indeed

Below: A Canadian sergeant loads his Smith & Wesson .38 revolver. The .38 was adopted by many armies since its lower recoil required less training to handle. The long rod protruding from the cylinder is used to push out all six cartridges for reloading.

.38 and .357 Magnum rounds have the same diameter, although there are significant differences. 'Magnum' simply means 'big' and the Magnum round certainly is that. Of the same diameter as a normal .38 round, the .357 Magnum cartridge is 2.5mm (0.1in) longer and can therefore hold correspondingly greater propellant charges.

A .38 round will fit in a revolver chambered for the .357 Magnum, but the Magnum round will not fit in the 'lesser' handgun, which is probably just as well since the chamber pressures created by such hot loads may damage the cylinder of a weapon not specifically designed to handle them.

'Hot' loads such as the .357 Magnum increase recoil considerably but also enhance the effectiveness and stopping power of the round. Modern revolvers are also commonly chambered for a light .32 and .22 LR ('Long Rifle') round, and for the enormous .44 Magnum cartridge, which can be considered as a pretty fair attempt to deliver artillery shells via a handgun. Other calibres have at times been common but today are less common.

Self-loading pistols

The 'six-shooter' offered enormous advantages over the single-shot flintlock pistol, but there was still an edge to be gained from a weapon holding more ammunition ready for use. Larger cylinders with more chambers were experimented with, but the real increase in effective firepower came with the self-loading pistol. Early self-loading weapons were rather clumsy and were generally fed from an internal magazine reloaded using 'clips' of ammunition rather than a detachable box. This is the origin of the mistaken practice of referring to magazines as 'clips'.

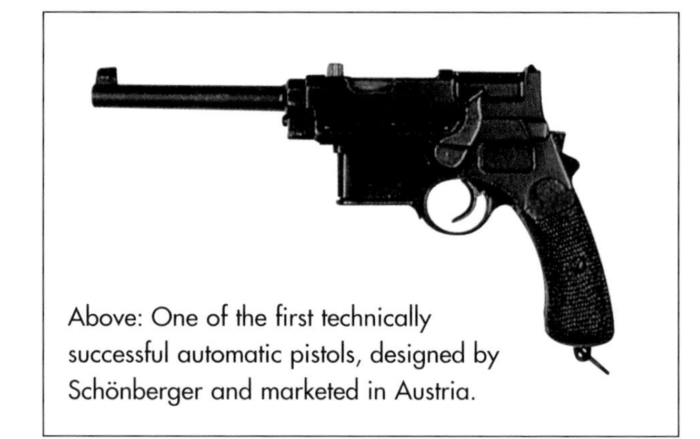

Above: One of the first technically successful automatic pistols, designed by Schönberger and marketed in Austria.

Semi-automatics

Self-loading handguns are often referred to as semi-automatic but sometimes as automatic pistols; terminology is a matter of preference to some extent. An 'automatic' weapon, correctly speaking, however, is one in which fire will continue until the trigger is released or ammunition runs out, so the term 'automatic' is not strictly accurate when applied to a weapon whose trigger must be pulled to fire each separate round.

In a self-loading weapon the recoil of a fired round is used to eject the spent cartridge and chamber the next one. The process can be carried out manually as well; in the typical semi-automatic pistol the 'slide' – a shroud around the actual barrel – moves back to align the ejection port on the barrel with that of the slide. The motion also trips a spring-loaded lever that throws

Left: A 'double tap' is two shots fired rapidly at the same target, increasing the chances of hitting and stopping the target: as soon as the weapon recovers from the recoil of the first shot, fire again. Note the spent cartridges in the air and the slide at full recoil, exposing the end of the barrel.

the spent round out, then pushes the hammer back to the cocked position. As the slide runs forward, a hole in the bottom of the breech aligns with the top of the magazine, whose spring forces the next round up and into the breech. Once the slide has reached its forward rest position the weapon is ready to fire.

Below: Hollow-point ammunition in a semi-automatic pistol magazine. Hollow points offer increased stopping power, which can be vital for self-defence or for the lone law enforcement officer faced with multiple assailants.

Self-loader ejection

Since self-loaders fire from a closed breech and have no holes to allow gas to escape, muzzle velocity from the same round is slightly higher than in a comparable revolver. In addition, most semi-automatics are in effect single-action weapons. Pulling the trigger allows the hammer to fall and the weapon to fire, and recoil or gas pressure drives the slide back to pick up the next round and reload the chamber. This has advantages in terms of accuracy but makes negligent discharges a little more likely than in a double-action weapon.

Some semi-automatics are constructed to use double-action fire either on the first shot or all shots. In the latter case the hammer is returned to a 'down' position after each shot and must be cocked and then fired by pulling the trigger. This means that the trigger pull is identical on the first and all subsequent shots, which, again, has advantages in terms of accuracy and safety.

'Condition One'

Double-action semi-automatics offer the advantage that they can be carried with the hammer down but still ready to fire, whereas single-action weapons must first be cocked. Users who carry the weapon without a round in the chamber must work the slide to chamber the first round and cock the weapon, while those who chamber a round and drop the hammer need only thumbcock the weapon, which is faster but still takes time.

The usual solution to the problem of bringing a weapon into action quickly is to carry it 'Condition One' – round chambered, hammer cocked, safety on. This is perfectly safe so long as the weapon is functioning properly, but carrying a weapon cocked makes some users nervous.

Above: Reloading a semi-automatic pistol is quick and simple. The hand holding the magazine can always find the user's other hand, which is wrapped around the grip and therefore the magazine well.

Above: Despite its slightly odd appearance, the Walther P38 was a fine handgun chambered for 9mm Parabellum. It replaced the Parabellum '08, or Luger, as the standard sidearm of German forces in World War II.

Bullet weight

Bullet weights are still sometimes measured in grains, though grams are commonly used today. Example weights:

- .22 Pistol round: 1.8 grams (27 grains)
- .38 Pistol round: 9 grams (140 grains)
- .44 Magnum round: 15.6 grams (240 grains)
- .223 Rifle round: 3.6 grams (56 grains)
- .50 Machine gun round: 46.7 grams (721 grains)

Self-loader safety systems

The development of other safety systems, replacing or in addition to the traditional safety catch, creates other possibilities. Some weapons use a double-action system coupled with a decocking lever, allowing the hammer to be safely lowered on a loaded chamber. The hammer is disconnected until the trigger is pulled, at which point the weapon fires normally. Other safety devices include grip and trigger safeties. These normally work by disconnecting the hammer, unless the weapon is properly held and the trigger pulled.

Such systems prevent accidental discharge if the trigger is snagged or dropped, but do not prevent a nervous or clumsy user from shooting himself or someone else as he draws the weapon. Just because the weapon will not fire unless the trigger is pulled does not mean it is always foolproof.

Interrupter mechanism

It is normally desirable for a handgun to fire just one round when the trigger is pulled. Apart from anything else, recoil under full-auto fire is likely to cause a handgun to jump around or point itself at the sky, resulting at best in a great waste of ammunition and the real possibility of collateral damage. For this reason self-loading pistols have an interrupter mechanism that prevents the firing of the next cartridge until the trigger is released and pulled again, hence their 'semi-automatic' designation. Some full-automatic pistols have been produced, sometimes termed 'assault pistols'. These often include minimal foregrips or stocks to make them more controllable, although generally these are not very effective.

Reloading

Semi-automatic handguns are reloaded using a magazine that fits into the handgrip. It is also possible to insert a single round directly into the breech, and one common cause of accidents is the possibility that a round may remain in the chamber, ready to fire, after the magazine is removed. Some weapons lock the slide in an open position when the last round is fired, preventing such an occurrence. This also has the advantage that, when a new magazine is inserted, the slide can run forward and chamber the first round at the touch of a lever – that is, without changing hand position – whereas in handguns where the slide remains forward, the firer must work the action to chamber the first round of the new magazine and recock the weapon. The delay in this case is minimal, but still potentially serious in a close-range fire-fight.

Advantages

It is far easier to create a 'silenced' semi-automatic pistol than a revolver. The addition of a suppressor on the end of the barrel brings down muzzle velocity and muffles the report of the weapon, although the action of the slide can cause enough noise to be significant during a stealthy infiltration.

While revolvers do offer some advantages in terms of ease of use and perhaps a marginally better reliability record, semi-automatic pistols are the modern sidearms of choice. Easy to carry, with a high magazine capability and reasonable stopping power, the semi-automatic is a good choice for backup or personal defence work. Attempts to turn the handgun into a 'combat' or 'battlefield' weapon, such as extended magazines, full-auto fire and other gimmicks, are of limited utility and may actually make the weapon less effective.

Semi-automatic calibres

Semi-automatic weapons are most commonly chambered for either 9mm Parabellum or .45 ACP (Automatic Colt Pistol) ammunition. The 9mm versus .45 debate has raged for decades and will likely continue. The smaller 9mm round allows a higher magazine capacity, while .45 fans say that no amount of high-velocity 9mm is as useful for stopping an assailant cold as the mighty .45 ACP round. In part because of the endless debates over ammunition qualities, modern handguns are commonly made in several versions, each version chambered for a different round but retaining the same general characteristics.

Right: A modern Smith & Wesson combat revolver, and its semi-jacketed .44 Magnum ammunition. Note the contoured grips and easy-to-reach cylinder catch below the hammer spur. The two devices on the left are speedloaders. Pressing the plunger pushes six rounds directly into the cylinder.

The .44 Magnum remains an awesome handgun, but it has now been superceded by the .454 Casull as the world's most powerful handgun.

Magnum ammunition

The .357 Magnum round was invented in 1935. The .44 Magnum cartridge (more correctly named .44 Remington Magnum Pistol) appeared in 1956, but it was not until the 1970s – and the movie *Dirty Harry* – that Magnum weapons really became popular.

Above: Captain Schwartz, a sharpshooter during the American Civil War, poses for this photograph with his Savage revolver held in the firing position.

In addition to 9mm and .45 ACP, small semi-automatics are often chambered for .380 ACP or 7.65mm calibre ammunition. The latter is a pistol round and not to be confused with the NATO or ex-Warsaw Pact 7.62mm rifle rounds. Light calibres make for lower recoil and a smaller, lighter weapon, useful for carrying concealed or as a personal weapon for civilians who do not want to lug around a hand cannon for use in case someone tries to mug them.

Stopping power

More powerful handguns are also popular. The .40 and 10mm calibres are intended to offer a handgun user greater stopping power without a ridiculous increase in recoil or a reduction in magazine capacity. The FBI, for example, now uses 10mm handguns, which can be easily controlled by a well trained agent and have sufficient stopping power to almost guarantee to disable the target. Such powerful weapons, however, may be too much for less well trained users.

Once the preserve of the heavy-frame revolver, Magnum ammunition is now available for use in semi-automatics in .357 and .44 calibres – there is even a .50 calibre version of the awesome Desert Eagle semi-automatic. While the ability of such weapons to intimidate an opponent or demolish him with a single shot is not in dispute, their usefulness for normal handgun users is open to question, since these weapons are heavy, bulky and possess ferocious recoil.

Enormous calibres and other performance-increasing measures are of questionable value since all such measures attempt to turn the handgun from what it is – an excellent close-in personal defence weapon – into something that it is not, and will probably never be: a capable weapon for a battle situation. If you think you are going to encounter a situation that requires more than a handgun, in truth you are better off obtaining a rifle, shotgun or submachine gun rather than an overgrown handgun.

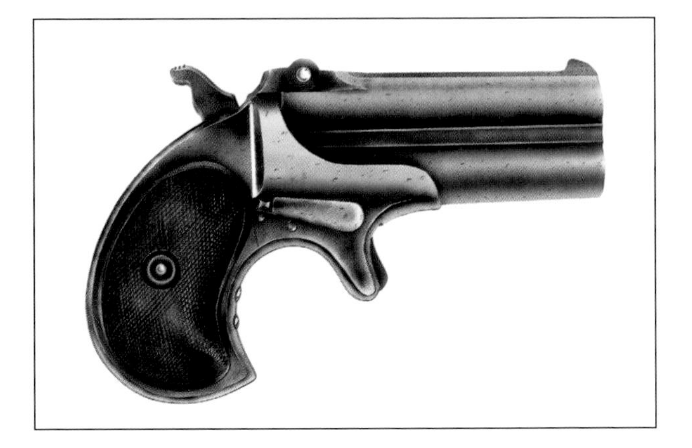

Above: A double-barrelled Remington derringer. This tiny pistol holds two powerful rounds, probably .44 or .45 calibre. It breaks open for reloading, but any situation that requires reloading your derringer is a losing proposition.

Derringers

The advent of percussion weapons and later cartridge firearms allowed the manufacture of very small handguns that could be concealed and brought into use by surprise, perhaps getting the user out of an otherwise impossible situation.

Many of these 'concealables' or 'holdout pistols' are simply small but entirely conventional weapons, often chambered in small calibres. Lacking much capacity or stopping power, such weapons are very much the tools of last resort.

The derringer is an extreme version of this concept. A single- or double-barrelled weapon with minimal grips, a derringer offers one or at most two shots. Since there is no feed mechanism, the weapon can be chambered in fairly large calibres and still remain small. Favoured by gunfighter-gamblers in Western movies, derringers are of little combat value and never found much favour.

Right: *Cavalry Charge on the Southern Plains*, by Frederick Remington (1907). The troopers carry their revolvers pointing straight up to avoid accidental casualties as the charging horses jar the riders' hold on their guns.

The heyday of the revolver

Fans of Westerns may be surprised to realize just how recent the 'gunfighter' period actually was, and how short. Expansion into the far west of the North American continent took place more or less from the time of the earliest attempts at colonization, and several important cities were established quite early on the west coast. However, due to the long travel times involved the West was only really opened up by the railroads: at the time when European nations were fighting their colonial wars and the United States was making its presence known worldwide, the West was a poorly developed and somewhat primitive region.

The American Civil War of 1861–5 had important consequences for world history. From 1865 North America no longer was simply an influence on events; the United States was a major world power. Unification had been established and the national identity of the US as a single entity made up of distinct parts rather than as a loose alliance of parts had been firmly established.

Another consequence of the Civil War was the return home of thousands of men who had 'seen the elephant' and endured the hardships of war. Some of these men could not settle easily back into regular civilian life. Some could not stomach the defeat of their ideals. Others had simply become infected with an adventurer spirit. The West offered these individuals a chance to start a new life, to find adventure, or to escape the aftermath of the war.

Guns and the West

Such a vast area, sparsely populated and with travel made difficult by the distances and lack of infrastructure, was an ideal location for lawlessness. Criminals could keep on the move and elude pursuit, or take what they wanted from less well armed people. In such a climate, and without the weight of civilization to assist them, citizens were forced to defend themselves as best they could. Justice was by necessity somewhat rough and ready.

The common denominator in all this was firepower. Possession of good-quality firearms allowed the citizen to defend his property and family and the lawman to back up his powers of arrest with a very convincing threat. In the hands of criminals they allowed violent men to force their will on others, taking whatever they pleased.

As if this was not enough, there were troubles between the settlers moving west and the Native Americans displaced by them. Again, possession of the best weapons was the decisive factor in these conflicts – and it was not always the settlers, nor even the US Army, who were best armed.

This was of course the age of the 'gunfighter', around whom so many myths have sprung up. It is true that the Hollywood-style draw-and-shoot duel

Above: A woodcut of Samuel Colt holding one of his revolvers. Colt did not invent the 'wheelgun' as he claimed, but he did create all-time classic revolvers like the M1861 'Navy' Colt and the M1873 Peacemaker.

Early revolvers

There were no safety devices on early revolvers. This could be an asset. If, for example, the trigger assembly became damaged such a weapon could still be fired by hitting the hammer with something hard.

did sometimes take place, but this kind of honourable conflict was uncommon. More often, gunfights were sudden, bloody affairs taking the form of ambushes or bushwhackings. The gunfighter of old was no more likely to challenge his target to a fair fight than today's urban gunman. More gunfighters were shot in the back in an ambush than in a fair fight – and nobody ever shot the gun out of his opponent's hand.

Samuel Colt

From the 1850s onward, revolvers were increasingly available in the West, although many ordinary people were forced to rely on black powder weapons to defend their homes. Revolvers were expensive, and some were of very poor quality indeed. Among those that stood out were the fine weapons made by Samuel Colt.

Colt had a varied and somewhat chequered career prior to his entry into the firearms trade. He claimed to have invented the concept of the revolving pistol during his time as a seaman, basing the idea on the ship's wheel. His other exploits included a period touring small settlements in the backwoods of the USA as 'Doctor Colt' (sometimes spelled 'Coult'), amusing the uneducated residents with geegaws in a manner not uncommon at the time. Given his activities during this time and the showmanship naturally indulged in, Colt's claim about the origins of his revolver concept may have been a colourful invention, since revolving flintlock weapons existed before Colt's time.

Whatever the truth, Samuel Colt founded an arms factory in 1836, producing five-shot revolvers that were put to effective use by the Texas Rangers in the 1840s, but this venture was not a success and the factory closed down in 1842. Colt went on to other things, including work on electrical and telegraph applications.

Military Colts

The outbreak of the Mexican War prompted the United States government to order 1000 revolvers for use by its small forces. Colt had recently

Above: A studio photograph of a Union cavalryman with a pair of Colt 'Navy' revolvers and a sabre. The sabre was by this time an anachronism; the cavalry trooper's main weapon was the revolver on horseback and the carbine on foot.

designed a new six-shot revolver and founded a new factory to produce them in Connecticut. The new weapon was a huge success, ensuring that by 1855 Colt owned the world's largest private arms factory.

The American Civil War created a massive demand for small arms, and Colt's factory supplied over 400,000 of them – 300,000 rifles and 100,000 revolvers – to both sides. Some of Colt's products, such as a repeating carbine using a revolving cylinder similar to that in his handguns, were not a success. This was due in part to an unfortunate tendency for the firing of one round to ignite all those remaining in the cylinder, with serious consequences for the firer, whose left hand was in front of the cylinder and his face in close proximity.

Despite these occasional glitches, Colt became a household name during the Civil War, and even though Samuel did not live to see the end of the war (he died in 1862), his wife, Elizabeth, took over a company that employed 1500 personnel. What Colt brought to the arms trade was not so much an innovative weapon but new manufacturing processes that allowed mass-production of high-quality weapons.

Colt M1860 & 1861

The Colt weapons of the period were not true all-in-one cartridge firearms, using a cartridge and separate percussion cap. Although six shots were a lot better than one, once all had been fired these weapons were rather slow to reload. Two major variants saw use, the M1860 'Army' Colt, chambered in .44 calibre, and the M1851 'Navy' Colt, which was chambered for .36. A new 'Navy' revolver, the M1861, based on the 'Army' design,

M1860 'Army' Colt

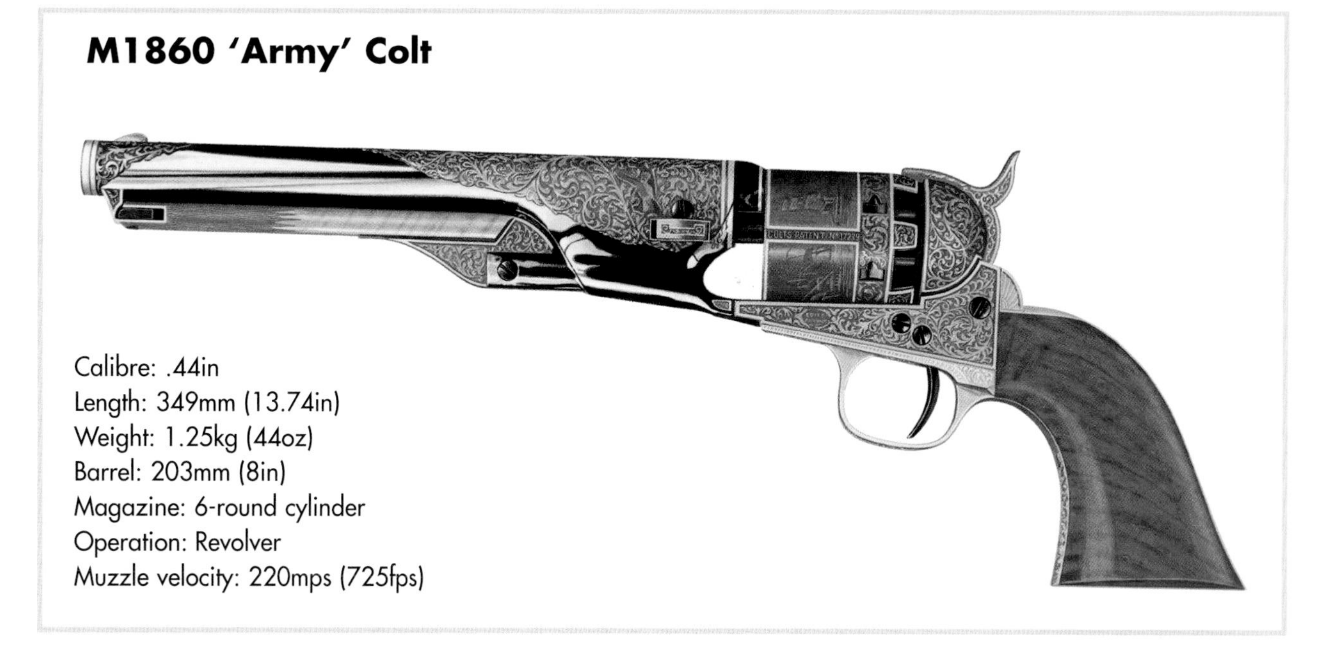

Calibre: .44in
Length: 349mm (13.74in)
Weight: 1.25kg (44oz)
Barrel: 203mm (8in)
Magazine: 6-round cylinder
Operation: Revolver
Muzzle velocity: 220mps (725fps)

M1861 'Navy' Colt

Calibre: 0.36in
Length: 328mm (12.91in)
Weight: 1.02kg (36oz)
Barrel: 190mm (7.5in)
Magazine: 6 -ound cylinder
Operation: Revolver
Muzzle velocity: 300mps (750fps)

Above: One of the greatest – or most famous – gunfighters of all time: 'Wild Bill' Hickok. Despite his reputation, the frontier scout turned US Marshal favoured careful aim over rapid but wild shooting.

was fielded but did not achieve commercial success. The US Army purchased almost 130,000 'Army' model Colts and 17,000 'Navy' Colts during the war, while the Confederate forces favoured the 'Navy' model and produced several copies to arm their officers and cavalrymen. Not all of these weapons remained in Government hands after the war; large numbers were taken home or otherwise found their way into general circulation.

The amount of guns in circulation following the Civil War did little to reduce demand. Perhaps it even stimulated it, since the only effective counter to a sixgun was another sixgun. Thus, as the dust of war settled and the move westward began, the Colt company supplied arms to the frontiersmen by the ton. This was the defining moment in the development of modern firearms; the point at which flintlocks were pronounced dead and cap-and-ball weapons were eclipsed by all-in-one cartridge weapons. Samuel Colt's revolvers were at the forefront of the firearms revolution and truly deserve their place in history.

Colt Peacemaker

The Colt M1873 was Colt's classic revolver of the era. A single-action, six-round revolver with excellent 'pointability', the Colt will be forever associated with the western frontier. Indeed, its other names – the Frontier or the Peacemaker – firmly anchor it in that short but fascinating period of American history.

Much favoured by gunslingers and lawmen, the Colt Peacemaker was a reliable weapon, and very accurate over the sort of ranges a handgun is used at. Contrary to Hollywood myth, even a *High Noon* draw-and-shoot confrontation is not about clearing leather and getting lead in the air – it is about getting the first shot on target. The legendary gunfighter 'Wild Bill' Hickok rarely shot first. This was nothing to do with misplaced chivalry but was because Hickok would take aim carefully and deliberately shoot his opponent, who would usually waste his first shot through nerves and excessive haste.

Taking even a second to aim while standing under fire would require nerves of steel, but Hickok knew a fundamental truth of gunfighting: beyond very close range, unaimed rapid firing hits its target only by accident. Hickok risked being hit by such a stray round, knowing the chances it would happen were slim, and that a second later he would definitely hit his opponent and take him out of the equation.

Gunfighters rarely shot from the hip, other perhaps than in a very close range fight. Since they were using single-action revolvers, recocking the weapon wasted a short time that might allow an opponent a fatal opportunity. Thus each shot had to count, and would be fired from a single-handed, from-the-shoulder stance, aimed as carefully as stress and incoming gunfire allowed.

Remington

The second most popular handgun manufacturer of the American Civil War was Remington, who sold some 127,000 revolvers to the US Army between 1861 and 1865. These weapons, very similar to the more popular Colts, had been designed in 1857 and came in .45 and .36 calibres. One interesting innovation was the strap over the cylinder, which adds to the strength of the weapon and is a feature of modern heavy-frame revolvers.

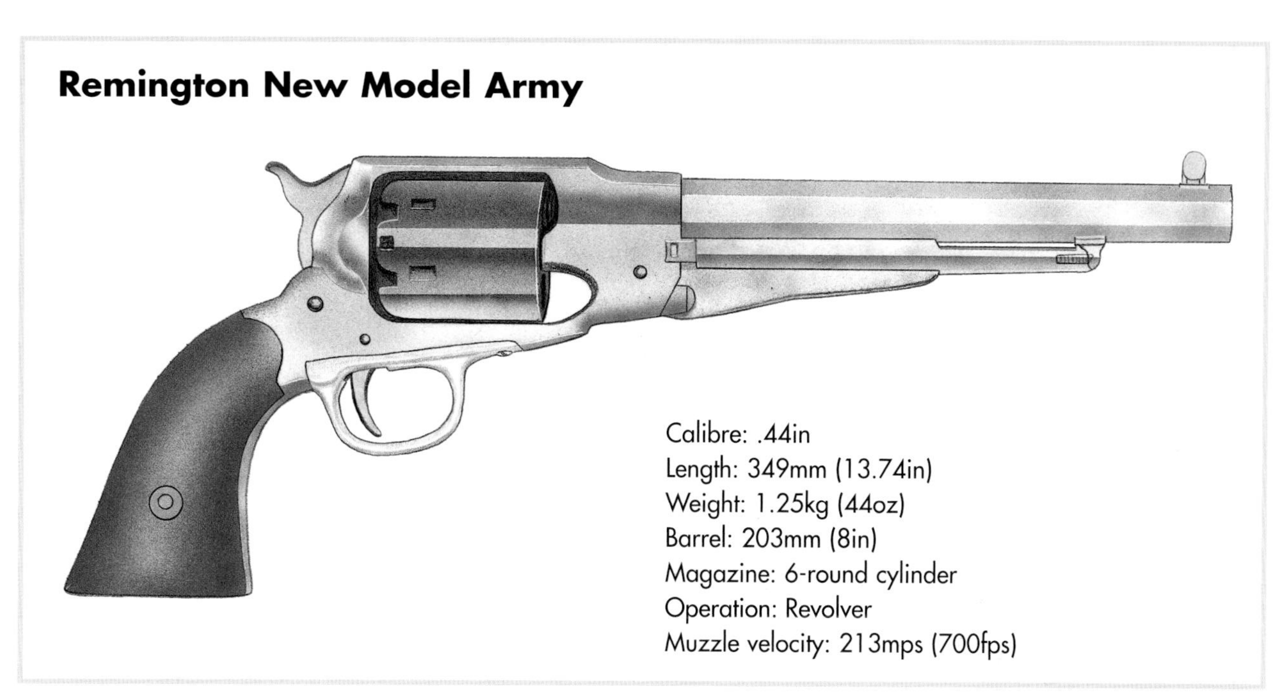

Stance

Whether carefully using the sights or engaging in point-and-shoot combat, a good, steady stance is vital. A weapon cradled in two hands or braced on something is more likely to put its bullets where the user wants them. Gunfighter and marshal Bill Hickok proved this point in many of his duels.

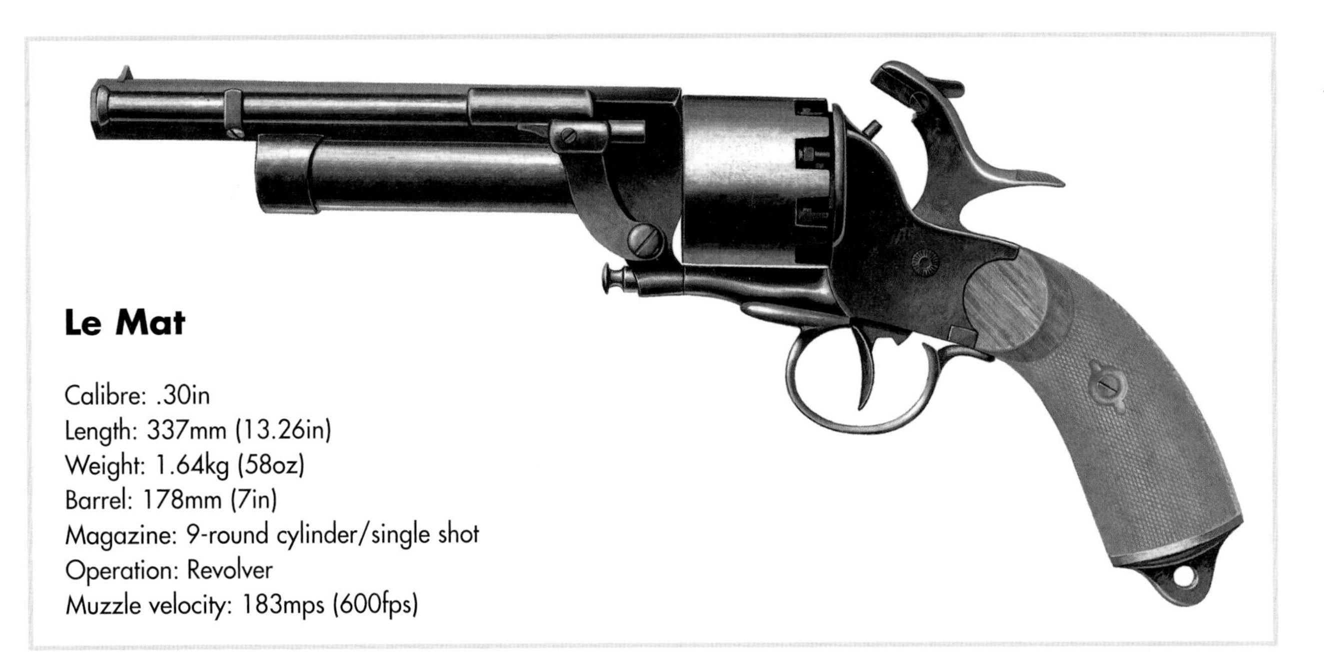

Some gunfighters, including Jesse James's brother Frank, maintained that the Remington was superior to the Colt. Remington's New Model pistols continued in production until 1888.

Smith & Wesson

The Civil War period and subsequent expansion westwards saw the ascent of another household name in small arms, Smith & Wesson, whose first revolver was produced in 1857 and was taken up in small numbers by both sides. In 1870, the Imperial Russian government placed an order for 20,000 Smith & Wesson revolvers, and an adapted version known as the Schofield-Smith & Wesson, after Major George W. Schofield, was purchased for the US Army. Perhaps 8000 such weapons were issued beginning in 1870. Schofield-Smith & Wessons were also purchased by the Wells Fargo company to arm their security personnel.

The outlaw Jesse James owned and used a Smith & Wesson revolver, and was killed by one in the hands of his one-time ally, Robert Ford. This was no Hollywood gunfight but an assassination; Ford visited his ex-friend and shot him in the back of the head when he turned to straighten a picture.

Le Mat

Another weapon from the Civil War deserves attention, albeit mainly for its novelty. Designed by a New Orleans doctor and manufactured in France, the Le Mat 'Grapeshot' revolver was an interesting concept that proved rather impractical in the field, even though the legendary cavalry commander J.E.B. Stuart owned one.

The Le Mat was a nine-shot revolver chambered for either .40 or .30, with the nine chambers of the cylinder grouped around a central smoothbore barrel of either 16- or 18-gauge, which was loaded with a single shotgun cartridge. Although this extra firepower seems useful, especially in the scramble of a cavalry engagement, the weapon never caught on. This was perhaps because the Le Mats that reached end users were of poor quality.

Subduing the colonies

The cartridge revolution was occurring elsewhere, too. By the middle of the nineteenth century several European powers had established colonies and dominions in far corners of the world. The greatest of these was the British Empire, which included territories in every continent and on islands in every ocean of the world.

It is a truism that a nation develops a military tailored to the role it performs. Thus, although other European powers engaged in conventional massed hostilities within their shared continent at various times, for the British the main role of the armed forces was colonial warfare. This generally involved small units engaged against vastly superior but relatively ill-equipped local forces.

The history of the so-called 'Colonial Period' is a bloody one, with conflict taking place on at least one continent at any given time. Distances, communication lags and the lack of sufficient reserves to deploy to all trouble spots meant that the local commanders of the colonial powers had to make do with what they had. Their only advantages were the quality of the troops at hand and the superiority of their weapons.

Auxiliary sidearms

The rifle was the main instrument of colonial power, sometimes backed up by early machine guns. High-quality sidearms, however, provided their users with a last line of defence that was – sometimes – just enough. Revolvers were carried by officers and non-combat troops such as artillery and logistics wagon drivers, and were not considered particularly effective against a determined and courageous warrior.

Captain P.C. Newbigging of the Royal Artillery observed that, if being rushed by a Zulu warrior armed with an assegai (a short stabbing spear), it is pointless 'to keep popping at him with a revolver' since he would surely still manage to stab the target to death, whether mortally wounded or not. A rifle shot at 10 to 15 yards was considered the sovereign remedy for such problems.

Right: Although it was the rifle that was the foremost infantry weapon during the colonial period, revolvers were frequently carried by officers and auxiliaries. This fire-damaged picture from 1887, in a series depicting recipients of the Victoria Cross, shows Lieutenant Reginald Hart using his revolver to defend a wounded Bengal Lancer.

Adams Revolver

Despite such misgivings, revolvers were carried and sometimes saved the life of the user. One of the most important weapons of the time was the Adams revolver. This weapon can be considered a British equivalent of the Colt in terms of its importance. Patented by Robert Adams in 1851, the Adams was a development of the 'pepperbox' type revolver, in which six independently loaded barrels were rotated one by one in front of a fixed firing mechanism. Adams applied some of the principles of this weapon but used a fixed barrel and rotating cylinder to improve the revolver's lightness and aesthetic qualities.

The Adams was trigger-cocked, allowing rapid double-action fire, and was adopted by the Prince

Adams Self-Cocking Revolver

Calibre: .49in
Length: 330mm (13in)
Weight: 1.27kg (45oz)
Barrel: 190mm (7.48in)
Magazine: 5-round cylinder
Operation: Revolver
Muzzle velocity: 213mps (700fps)

Left: A World War I British officer armed with a Webley revolver leads his men 'over the top'. Revolvers were used mainly as a status symbol for officers but sometimes saw use for self-defence or to enforce discipline – either as a threat or rather more directly.

Consort, creating much positive publicity. By the 1860s Adams revolvers were in mass production and were being ordered for the British armed forces, depriving Colt of further orders. Adams revolvers were bought by both sides in the American Civil War, although the Confederacy had difficulty in paying for its orders.

The Boxer cartridge

Like early Colts, the Adams self-cocking revolver used separate cartridges and percussion-cap ignition, but by the mid-1860s military procurement committees were becoming interested in breech-loading cartridge weapons. In 1866 Colonel Edward Mounier Boxer, of the Royal Laboratory at Woolwich, designed a .450 cartridge with set-in primer. The emergence of the Boxer cartridge at this time prompted Adams to convert some muzzle-loading revolvers to this more powerful round, and later to produce a revolver built around the Boxer ammunition.

The Boxer round offered good stopping power, unlike earlier .36 rounds, and found favour among British forces posted to colonial outposts. However, the standard round adopted by the British forces was of .455 calibre. This powerful cartridge remained the standard for service sidearms until the end of World War I. British officers were expected to provide their own revolvers and could choose whatever they wanted so long as it was chambered for the standard .455 service round.

Webley & Scott

The most famous revolvers in British service at this time were made by Webley & Scott. The 'classic' was the Mk IV, a heavy but powerful weapon using a break-open ('tip-down') mechanism rather than a hinged cylinder. With its octagonal barrel the Webley remains a distinctive weapon. Versions up to the Mk VI, the final evolution of this fine handgun, saw service throughout the end of the Colonial period and both World Wars.

Conditions in the trenches were not kind to men or their weapons, but the Webley developed a reputation for reliability in the most horrific conditions. In close-quarters trench fighting, rifles were simply too unwieldy, so handguns, knives and a range of improvised clubs saw frequent and brutal use. A 'revolver-bayonet' was available for the Webley pistol, for use in such circumstances, although it was not particularly effective.

Further developments

Another experiment of the period was the Webley-Fosbery. Based on a Webley revolver, the Webley-Fosbery used recoil to drive the cylinder backwards. A stud on the frame engaged with grooves on the cylinder to drive it round, while the hammer was recocked by the rearward motion. Mauser fielded a similar weapon, the 'Zig-Zag', named after the zigzag groove on the cylinder.

Despite being based on a clever idea, the Webley-Fosbery and Mauser offered few advantages and tended to fail in dirty conditions. This made such weapons unsuitable for the colonial and trench-warfare environments, and so this innovative weapon never achieved any real success.

Webley & Scott MkVI

Calibre: .455 British Service
Length: 286mm (11.25in)
Weight: 1.09kg (2.4lb)
Barrel: 152mm (6in), 7 grooves, rh
Magazine: 6-round cylinder
Operation: Revolver
Muzzle velocity: 200mps (655fps)

As the Colonial period came to an end and the world lurched towards the Great War to End All Wars, experimenters of all nations were seeking to develop better firearms. The revolver had seemingly reached its pinnacle of development. Powerful, reliable but slow to reload and holding only six rounds, the revolver was becoming archaic. It was time for progress to march onward.

Enter the self-loader

The self-loading pistol was the weapon of the future. While conservatives clung grimly to their wheelguns, the more progressive elements in the arms industry were finding ways to overcome the problems inherent with self-loading weapons. Taking ideas from the machine guns of the time,

Revolver safety systems

Many modern revolvers use a 'transfer bar' between the hammer and firing pin. The transfer bar is only moved into place when the trigger is pulled. When the bar is not in place, the hammer sits too far back to reach the firing pin – even if the hammer is accidentally bashed against something it cannot impact the firing pin and the revolver will not discharge.

Another useful safety feature found on many revolvers and semi-automatics, is a decocking lever. This allows the hammer to be moved from the cocked to the uncocked position with no danger of the weapon firing. A double-action pistol can be fired from this position; a single-action weapon cannot.

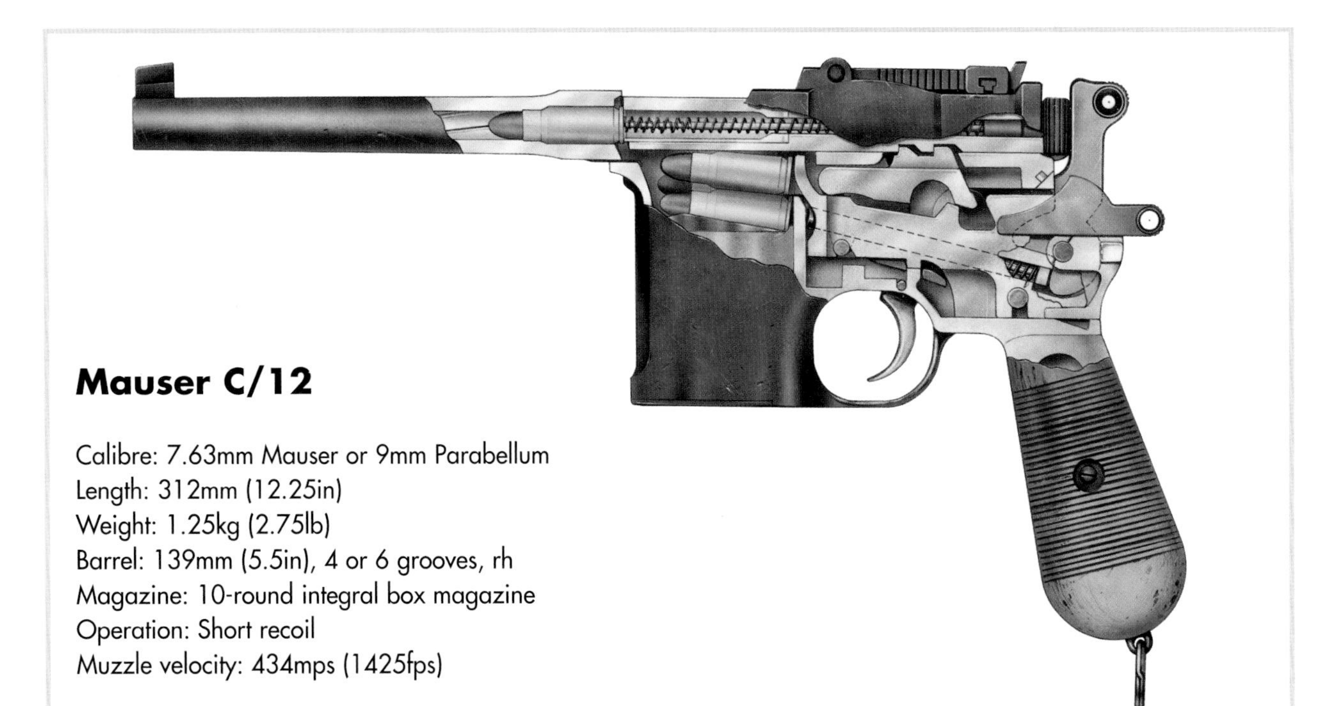

Mauser C/12

Calibre: 7.63mm Mauser or 9mm Parabellum
Length: 312mm (12.25in)
Weight: 1.25kg (2.75lb)
Barrel: 139mm (5.5in), 4 or 6 grooves, rh
Magazine: 10-round integral box magazine
Operation: Short recoil
Muzzle velocity: 434mps (1425fps)

Cover vs. concealment

Cover is something that will stop a bullet whereas concealment is something that will obscure an opponent's sight of you. The first protects you while the second merely hides you. A brick wall is, usually, cover; a cardboard box is not.

Borchardt C/93

Calibre: 7.65mm
Length: 279mm (11in)
Weight: 1.1kg (2.56lb)
Barrel: 165mm (6.5in), 4 grooves, rh
Magazine: 8-round detachable box magazine
Operation: Short recoil
Muzzle velocity: 326mps (1070fps)

some of these weapons were clever but impractical, often with complex and fragile mechanisms required to get the next round loaded.

Borchardt C/93

One example of these innovative but ultimately less than useful weapons is the Borchardt C/93. This masterpiece of engineering was unwieldy and fragile on account of the protruding mechanism for recoil-operation. It was significant in one way, however, since the Borchardt was the first handgun to be loaded from a detachable box magazine. Previous self-loaders had an internal magazine loaded from a charger or clip. Although the Borchardt ceased production before 1900, examples of this weapon served for some years, some fitted with a shoulder stock for use as a marginally effective carbine.

Weapons like the Borchardt were simply too clumsy for the sort of combat seen by handguns, but semi-automatics quickly adapted to fill their destined role. One advantage of a self-loader is that the weapon has a slimmer shape than a revolver in the same calibre, since it does not need a bulky cylinder. While this may be of limited benefit to that traditional user of pistols, the cavalry soldier, there were advantages for troops operating in close or urban terrain, or for anyone who had to carry a concealed handgun.

The main reason for selecting semi-automatics during this period, other than the fact that they were new and exciting, was firepower. Some users preferred the tried-and-tested reliability of the revolver, but many others wanted the faster loading and greater capacity that became available.

Above: Royal Navy officers at marksmanship practice. Most are armed with Webley & Scott semi-automatic pistols, though one has a Webley revolver. Note the formal posture; few people would take this position in a firefight!

Mauser C/12

One classic of this period was the Mauser pistol. A bulky yet beautiful weapon fed from an internal magazine in front of the trigger mechanism, the Mauser was originally chambered in 7.63mm and reloaded from the top. Its mechanism was complex but well made and the weapon was so successful that many variants were created. Versions in 9mm, full-automatic versions and variants with six-, ten- or twenty-round magazines were marketed. Some Mausers were used with shoulder stocks as carbines.

The definitive Mauser is the C/12 model, which is probably the weapon used in the famous Sidney Street Siege of 1911. Having been interrupted during a robbery, the two criminals killed three policemen during their escape and were eventually cornered in a house in east London. Their Mauser pistols delivered so much firepower that the police, armed with shotguns and Bulldog revolvers, could do little. The siege was eventually resolved by Army marksmen acting under the direct orders of the Home Secretary, Winston Churchill.

Parabellum P-08 (Luger)

Calibre: 9mm Parabellum
Length: 233mm (8.75in)
Weight: 0.87kg (1.92lb)
Barrel: 102mm (4in), 6 grooves, rh
Magazine: 8-round detachable box magazine
Operation: Short recoil
Muzzle velocity: 380mps (1247fps)

Parabellum P-08

Another classic German pistol developed in the years immediately before World War I was the Parabellum P-08, designed by Georg Luger and forever known by that name. Chambered for 7.65mm and 9mm, the P-08 was accurate and comfortable to shoot, and was taken up in large numbers by the German army and navy. More than 2.5 million were produced between 1908 and 1945. The pistol was comfortable to use and the mechanism was effective although prone to malfunction in dirty conditions. Despite its age, the 'Luger' is still popular among enthusiasts.

Webley & Scott

Webley & Scott also experimented with self-loading pistols at this time, developing the Self-Loading Pistol 1912 Mk 1 around a version of the standard .455 cartridge. This extremely

Colt M1911

Calibre: .45 ACP
Length: 216mm (8.5in)
Weight: 1.13kg (2.49lb)
Barrel: 127mm (5in), 6 grooves, rh
Magazine: 7-round detachable box magazine
Operation: Short recoil
Muzzle velocity: 253mps (830fps)

Above: Perhaps the pinnacle of cold-blooded courage: a US 'Tunnel Rat' prepares to wriggle into a Vietcong tunnel and search it, armed only with his .45 Colt M1911A1. He may face booby traps and enemy personnel as well as natural hazards such as snakes or a roof collapse.

powerful round was not compatible with revolvers – it would fire but sometimes caused the revolver to explode. Interestingly, the Webley self-loader was not issued to troops fighting in the trenches but was used by the Royal Navy, Royal Flying Corps and some police personnel.

The self-loader comes of age

In the early years of the twentieth century John Browning designed a semi-automatic pistol chambered in .38. In conjunction with revolvers of the same calibre then in common use, this was taken by the US Army to the Philippines, where it proved ineffective as a man-stopper. One problem encountered by US forces was the tendency of distraught Filipinos to 'run amok'. Today such behaviour is recognized as a dissociative mental condition, but all that was then known was that an amok individual possessed near-superhuman strength and endurance, and would kill anything and anyone in his path, usually with the machete that was so fundamental to life in the jungle-covered Philippines. Amok individuals were more or less immune to shock or trauma. Like the users of some drugs, any injury that did not kill them immediately was of no consequence.

A weapon was needed that would knock over the attacker with massive stopping power. Having seen too many injured or dead servicemen with empty .38 weapons lying beside them, the US Army sought a weapon that would stop the most determined and aggressive individual, and in the Colt M1911 they got it.

Colt M1911 & 1911A1

Considered by many to be the best handgun of any kind, ever, the Colt M1911 was the ultimate self-loading pistol of the period before World War I. It reached service just in time to go to the trenches, where it performed sterling service.

Conditions in the trenches were hard on men and weapons, and the M1911A1, entering service in 1926, was based on the lessons learned in that environment, including such features as a wider ejection port. The A1 was a fearsome weapon and remained the standard US military sidearm for six decades. The pistol was widely copied, though not always produced to Colt's high standards, and was adopted by police and military forces around the world, plus countless private weapons users.

The M1911 (and A1 version) is a simple weapon, using a swinging link short-recoil operation to drive the slide back and eject the spent round before recocking the weapon, picking up the next round and chambering it in the breech ready to fire again. Firing is single-action, requiring that the weapon be cocked before bringing it into use. Users expecting combat often carry the Colt 'cocked and locked' – a round in the chamber, hammer cocked, safety on. This is known as Condition One. The weapon can be ready to fire in one movement – taking the safety off as the pistol is drawn – but remains entirely safe to carry.

Right: The venerable Colt M1911A1 in the hands of a US artilleryman. The Colt was a formidable weapon with excellent stopping power, which served well for many years. Its replacement with the 9mm Beretta 92 still rankles with some personnel.

Recoil

By the time the user feels the recoil of his shot, the bullet has already left the barrel.

The barrel of a gun is sometimes 'ported': small angled vents are drilled into it, to redirect exhaust gases in a direction that opposes muzzle flip, reducing 'felt' recoil and aiding control.

Officers and auxillaries

The .45 Colt served through both World Wars and beyond as a sidearm for officers and troops assigned to non-rifleman roles, as a weapon for security personnel at installations and aboard ships, and for use at close quarters. For example, the 'tunnel rats' of the Vietnam War would crawl into tunnel networks equipped with torches and .45s to clear them of determined guerrillas. Such applications require a powerful, reliable weapon, and the M1911A1 was all of that. The A1's long and distinguished military service history finally came to an end in the 1990s with the adoption of the 9mm Beretta by the US armed forces, but it remains a well loved (and much-missed) weapon. Thousands still remain in the hands of private shooters who value its qualities, even though its seven-round magazine offers little more firepower than a good revolver.

Above: Suited against chemical attack, these troops are armed with the 9mm Browning Hi-Power. The guns are modified with longer barrels for more accurate shooting.

Browning Hi-Power

Revolvers of various sorts remained in military use throughout World War I and even into World War II, although gradually the balance shifted in favour of self-loaders. Many classics emerged in the inter-war years, including another all-time favourite: the Browning Hi-Power.

John Browning had been involved in handgun design for many years (and indeed co-designed the Colt M1911), but his fortunes took him away from the USA to Belgium, where the Fabrique Nationale (FN) company took up his self-loading pistol design. This, the HP-35 (or GP-35 – 'Grande Puissance'), was taken up by the armed forces of several countries, including Britain.

Holding 13 rounds of 9mm ammunition in its magazine, the HP-35 is cocked by working the slide, which chambers a round and cocks the weapon. Although the Browning has a safety catch, which locks the slide and hammer, it was not intended to be holstered in the cocked position or carried 'Condition One'. This means that the user must carry the weapon without a round chambered and work the action before firing, delaying readiness by a short but possibly significant period.

Operation is similar to the M1911, but instead of a swinging link the Browning uses a cammed slot to unlock the slide from the barrel as the weapon recoils. The barrel is stopped but the slide continues backwards to complete its action.

The 9mm round has less stopping power than .45, but the Browning carries nearly twice as many rounds. Given that in the stress of combat even trained shooters operating at close range miss a lot of their shots, this extra firepower can be significant. Recoil is a lot lower for a 9mm than with a larger calibre handgun, so the Browning can be used effectively by less well trained personnel. This was particularly important in wartime, with accelerated training being the norm.

Modern developments

Although it was used by both sides during World War II, the Browning was not adopted by the British Army as a standard service pistol until 1954. It remained in service for many years but is becoming quite dated compared to modern self-loaders. The design has been copied extensively and will likely remain in service for many years to come, but as a service pistol the 9mm Browning is no longer competitive.

A modernized version of the High-Power, the Browning Double-Action (or DA), is currently available and includes all the best features of the old Hi-Power along with modern developments, such as redesigned grips for a two-handed stance and an ambidextrous de-cocking lever.

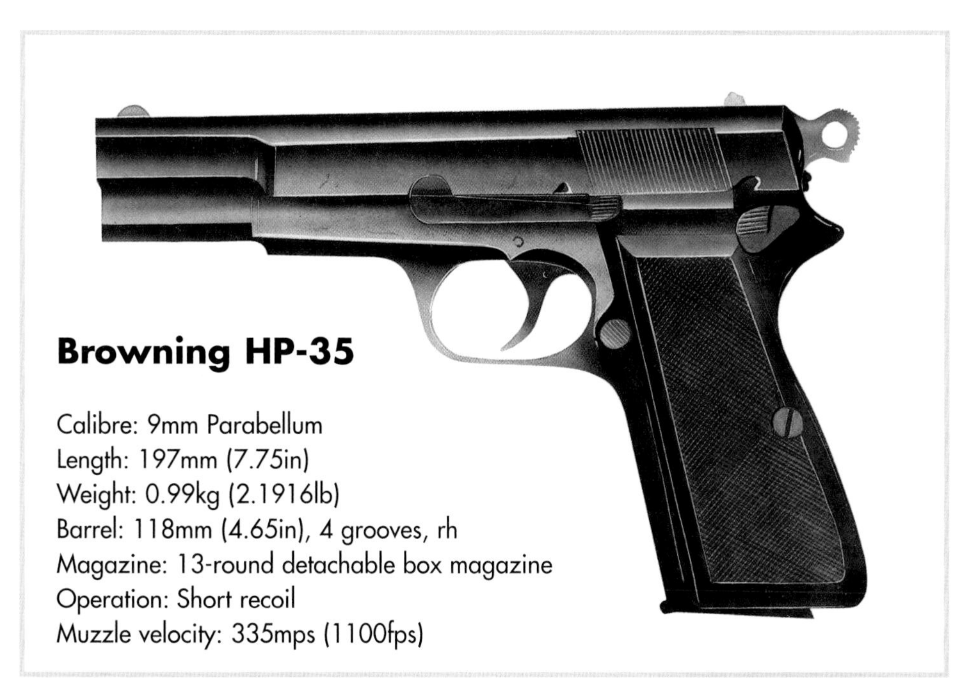

Browning HP-35

Calibre: 9mm Parabellum
Length: 197mm (7.75in)
Weight: 0.99kg (2.1916lb)
Barrel: 118mm (4.65in), 4 grooves, rh
Magazine: 13-round detachable box magazine
Operation: Short recoil
Muzzle velocity: 335mps (1100fps)

Tokarev TT30

Calibre: 7.62mm Soviet
Length: 196mm (7.68in)
Weight: 0.83kg (1.83lb)
Barrel: 116mm (4.57in)
Magazine: 8-round detachable box magazine
Operation: Short recoil
Muzzle velocity: 420mps (1380fps)

Tokarev TT30

The success of the Colt/Browning action meant that other weapon designers copied it for their own handguns. Thus when the Russian designer Fedor Tokarev introduced his TT30 pistol, chambered for the standard 7.62x25mm round, it was based on the 1911 mechanism. The Russian military has never considered the pistol to be particularly useful, and as a rule they are not as effective as their Western equivalents. Owing to the range of conditions (most of them appalling) likely to be encountered by Russian service pistols, however, they're designed to fire under almost any condition.

The Tokarev was underpowered by handgun standards, but it could be relied upon to fire in snow, mud or dusty and dry conditions. It was also resistant to abuse and easy to manufacture, being turned out in vast numbers to arm the mass armies of World War II. Production ceased in the 1950s, but licensed versions, often chambered for 9mm, have been manufactured in Egypt and China in large numbers, and ageing TT30s and TT33s (a slightly modified version) can still be found in service with some military forces.

Makarov

The Tokarev's replacement, the Makarov, was based upon lessons learned in World War II and drew heavily on the design of the Walther PPK. Built around a 9x18mm round, which is slightly less powerful than the standard 9x19mm Parabellum or 'Luger' round used elsewhere, the Makarov is more powerful than its predecessor and just as reliable. Its awkward shape makes accurate shooting tricky, but it will always fire when the trigger is pulled; everything else is just a bonus.

Walther P38

Just before World War II the ageing Luger P-08 was replaced in service with the German armed forces by the Walther P38. Using a 9mm cartridge fed from an eight-round magazine, this weapon was much more tolerant of poor conditions and the vagaries of ammunition, making it far more reliable. It could be stripped easily and included

Walther P38

Calibre: 9mm Parabellum
Length: 196mm (7.68in)
Weight: 0.83kg (1.83lb)
Barrel: 116mm (4.57in)
Magazine: 8-round detachable box magazine
Operation: Double-action short recoil
Muzzle velocity: 420mps (1380fps)

safety features such as a chamber loading indicator and a hammer safety. It was also quick and easy to produce – an important quality in view of Germany's drive for rearmament during the 1930s.

The P38 used a double-action trigger mechanism, allowing the weapon to be brought into action much more quickly than other self-loaders. The P38 is still in production, now designated the P1. Despite its slightly odd appearance it is still popular and elements of its design have been copied extensively.

Stechkin

Another Russian idea based upon wartime experience was the Stechkin pistol. Again drawing on the Walther PPK design, the Stechkin was a full-automatic pistol using 9x18mm ammunition and capable of 850 rounds per minute.

Too small to be useful as a machine pistol but large and bulky for a true handgun, the Stechkin was also almost uncontrollable on full-auto. The pistol could be fitted with a shoulder stock, which made the weapon as bulky as a real submachine gun but otherwise did little to help. Production ceased in 1975 and the weapon was soon withdrawn from use.

Liberator

The Liberator was primarily manufactured for the US Office of Strategic Services, the OSS. An unbelievably crude and cheap weapon, the Liberator was a single-shot smoothbore pistol intended to be used for close-range killings by resistance forces. Chambered for .45 ACP, it was capable of killing an enemy soldier at close range but was of no value in conventional combat.

As is common with 'unconventional' operations, it is not possible to discover how effective measures to place these weapons in the hands of resistance fighters actually were, nor how many were used successfully. The Liberator, however, cost almost nothing to make and did its job, so it is virtually certain that determined people were able to use it to cause mayhem behind enemy lines.

The triumph of the semi-automatic

Handguns saw extensive use throughout the two World Wars in the hands of soldiers, resistance fighters and special operatives. During close quarters fighting, such as in the trenches or during the desperate urban scrambles of World War II, handguns were valuable close assault weapons, while for those whose war was one of stealth, they offered firepower balanced with concealability.

By 1945 it was obvious that the semi-automatic pistol had come of age. Reliable, rugged and

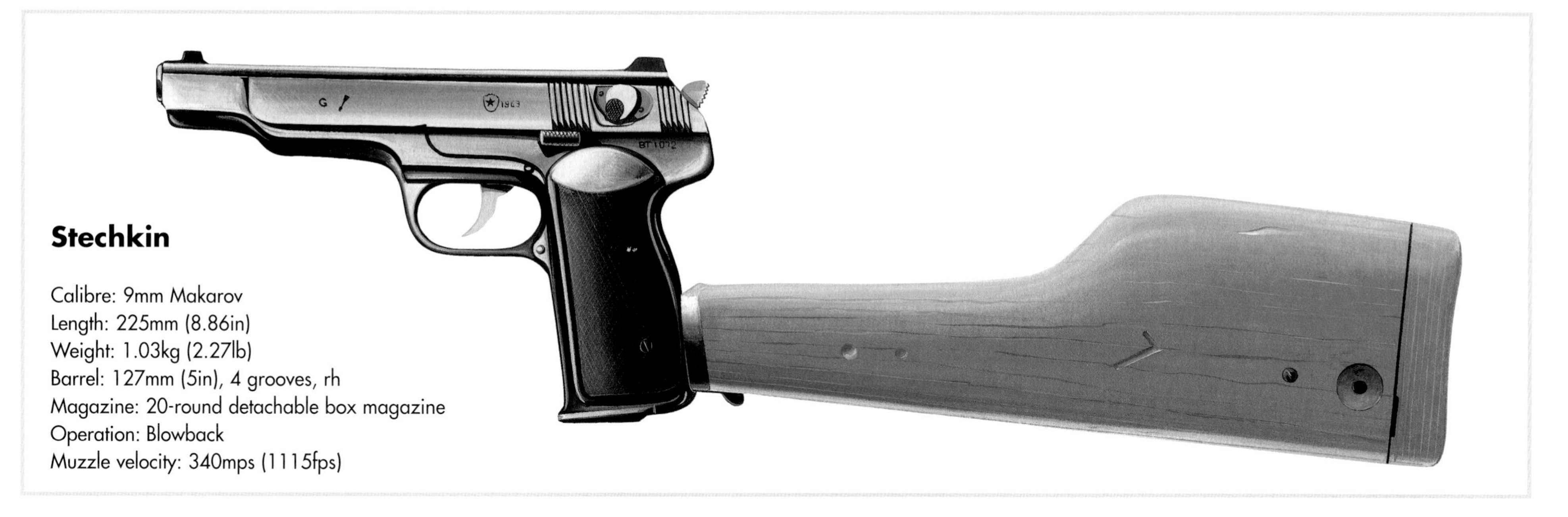

Stechkin

Calibre: 9mm Makarov
Length: 225mm (8.86in)
Weight: 1.03kg (2.27lb)
Barrel: 127mm (5in), 4 grooves, rh
Magazine: 20-round detachable box magazine
Operation: Blowback
Muzzle velocity: 340mps (1115fps)

powerful it had proven its worth in action and would be adopted by military forces worldwide in the next few years.

The resurgence of the revolver

Despite the ascendance of the semi-automatic pistol, the development of revolvers continued. Many police forces continued to use them for various reasons – not all of them good ones. Some forces believed that 'if you can't do it with six, you can't do it!', and saw no need for increased firepower. Others mistrusted the new weapons despite evidence that they were sound. For example, during the attempted kidnap of Princess Anne in 1970 a member of the British Royal Protection Squad suffered an ammunition stoppage on the first round, shaking British police confidence in semi-automatic weapons. Isolated

Makarov

Calibre: 9mm
Length: 160mm (6.3in)
Weight: 0.66kg (1.4lb)
Barrel: 93mm (3.66in)
Magazine: 8-round detachable box magazine
Operation: Gas
Muzzle velocity: 315mps (1033fps)

Liberator

Calibre: .45 ACP
Length: 141mm (5.55in)
Weight: 0.45kg (1lb)
Barrel: 101mm (3.97in), smoothbore
Magazine: 1 round inserted directly into chamber
Operation: Single shot
Muzzle velocity: 250mps (820fps)

Close quarters

When using a handgun at very close-quarters, the weapon should be kept close to the body. If necessary, the attacker should be 'checked' with the free hand as the gun comes on line to shoot.

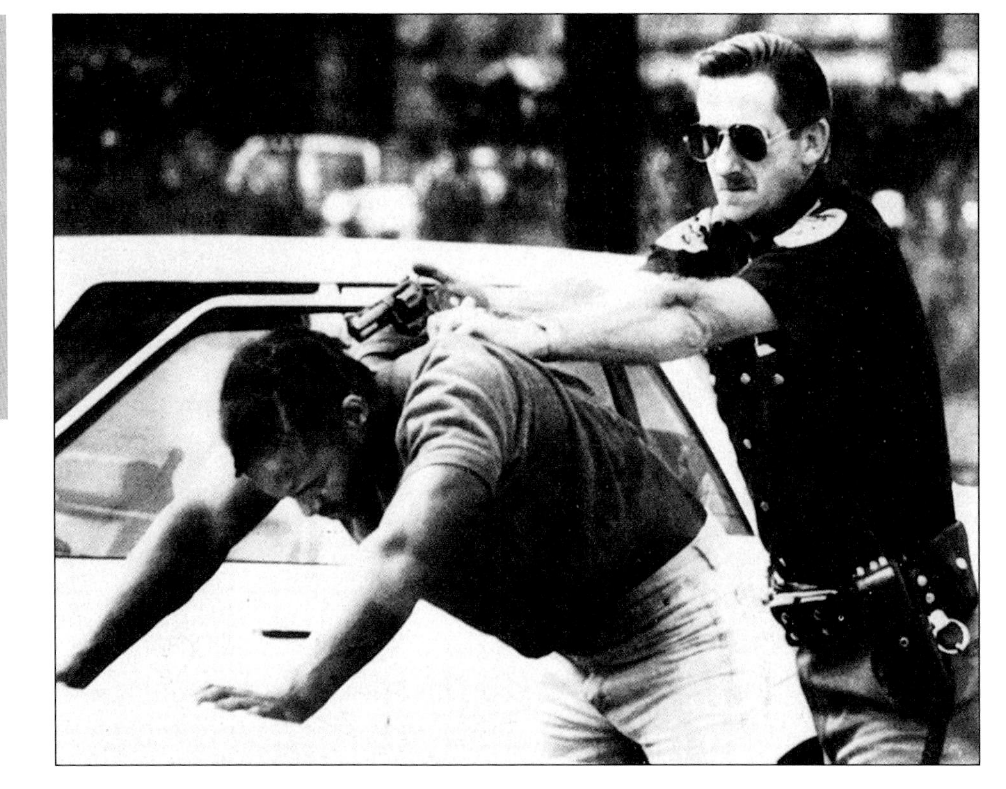

Right: Indianapolis police chief Jerry Priest makes a succesful arrest; the Colt Python has an air of authority that can deter opponents, making shooting unnecessary. Note how the suspect is 'checked' with one hand.

incidents like this made police forces wary, although there were other reasons too.

Police forces operate in an environment where stray shots will endanger the very people they exist to protect, and training budgets are not large. Thus some forces felt that more ammunition would promote less deliberate shooting on the part of officers whose marksmanship might not be of the highest levels. The same lack of budget made switching an entire force's weapons to a different type, and setting up new ammunition stocks, an undertaking to be delayed as long as possible. The reality, however, is that the more bullets someone has in his gun, the more of an advantage he has over someone with fewer, especially if he can also reload quickly. The self-loader has become the standard firearm of military and law enforcement personnel over the past few years and to some extent is the default choice.

Weapons users need a reason to pick an old-style six-gun over a modern semi-automatic pistol. One good reason is, of course, simplicity. A revolver is easy to use, uncomplicated and perhaps easier to load with shaking hands at 2 a.m. while listening for footsteps on the staircase. These factors alone make revolvers a popular choice for personal defence, and the gun makers have given us many other good reasons not to abandon them.

The modern revolver, even a cheap one, is well made, robust and reliable. Tolerant of abuse and poor ammunition quality, it can be left in a drawer for years and still function first time. It is also a well balanced and reassuring shape to the user, and an intimidating presence to the prospective target.

S&W M29

While many revolvers are manufactured in traditional calibres (.32, .38 etc.), the revolver's robust construction is ideal for weapons using powerful Magnum cartridges. Made famous by Clint Eastwood and the popular *Dirty Harry* movies, the Smith & Wesson Model 29 (or 629), chambered for .44 Magnum ammunition, is perhaps the modern equivalent of the Colt Peacemaker; the handgun everyone has heard of, although it has entered the popular vocabulary as simply the .44 Magnum or just 'the Magnum'.

The 629 is an awesome beast of a handgun. Available with barrel lengths ranging from 75mm to 200mm (3–8in) long, the muzzle blast and recoil of this personal artillery piece are unpleasant enough without considering the effect on the target. Stopping power is not in question with the .44 Magnum since the 629 can crack a truck engine block, although accuracy can be reduced by muzzle flip and 'Magnum flinch' on the part of the user.

Capable of double or single-action operation, the 629 is in use with the Tennessee State Police, but most law enforcement users consider the .44 Magnum to be simply too powerful for most shooters. Nevertheless, the businesslike appearance of this beautiful piece of engineering is generally enough to bring any incident to a rapid close.

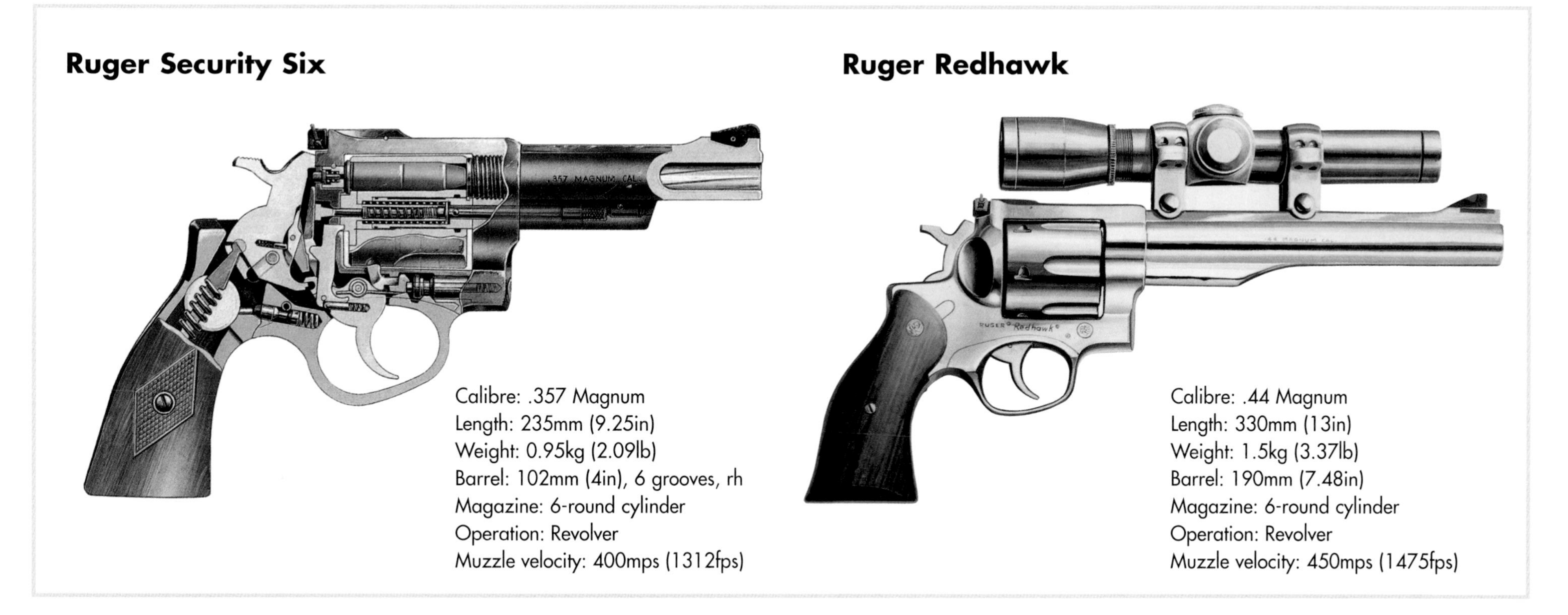

Colt Python

Another excellent and deservedly well known combat revolver is the Colt Python. The distinctive ventilated rib along the top of the barrel has been copied by other manufacturers, some of whom have come close to Colt's extremely high quality of manufacture. Available in various barrel lengths, the Python is chambered for .357 Magnum (and can therefore fire .38 Special ammunition as well).

While not as awesome as the .44 Magnum, the .357 Magnum is a powerful round and users who perhaps could not handle an M29 find the Python quite controllable. The Python is an expensive handgun, however, so cheaper copies are encountered more often than the real thing.

Ruger Redhawk & Six Series

Sturm, Ruger & Co. joined the revolver renaissance in the 1970s with their 'Six' range: the Security Six, Speed Six and Police Six. The Security Six was based on a 1950s-vintage single-action revolver that was one of Ruger's early designs. It was intended to become a standard police weapon and was built around the .357 Magnum cartridge, offering law enforcers the ability to penetrate buildings and vehicles used as cover. The Speed Six was almost identical, but with a rounded butt and short barrel.

The Ruger Redhawk, a .44 Magnum revolver, was aimed at private users rather than government bodies. With nearly 200mm (8in) of barrel and a telescopic sight, the Redhawk is accurate beyond normal handgun ranges and can even bring down game. Such huge revolvers are at the outer extreme of what can be considered 'sidearms', but the Redhawk has achieved worldwide success due to its performance and reliability.

COMBAT MAGNUMS: COLT PYTHON VERSUS

In what appears to have been a vintage year for handguns, the Colt Python and the Smith & Wesson M29 were both first produced in 1955. These fine weapons put the revolver back on the map and established the 'combat Magnum' concept. Today's big Magnum revolvers offer massive knockdown power from even a glancing hit, and their incredible muzzle blast may be enough to discourage an attacker even if the shot misses. High recoil, however, can cause 'Magnum flinch' in some users, spoiling accuracy as the firer instinctively flinches away from the discharge of his own weapon. It may be that some handguns are just too powerful for their own good.

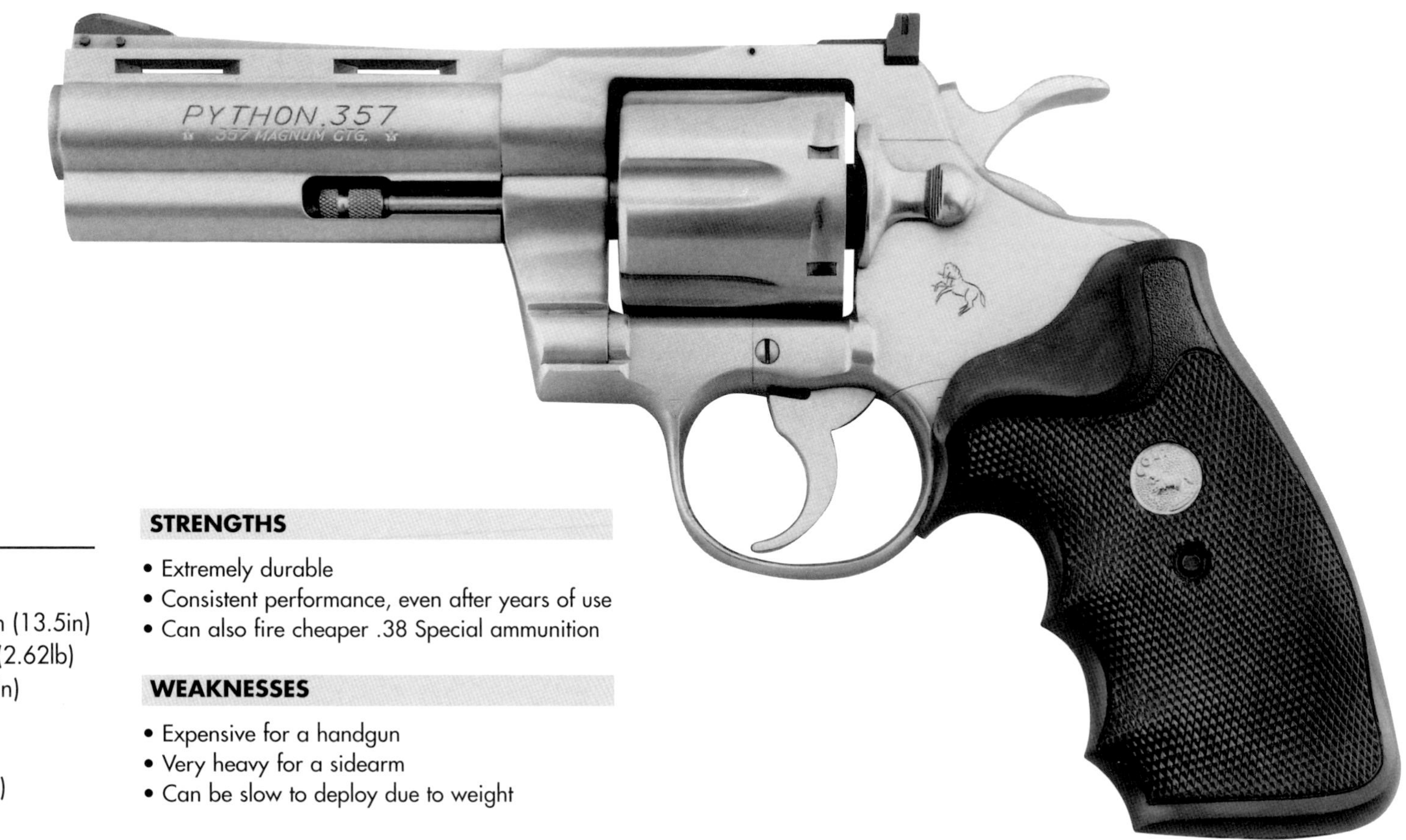

Colt Python

Calibre: .357 Magnum
Length: 235mm (9.25in) to 343mm (13.5in)
Weight: 1.08kg (2.37lb) to 1.2kg (2.62lb)
Barrel: 102mm (4in) to 204mm (8in)
Magazine: 6-round cylinder
Operation: Revolver
Muzzle velocity: 455mps (1500fps)

STRENGTHS

- Extremely durable
- Consistent performance, even after years of use
- Can also fire cheaper .38 Special ammunition

WEAKNESSES

- Expensive for a handgun
- Very heavy for a sidearm
- Can be slow to deploy due to weight

SMITH & WESSON M29

The .357 Magnum Colt Python has been described as the world's best production revolver. It has been copied but never equalled in terms of quality and ruggedness. Only its high price prevented it from being adopted by many police forces. The Smith & Wesson Model 29 has been available for nearly 50 years, and is now manufactured in several variants as the '629' series. In the *Dirty Harry* films Clint Eastwood used the 203mm (8-inch) barrel version. Although most police departments consider .44 Magnum to be too powerful for law enforcement issue, there are plenty of private users who appreciate its qualities.

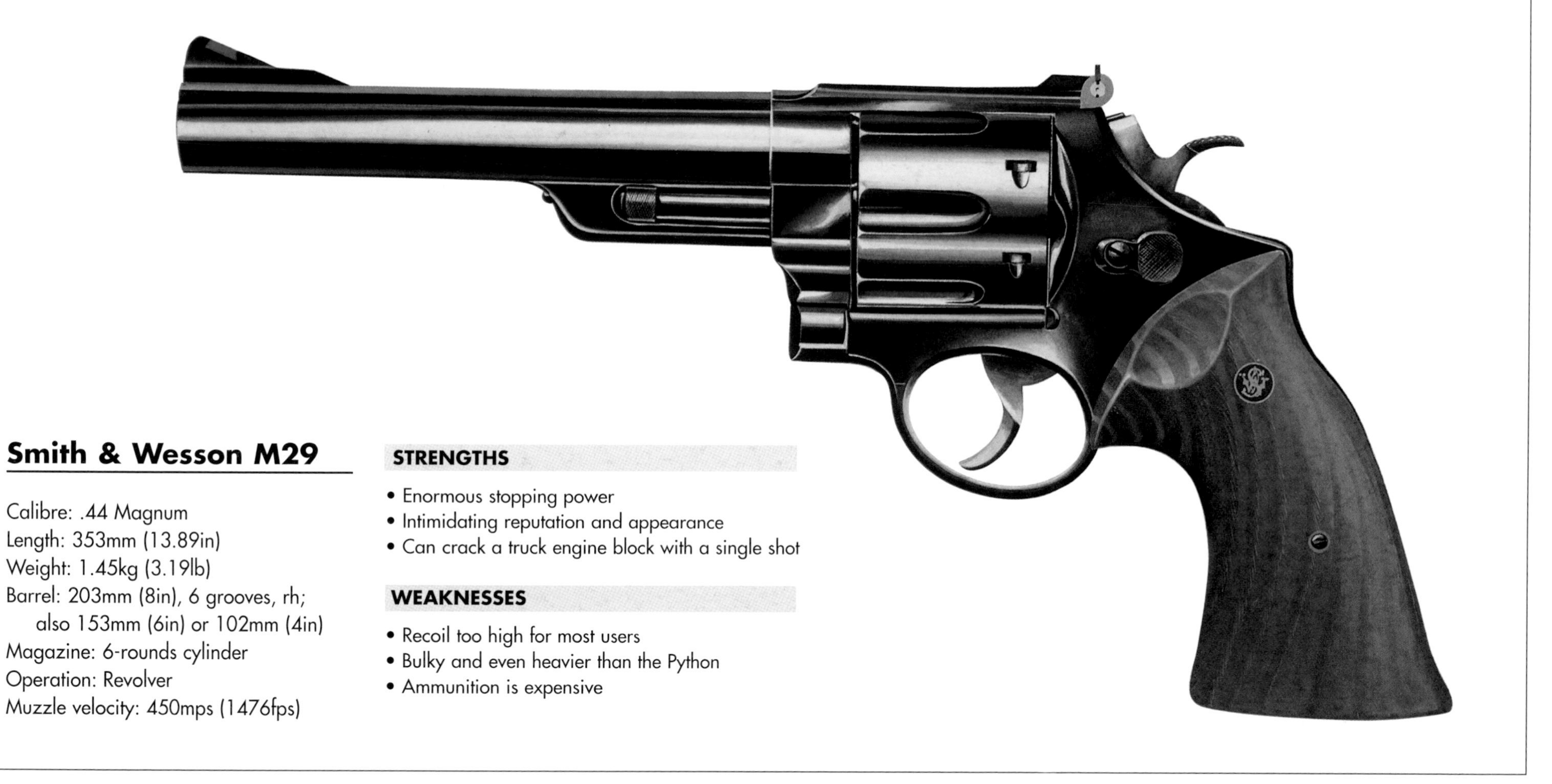

Smith & Wesson M29

Calibre: .44 Magnum
Length: 353mm (13.89in)
Weight: 1.45kg (3.19lb)
Barrel: 203mm (8in), 6 grooves, rh;
also 153mm (6in) or 102mm (4in)
Magazine: 6-rounds cylinder
Operation: Revolver
Muzzle velocity: 450mps (1476fps)

STRENGTHS

- Enormous stopping power
- Intimidating reputation and appearance
- Can crack a truck engine block with a single shot

WEAKNESSES

- Recoil too high for most users
- Bulky and even heavier than the Python
- Ammunition is expensive

Above: Revolvers are still issued as security pistols, even by major armed forces. Here, US Marines assigned to embassy protection practice draw-and-shoot marksmanship with their 4-inch Ruger revolvers. A .357 Magnum slug is a fearsome manstopper at short ranges.

The modern revolver is capable of surviving chamber pressures that would burst a nineteenth-century handgun, allowing extremely powerful rounds to be used. This, coupled with their resistance to abuse and the simplicity of their operation, ensures that the 'combat revolver' will remain in service for many years to come. Although mechanical repeaters have fallen out of favour with military and law enforcement bodies apart from some special units, such as 'combat swimmers' deployed by German hostage-rescue forces for operations in harbours and waterways, for the average user the revolver is a credible deterrent and an effective combat weapon.

Concealable handguns

People tend to be alarmed at the display of weapons, so the average citizen going about his business armed for self-defence will not usually wish to have his weapon on display. Bodyguards and non-uniformed police officers may need to blend in or may wish to maintain a discreet presence. Of course, criminals and assassins can also benefit from concealing their weaponry until they are ready to use it.

Thus for a number of reasons, it is not always desirable to advertise that you are carrying a weapon. Some handguns are naturally concealable due to their small size. Others are deliberately designed to be kept hidden or disguised.

Concealables are a sensible choice for those who do not wish to advertise that they are armed, who need a backup gun, or who simply want a weapon for self-defence that they can carry easily and will probably never use. A weapon intended to be carried in a purse or bag, or hidden under clothing, cannot have numerous large protrusions that will snag and interfere with a clean draw. Ideally, concealable weapons should also be able to be carried ready to use, since valuable time is already wasted in deploying the weapon.

Instinctive shooting

Most self-defence or security handgun shooting is based on hand-eye coordination. The firer looks at the target, points his weapon at the spot that his eye tells him it needs to point, and shoots.

Many handgun users tend to resort to desperately filling the air with lead in the general direction of the target. Unless firing from very short ranges this is unlikely to result in a direct hit.

Walther PPK

One of the most famous concealable handguns, although not constructed specifically for the purpose, is the Walther PPK. This very small self-loading handgun was introduced in 1931 as a smaller version of Walther's PP, or Polizei Pistol.

Made famous as the sidearm of several incarnations of James Bond, the PPK is available in a range of calibres from 6.35mm to .380 ACP. Its magazine holds seven rounds. The PPK can be carried with a round in the chamber and brought into action quickly with a double-action shot; subsequent shots are single-action. Despite embarrassment in 1970 when a police officer's pistol jammed at a critical moment, the PPK is a reliable weapon, though like all small-calibre handguns it lacks stopping power.

PSM

The Russian equivalent of the PPK, the Pistolet Samozaryadniy Malogabaritniy, or PSM, uses an underpowered 5.45mm cartridge feeding from an eight-round magazine. It can be used double-action like many such weapons and was probably issued to undercover police agents.

Detonics Pocket 9

No longer in business, the US firm Detonics produced a range of excellent combat handguns including the Pocket 9. As the name suggests, this pistol is a small 9mm with a six-round magazine, intended for close-range personal defence. The Pocket 9 has no sights to snag on clothing (they are of no use at the sort of range for which this weapon is intended) and the pistol can be used as either double- or single-action.

H&K P7 & P9

Pocket and concealable handguns present a number of engineering challenges. While most are simply 'slimline' versions of combat handguns, some are innovative in their own right. Heckler & Koch manufactures the distinctive P7, available in 9mm Parabellum or .45 ACP. The P7 is cocked by squeezing the grip, meaning it cannot fire unless it is properly held in the hand. Different magazine capacities are available in the 9mm version: the P7M8 holds eight rounds but is more concealable than the P7M13, which contains thirteen.

Walther PPK

Calibre: .22LR, 6.35mm or 7.65mm Browning
Length: 148mm (5.8in)
Weight: 0.59kg (1.3lb)
Barrel: 80mm (3.15in), 6 grooves, rh
Magazine: 7-round detachable box magazine
Operation: Blowback
Muzzle velocity: 290mps (950fps)

Hair triggers

Some users like to adjust their weapon to create a 'hair trigger', so that the merest touch on the trigger will fire the weapon once it is cocked. This is a highly unsafe practice unless the user is very skilled and very careful, and has few practical advantages.

Right: The Walther PP was designed for law enforcement operations. It is small, easily concealable and has no projections to impede a fast draw. Its tiny size and low-powered cartridge prevented some users from taking it seriously, although James Bond seemed to find the even smaller PPK quite satisfactory!

Heckler & Koch also manufactures the rather more conventional P9, which is available in 9mm or .45 ACP; a few examples were chambered in 7.65mm. The .45 ACP version is aimed at the American market, since so many American shooters will not consider any other calibre. The P9 is a little larger than the P7, though not much heavier, and is in service with German police units.

The standard P9 is a single-action pistol, but a double-action P9S is also available. Both use the roller-locked delayed-blowback system used in the Heckler & Koch G3 assault rifle.

Ruger Speed-Six

Concealable handguns are not limited to semi-automatics. A range of 'pocket' revolvers are available, including the Ruger Speed Six. A double-action revolver with a short (76–102mm/3–4in) barrel, the Speed Six can fire .357 Magnum or .38 Special rounds. The solid frame required to handle Magnum loads makes for a bulkier weapon than might be desirable, but this is a 'pocket' weapon rather than one intended to be hidden from a search, so bulk is a question of comfort rather than a life and death issue.

Firing Magnum loads from such a small, light handgun can be unpleasant, especially with the muzzle flip that results from a short barrel and the unavoidable rearward balance point. Most users of pocket pistols carry them 'in case' of conflict, however, rather than because they are expecting to use them regularly. If a situation has gone so badly wrong that gunfire is necessary, the discomfort of shooting a small Magnum pistol tends to become a secondary consideration.

Heckler & Koch P7

Calibre: 9mm Parabellum
Length: 171mm (6.73in)
Weight: 0.8kg (1.76lb)
Barrel: 105mm (4.13in), polygonal, rh
Magazine: 13-round detachable box magazine
Operation: Gas-actuated delayed blowback
Muzzle velocity: 350mps (1150fps)

Ballistics

Projectiles like bullets do not travel in a straight line. Instead they follow a ballistic arc. This 'bullet drop' means that beyond a very short range the gun must be angled slightly upwards if the round is to successfully reach its target.

Point-blank range is defined as the distance a bullet will travel if the gun is held level with the ground – in fact a surprising distance! However, the term is normally applied to very close ranges within which the drop is insignificant.

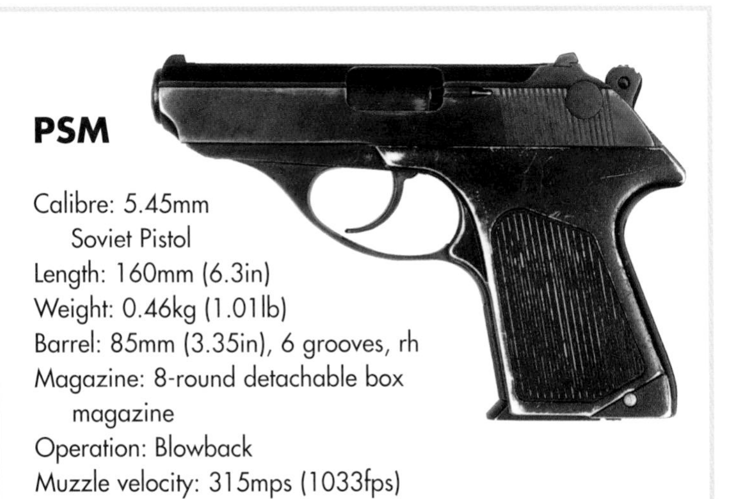

PSM

Calibre: 5.45mm Soviet Pistol
Length: 160mm (6.3in)
Weight: 0.46kg (1.01lb)
Barrel: 85mm (3.35in), 6 grooves, rh
Magazine: 8-round detachable box magazine
Operation: Blowback
Muzzle velocity: 315mps (1033fps)

Colt Detective Special

Another small revolver useful for carrying concealed is the Colt Detective Special. This weapon, which entered production in the 1920s, was based on the standard Colt police revolver, fitted with a short or 'snub' barrel only 54mm (2 inches) long. Chambered for .38 Special ammunition, the Detective Special is light enough to be carried in comfort for long periods, and can be drawn quickly from a concealed holster. In the 1950s the Detective Special was redesignated the Model D.1.

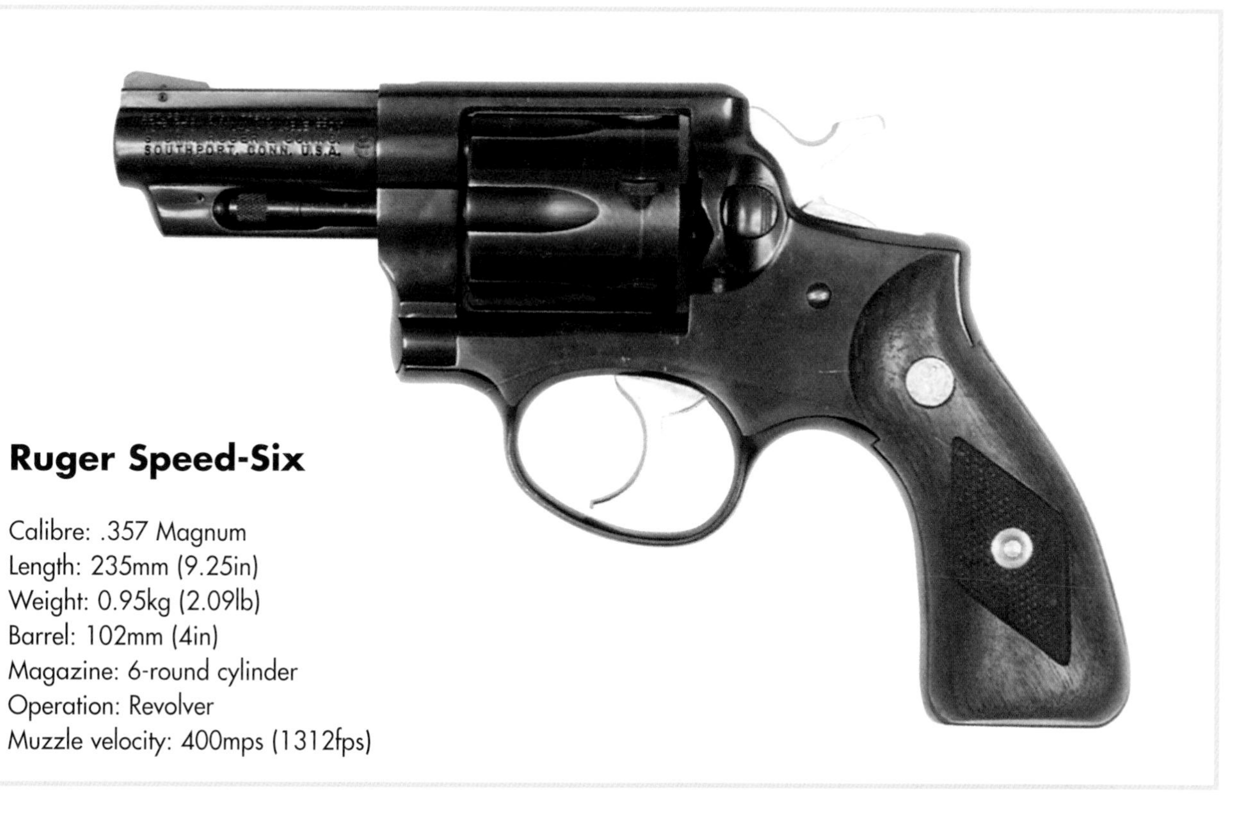

Ruger Speed-Six

Calibre: .357 Magnum
Length: 235mm (9.25in)
Weight: 0.95kg (2.09lb)
Barrel: 102mm (4in)
Magazine: 6-round cylinder
Operation: Revolver
Muzzle velocity: 400mps (1312fps)

Weapon noise and silencers

The other aspect of improving a weapon's concealability concerns devising means to minimize its audible signature when it is fired. For the citizen, there are few good reasons for owning a silenced weapon, except for vermin control officers who do not wish to wake the neighbourhood with early-morning gunfire or scare off the animals or birds they are sent to eliminate. In most regions, silenced weapons are illegal.

For most military users silencing is irrelevant. Indeed, the noise of a weapon discharge is a useful part of the weapon's effect, possibly scaring off an opponent even though he has not been hit. Special forces troops and similar covert operatives, however, do find it useful to be able to kill at distance but in silence, taking down guard dogs and sentries without alerting others to their presence by the noise of gunfire or by having to resort to close-quarters tactics.

Weapon noise comes from three sources: the sound of the cartridge firing, the noise made by a bullet travelling at supersonic speeds and the mechanical noise of the weapon itself. Bullet noise can be reduced by using lower-velocity ammunition and mechanical noise can be minimized by locking a weapon so that it is manually reloaded rather than allowing the slide to work normally. The major problem is the sound made by firing the weapon. A 'silencer' or 'suppressor' can be fitted to some weapons to muffle the noise of the report with a series of sound-absorbing baffles. A silencer makes the weapon muzzle-heavy and rather unwieldy for combat operations, but the whole point of using one is to avoid combat in favour of stealth.

S&W Mk 22

Perhaps the most famous of silenced pistols is the Smith & Wesson Mk 22, known as the 'Hush Puppy'. The name is a piece of rather grim humour, since silenced pistols are often used to kill guard dogs. The Hush Puppy is based on the S&W Model 39, with the slide locked to reduce manual noise. With subsonic ammunition, the Mk 22 is very quiet in operation: the noise it makes, even if audible, does not sound like gunfire. The 'Hush Puppy' remained in service until the 1980s.

Colt Detective Special

Calibre: .38 Special
Length: 171mm (6.7in)
Weight: 0.6kg (1.31lb)
Barrel: 54mm (2.13in), 6 grooves, rh
Magazine: 6-round cylinder
Operation: Revolver
Muzzle velocity: 213mps (700fps)

Ruger Mk II

In use with US Navy SEALs, Mossad and – at the other end of the scale – pest control officers, the silenced Ruger Mk II pistol is a semi-automatic target pistol chambered in .22 LR and fed from a nine-round magazine. The Ruger's target-pistol lineage is apparent in its great accuracy: it can hit its target at 70 metres (230 feet), which is a long way for any handgun. The .22 LR round has little stopping power, so is no use against a charging opponent, but for silent assassination (it does not matter if the target dies immediately, so long as he dies) or precise elimination of animals the weapon is ideal.

Space-age semi-automatics

While the semi-automatic pistol came of age during World War II and the immediate post-war years, there was still some way to go before the full potential of the handheld 'slugthrower' (a bullet is basically a 'slug' of lead, hence the name) was to be realized.

From the 1960s onward, the quest for ever better sidearms took designers down several roads. Experiments with different calibres and ammunition types continued alongside the use of new, space-age materials and manufacturing processes. The science of ergonomics was applied to weaponry in order to create comfortable and easy-to-use sidearms. In addition, some 'blue-sky' projects were undertaken that might have revolutionized the world of handguns, but ultimately fell by the wayside.

Glock 17

When advanced sidearms are mentioned, the Glock range leaps immediately to mind. The appearance of the Glock 17 in 1983 caused controversy, owing to claims by various ill-informed 'authorities' that this 'plastic pistol' could be carried through airport weapon detectors. Such authorities failed to note that only 40 per cent of the Glock is plastic and the metal parts, including the slide, barrel and ammunition, are of metal and will set off a metal detector. The weapon also retains a distinct 'pistol' shape on an X-ray scanner screen and will be spotted by an alert operator.

Subsequent events have shown that all kinds of things can be carried undetected through lax airport security; the Glock is no better or worse than any other handgun at remaining undetected.

Panic aside, the Glock was a truly revolutionary weapon. Its clean lines are made possible by a lack of external controls. Rather than the traditional safety catch the Glock uses a trigger safety and firing pin lock; the weapon will not fire unless the trigger is pulled. This does not prevent over-enthusiastic users suffering from an unfortunate condition known as 'Glock Leg', if their draw action takes up a little too much trigger slack, but this is a human failing, not a mechanical one. The Glock is as safe as a weapon can be while still remaining useful in combat.

The '17' designator was derived from the weapon's magazine capacity; an awesome 17 rounds

Safety systems

The standard safety catch on a semi-automatic prevents movement of either the trigger, the sear or the hammer, preventing the weapon from being fired until the catch is released. It may be mounted on the frame or the slide. Some weapons use a combination of safety devices, for example a standard safety catch and a grip safety.

Smith & Wesson Mk 22

Calibre: 9mm Parabellum
Length: 323mm (12.75in)
Weight: 0.96kg (2.1lb)
Barrel: 101mm (3.9in), 6 grooves, rh
Magazine: 8 round detachable box magazine
Operation: Blowback
Muzzle velocity: 274mps (900fps)

of 9mm Parabellum, double-stacked in the detachable box magazine. The firepower offered by such a large magazine, coupled with good marketing and overall simplicity of use, made the Glock 17 a winner. It has been adopted by police and military forces worldwide and is a popular sidearm for civilian weapon users.

Ruger MkII

Calibre: .22 Long Rifle
Length: 342mm (13.46in)
Weight: 1.43kg (3.15lb)
Barrel: 152mm (6in)
Magazine: 9-round detachable box magazine
Operation: Single-action blowback
Muzzle velocity: 246mps (807fps)

Glock variants

The success of the 17 prompted Glock to produce a family of handguns. The Glock 18 is a full-automatic machine pistol or 'assault pistol'. Chambered in 9mm and fed from a 19- or 33-round extended magazine, the Glock 18 is not a civilian weapon. Like similar assault pistols, it can get rid of a lot of ammunition very quickly (1300 rounds per minute) but it is of questionable use in combat. Altogether more practical are the Glock variants designated 20 to 23. These weapons are essentially 17s chambered for different ammunition. The 20 is chambered for the new 10mm Auto round, which is extremely powerful. Fed from a 15-round magazine, the 20 offers substantial firepower in a package very similar to the 17. The 21 is aimed at a certain segment of the US market that believes in .45 ACP or nothing, bringing Glock quality to this traditional and well respected calibre. The 22 and 23 models are chambered for .40 Smith & Wesson, another new and powerful round.

All Glock pistols have certain things in common. They are safe when used properly, extremely resistant to harsh conditions and easy to use. Features such as a reverse curve on the trigger guard make two-handed firing easier and have become standard on most modern semi-automatics.

Glock 17

Calibre: 9mm Parabellum
Length: 188mm (7.4in)
Weight: 0.65kg (1.44lb)
Barrel: 114mm (4.49in), 6 grooves, rh
Magazine: 17-round detachable box magazine
Operation: Short recoil
Muzzle velocity: 350mps (1148fps)

Left: The tough Glock pistol consists of only 33 component parts, making it simple to strip and clean in the field – a significant advantage over more temperamental handguns.

Durability as standard

Modern handguns are capable of withstanding horrific abuse while still functioning. During trials, a Glock 17 was left immersed in seawater for a week, brushed clean and taken to the range. It fired flawlessly. Modern finishes and materials are sufficiently robust that even fairly cheap weapons will fire thousands of rounds without trouble if properly maintained.

Beretta 92 & 93R

Rather more conventional, but nevertheless a fine weapon, is the Beretta 92. The eventual winner of the extended trials for a new US military service pistol, the Beretta 92 is a fairly conventional modern semi-automatic. It has an ambidextrous safety and magazine release and can be fired double-action on the first shot or manually cocked. Magazine capacity is 15 rounds of 9mm Parabellum, offering good firepower.

The weapon adopted by the US Forces was the 92SB, which was replaced by the 92F to meet the requirements of military service. Early in the Beretta's service life problems were encountered with some examples, including a tendency for the slide to crack or even, in the worst cases, come adrift and fly off into the firer's face.

Although US Navy SEALs dropped the Beretta in favour of other handguns, the problems were cleared up and Berettas have now given many years of fine service despite the grumbles of servicemen who, perhaps recalling stories of amok Filipinos a century ago, would have preferred something in a heavier calibre – say, .45 ACP.

The Beretta 92 is also a standard law enforcement sidearm and used by many private owners. An 'assault pistol' version, the 93R, is available. Fitted with a tiny foregrip and an extended magazine, the 93R can deliver three-round bursts. Even with the optional stock, a full-automatic pistol is not the most controllable of devices. Although the 93R is in use with Italian governmental protection officers, it has not achieved widespread popularity. A suppressed version of the standard 92F is also available to military users.

SIG-Sauer P-220 series

Another contender in the US Army Pistol Trials was SIG-Sauer, whose extremely high quality P226 was the only weapon other than the Beretta to meet all requirements. Designed by the Swiss firm SIG and manufactured by Sauer in Germany, SIGs are renowned for their quality but also their high price tag. This may have been the deciding factor between the two finalists.

Several SIG handguns are available. The P-210, featuring an unusual internal slide moving on rails, was taken up by Danish military and German police forces, while the P-225 and P-226 have found favour with a number of law enforcement

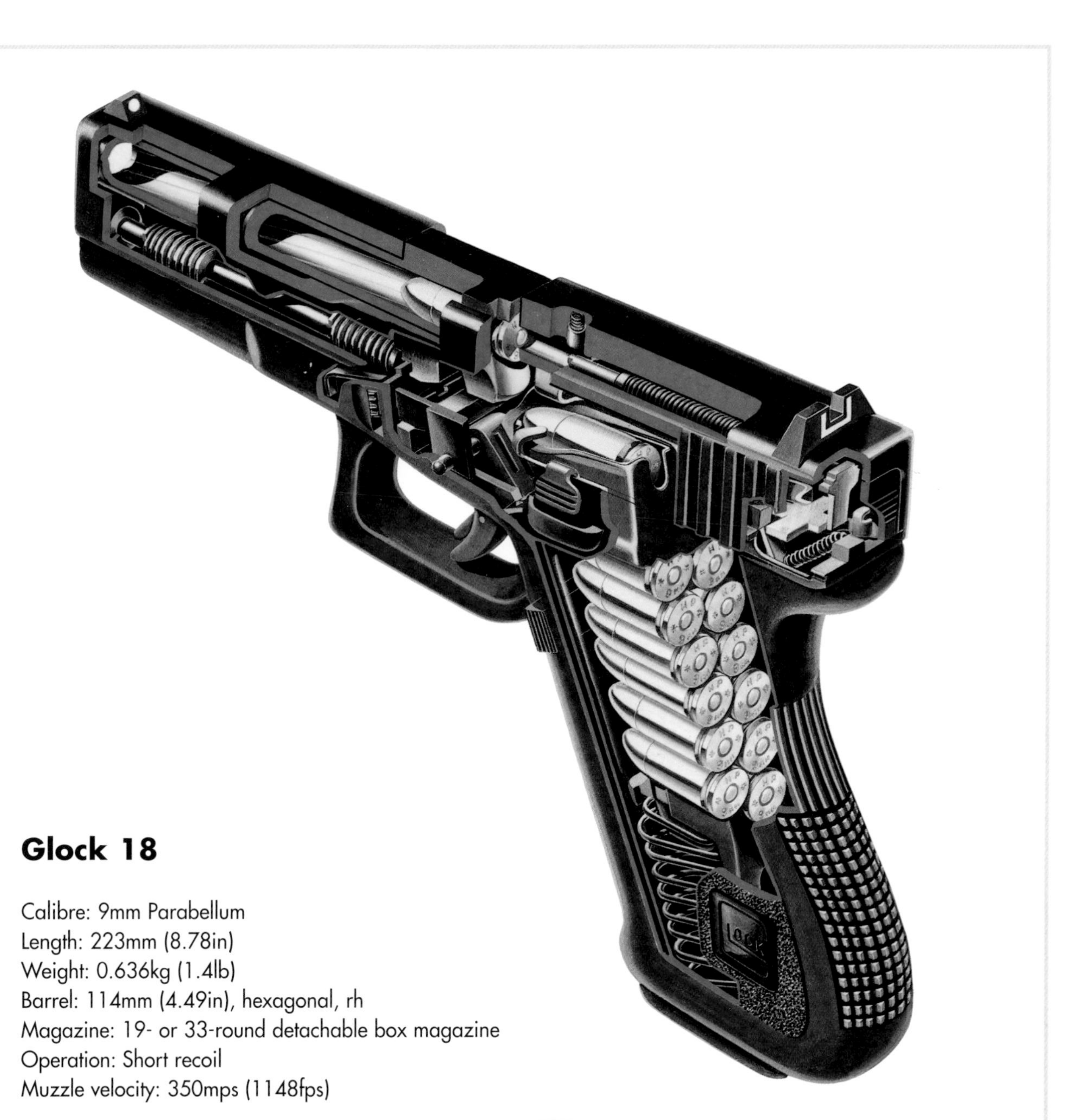

Glock 18

Calibre: 9mm Parabellum
Length: 223mm (8.78in)
Weight: 0.636kg (1.4lb)
Barrel: 114mm (4.49in), hexagonal, rh
Magazine: 19- or 33-round detachable box magazine
Operation: Short recoil
Muzzle velocity: 350mps (1148fps)

agencies and, according to unconfirmed but popular speculation, special forces, who can afford to buy the weapons they want, regardless of cost. The P-225 has a low ammunition capacity at only eight rounds of 9mm; the P-226 holds fifteen and is in service with the FBI.

Development of the SIG family continues; the P-228 is smaller and lighter than the 226, with a slightly lower ammunition capacity. It is available with a short trigger to make shooting easier for users with small hands. The P-228 can be used double- or single-action but cannot be carried 'Condition One'.

Above: Modern handguns are designed for ease of use in the hands of part-trained personnel. These Iranian women are training with 9mm Beretta 92 pistols as members of the Civil Militia although their formal stances are hardly realistic for real combat.

Right: The Beretta 93R machine-pistol, with its tiny shoulder stock, fold-down foregrip and extended magazine is a good way to get rid of a lot of ammunition very quickly. This may or may not be of use in actual combat.

CZ85

As an example of what can be done with an entirely conventional semi-automatic, the CZ85 stands out from the crowd. While Eastern Europe weapons manufacturers are sometimes associated with low-quality products, the CZ85 is an excellent weapon. Based around the Colt-Browning action used in the M1911A1, the CZ85 is an updated version of the CZ75, which first appeared in 1975. Chambered for 9mm Parabellum, the CZ was better received in the West than in what was then the Warsaw Pact, and was never taken up by the Czech armed forces.

The double-action CZ85 is fed from a 15-round magazine and has an ambidextrous safety. It is a very well made weapon and has remained popular with private users as well as several government and military forces. While there is little innovative about this weapon, it can be considered something of an 'industry standard' for a workhorse semi-automatic.

The designers, Ceská zbrojovka organisation, failed to take out adequate patent protection and it is perhaps an unwanted compliment to this excellent handgun that it has been copied so many times by so many different manufacturers.

Detonics Combat Master

By the 1970s the much-loved M1911A1 was showing its age. Many manufacturers sought to create a weapon that would offer the advantages of the venerable Colt but bring the .45 right up to date. One such weapon – and a very good one – was the Detonics Combat Master. Available in a number of configurations, and ultimately in several calibres, Detonics pistols are of extremely high quality, incorporating design features to reduce felt recoil and improve handling.

Now out of production, the Combat Master is a compact M1911-pattern handgun chambered for .45 ACP. Designed from the outset to handle hollow-point rounds, which improve stopping power, the Combat Master is fed from a six-round magazine and features two (or in later models, three) recoil springs as opposed to one in the Colt. Fairly heavy for its small size, the Combat Master offers the user .45 stopping power in a small and easily concealable handgun. Later Detonics pistols explored alternative calibres including 9mm and a '451 Detonics' round.

Despite being rescued from bankruptcy once, Detonics is no longer in business. This is probably because the market was not ready for such expensive little guns, despite their excellence.

Beretta 93R

Calibre: 9mm Parabellum
Length: 240mm (9.45in)
Weight: 1.12kg (2.47lb)
Barrel: 156mm (6.14in), 6 grooves, rh
Magazine: 15- or 20-round detachable box
Operation: Short recoil
Muzzle velocity: 375mps (1230fps)

Sig-Sauer P220

Calibre: 9mm
Length: 198mm (7.8in)
Weight: 0.83kg (1.83lb)
Barrel: 112mm (4.4in)
Magazine: 9-round detachable box magazine
Operation: Double-action recoil
Muzzle velocity: 345mps (1132fps)

Magazine safety

Some semi-automatic handguns have a magazine safety, which prevents the weapon from being fired if the magazine is removed. This prevents accidental discharge when a round is mistakenly left in the chamber. Similarly, most semi-automatic handguns will not fire if the slide is not fully home, which may occur due to dirt or fouling.

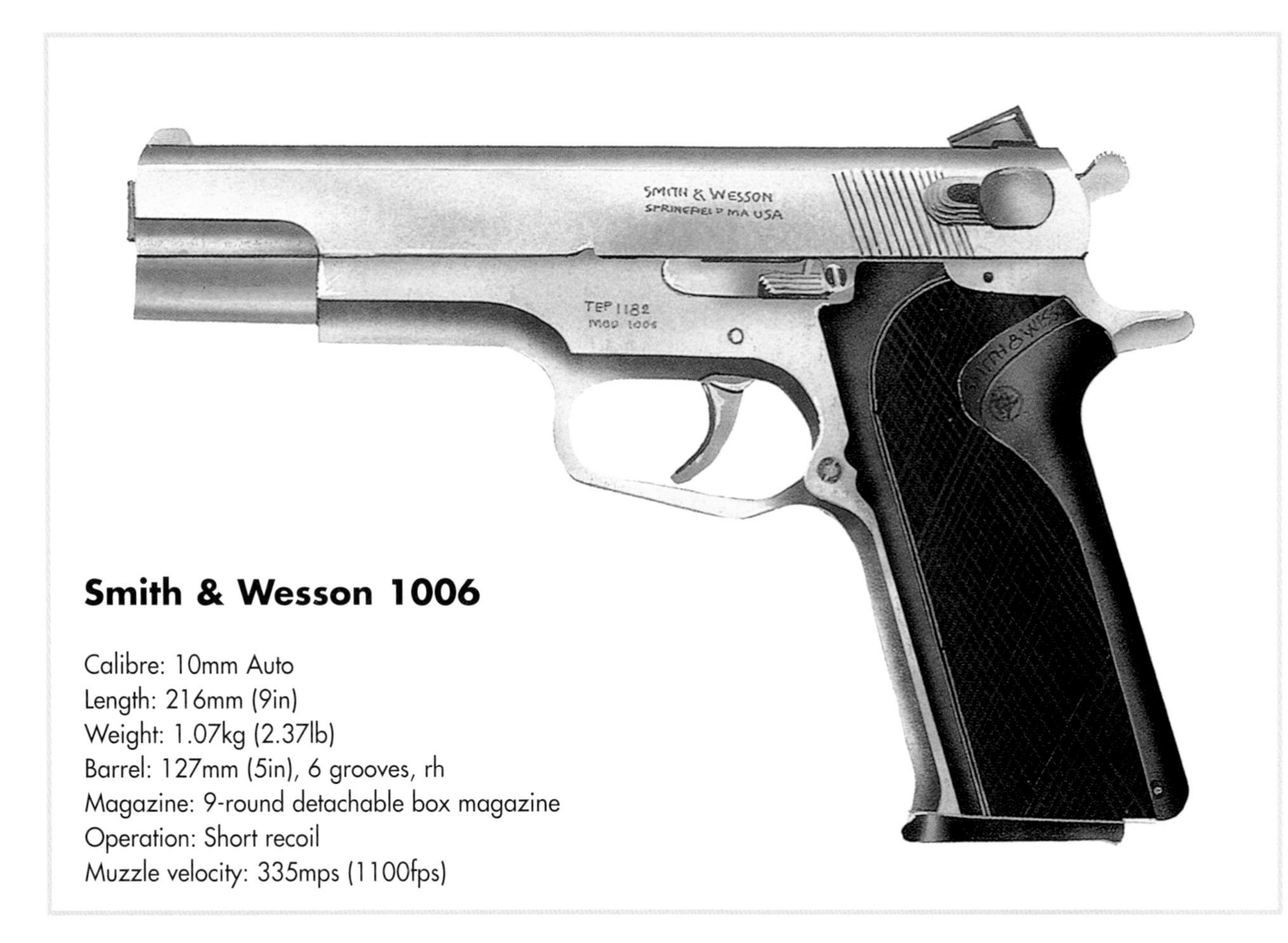

Smith & Wesson 1006

Calibre: 10mm Auto
Length: 216mm (9in)
Weight: 1.07kg (2.37lb)
Barrel: 127mm (5in), 6 grooves, rh
Magazine: 9-round detachable box magazine
Operation: Short recoil
Muzzle velocity: 335mps (1100fps)

S&W 1006 & 4506

In addition to contributing to the revolver renaissance, from the 1980s Smith & Wesson developed a range of excellent semi-automatics. Chambered for 9mm, 10mm, .45 ACP and .40 S&W, these weapons are all very similar, being based around a common frame. The various pistols are designated by a number system, with 1006 describing the 10mm and 4506 being the .45. Magazine capacities range from eight rounds in the .45 to 11 in the 4026. The latter is the .40 S&W variant, which uses a '10mm light' cartridge developed following FBI trials with the mighty 10mm round. Each weapon is also available with various features, including double-action only, double-action with ambidextrous safety, and double-action with a decocking lever rather than a regular safety catch.

The Smith & Wesson range is designed with the shooter in mind; all versions are as easy and comfortable to shoot as possible, though the 1006 is an extremely powerful handgun that requires a well trained user to control it properly. This handgun was adopted by the FBI since it offered sufficient stopping power to guarantee the safety of an agent, perhaps operating alone, dealing with multiple assailants. For police or civilian use the less powerful 4026 is probably a better option, as it is far more controllable yet still retains excellent ballistic characteristics.

It may be that in terms of Smith & Wesson's contribution to the future of handguns, the excellent .40 round may be even more important than the gun built to fire it.

One-handed use

The Czech CZ100 mounts a hook on top of the slide so that it can be cocked with one hand, by pushing the weapon against a hard surface.

Gyrojet

Some experiments with ammunition require a wholly new weapon to use it. One such, developed in the 1960s, was the Gyrojet pistol. Rather than a bullet propelled by conventional propellant and reaching its maximum velocity in the barrel, the Gyrojet fired a small 13mm calibre rocket that accelerated in flight. The rocket was spun in flight by offset propellant vents in a manner similar to some antitank missiles.

Gyrojet

Calibre: 13mm
Length: 234mm (9.2in)
Weight: 0.98kg (34.5oz)
Barrel: 127mm (5in)
Magazine: 6-round box magazine
Operation: Integral spring feed
Muzzle velocity: 274mps (900fps)

The Gyrojet needed no ejection system, since the entire round was ejected from the barrel, which made extraction an irrelevance and simplified the mechanism. The weapon, however, was highly inaccurate and, due to the low velocity upon leaving the barrel compared to a conventional bullet, not very effective at extremely close range. As a result, the idea never caught on.

It is possible to see only one circumstance in which Gyrojet-type weapons might be desirable. In some unpleasant future astronauts might feel the need to shoot at one another. The recoil of a standard firearm would pose a problem in microgravity, while a weapon firing powered projectiles would not throw the user around so much. The consequences, however, of gunfire of any sort aboard a spacecraft or station would probably be disastrous. Nevertheless the weapon deserves an honourable mention for demonstrating an intriguing concept that just might have revolutionized the world of handguns.

The quest for stopping power

For some users, no matter how potent their weapon there is always a need for more firepower: bigger magazines, better accuracy or more stopping power. One way to increase firepower is to shoot more bullets at the target, but burst-capable or fully automatic sidearms have never really caught on.

The alternative to firing more bullets is to give a single round unbelievable power. This is achieved by making it leave the barrel faster, making the bullet itself heavier, or both. The Magnum calibres offered an impressive increase in the power of each bullet, but initially required a large-frame revolver to withstand the awesome gas pressures developed within the firing chamber. Firearms users were forced to choose between the stopping power of a .44 Magnum revolver with six rounds aboard and the greater ease of carry, increased capacity and faster reloading of, say, a 'mere' .45.

The answer was to create a semi-automatic pistol abel to fire Magnum calibres. Various experiments have been conducted using pistol Magnum rounds and even cut-down rifle ammunition. Of all the huge-calibre semi-automatics to emerge from these experiments, two stand out as truly great firearms.

.44 Automag

The first is the Automag. Developed in the 1960s, this large, solid self-loader has been manufactured by several companies, though never in large numbers. Originally chambered for .44 Magnum, Automags are available in several calibres. Barrels can be swapped easily, and some users have barrels in different calibres to allow a quick change if desired.

MILITARY SIDEARMS: COLT M1911A1 VERSUS

The decision of US armed forces to replace the ageing M1911A1 as the standard service handgun led to a long, drawn-out series of trials, legal wrangles and re-evaluations. The eventual adoption of the Beretta 92F, a 9mm semi-automatic, did not please everyone involved. Indeed the move away from .45 ACP-chambered handguns upset many users. The .45 cartridge was originally adopted for its stopping power; returning to a smaller calibre seemed like a retrograde step. In addition, some manufacturers felt that they had not been given a fair chance to show what their weapons could do. But whatever recriminations may have been made, the 9mm Beretta replaced the .45 Colt in US service – for better or for worse.

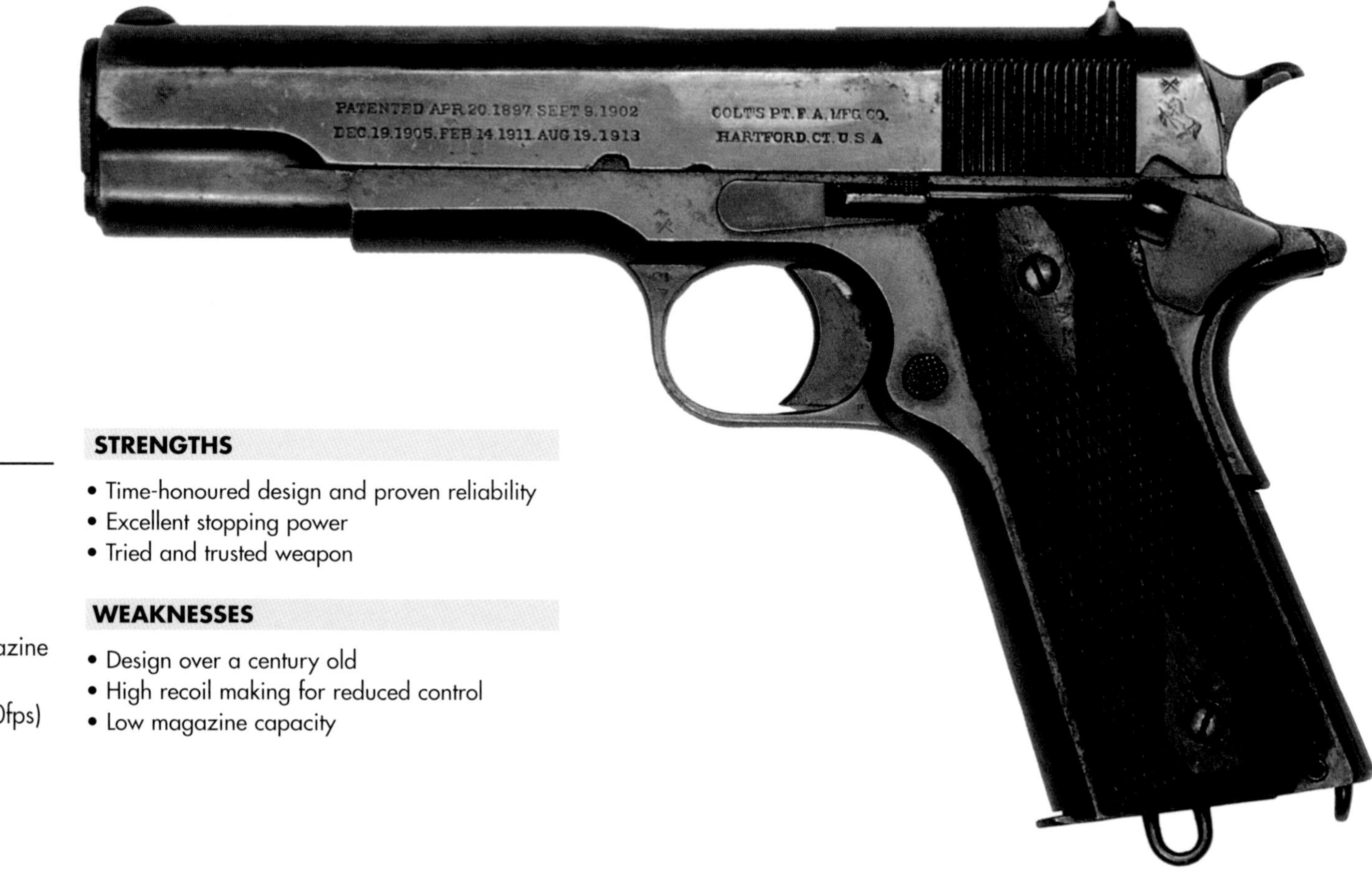

Colt M1911A1

Calibre: .45in
Length: 219mm (8.6in)
Weight: 1.1kg (39oz)
Barrel: 127mm (5in)
Magazine: 7-round box magazine
Operation: Short recoil
Muzzle velocity: 253mps (830fps)

STRENGTHS

- Time-honoured design and proven reliability
- Excellent stopping power
- Tried and trusted weapon

WEAKNESSES

- Design over a century old
- High recoil making for reduced control
- Low magazine capacity

BERETTA 92F

The M1911A1 had decades of sterling service behind it, from the trenches of World War I, through jungle and desert to the urban conflicts of the later twentieth century. Its reliability and stopping power had been proven time and time again. On the other hand, the 9mm Beretta carries more ammunition and has a lighter recoil, making it more controllable for the average soldier. It also achieved a measure of recognition as the weapon used by Mel Gibson's character in the *Lethal Weapon* films. The Beretta comes from a well-respected maker – its pedigree is not in any doubt – but after it was adopted there were doubts about its longevity, since firing large numbers of rounds seemed to bring on component failure.

Beretta 92F

Calibre: 9mm
Length: 217mm (8.54in)
Weight: loaded 1.145kg (2.524lb)
Barrel: 125mm (4.92in)
Magazine: 15-rounds box magazine
Operation: Short recoil
Muzzle velocity: 390mps (1280fps)

STRENGTHS

- Large magazine capacity
- Modern ergonomic design
- Ambidextrous operation

WEAKNESSES

- Lower stopping power than M1911A1
- Reliability issues with early models
- Long-term service life in some doubt

IMI Desert Eagle

Calibre: .357in, .44in or .50in Magnum
Length: 260mm (10.25in)
Weight: 1.7kg (3.75lb) for .357; 1.8kg (4.1lb) for .44;
2.05kg (4.5lb) for .50
Barrel: 152mm (6in)
Magazine: 9 rounds (.357 Magnum); 8 rounds (.44 Magnum);
7 rounds (.50 Magnum), detachable box magazine
Operation: Gas
Muzzle velocity: 436 mps (1430fps) for .357; 448mps (1470fps) for .44

The .44 Automag can hurl out a 240-grain bullet at 457 metres (1500 feet) per second, a good 30.5 metres (100 feet) per second more than an equivalent round from a revolver. Performance with .357 Magnum ammunition is likewise better than in an equivalent revolver. Even with such a heavy weapon recoil is considerable, although the recoil-operated slide helps soak up some of the kick. Automags have been out of production since 2000 but it is possible another company might take up manufacture of this influential and powerful weapon.

IMI Desert Eagle

More famous than the Automag is the Desert Eagle. Originally developed in the USA by M.R.I. Limited, the design was taken up and developed by Israeli Military Industries, who gave the weapon its current name. The original Desert Eagles, chambered for .357 and .44 Magnum, are both extremely powerful weapons. As if this were not enough, a massive .50 calibre version followed.

The standard Desert Eagle is a huge and bulky handgun, quite unsuitable for concealed carry but offering massive stopping power. Its nine-round magazine allows reasonable sustained fire, although such an awesome weapon is difficult to control despite being designed to cut felt recoil to manageable levels.

Desert Eagles are available with long barrels and telescopic sights, like some revolvers. The usefulness of such extras is debatable. Indeed, it could be argued that weapons such as the Desert Eagle have outgrown the best characteristics of handguns – concealability and portability. A .50 Desert Eagle is about half as long as a 9mm Mini-Uzi (a small submachine gun marketed by the same company) and weighs 2.05 kilograms (4.5 pounds) as opposed to the submachine gun's 2.7 kilograms (5.95 pounds). It is unlikely that an even bigger production handgun will appear in the near future, so perhaps the .50 Desert Eagle represents the pinnacle of development of the monster handgun.

Size and intimidation

For most users, huge and powerful handguns are simply too big and too heavy for the normal uses to which handguns are put. As an alternative to a carbine or submachine gun, however, or for situations where a larger weapon is inappropriate yet the target must be disabled on the first hit without fail, these weapons represent the ultimate in handheld stopping power.

However huge and bulky they may be, giant pistols are still easier to carry than a carbine and in many ways more intimidating. There is something very personal about a handgun aimed in your direction, and few people are brave enough to try anything when looking down a cavernous barrel.

Right: The monstrous Desert Eagle is not a weapon for the faint of heart. Big Magnums can be unpleasant to shoot. Anticipation of the massive kick can cause 'Magnum flinch' before firing, reducing accuracy.

The future of handguns

Handguns are supremely useful tools and have never gone out of fashion. Where other weapons such as submachine guns have been threatened with extinction by competitors (in this case lightweight assault rifles), the need for a small, easy-to-carry sidearm has remained constant.

The future of the handgun is assured: the only question is what form will it take? The general shape of the weapon seems likely to remain more or less the same, allowing for slight tweaks dictated by ergonomics. Rocket ammunition has been proven ineffective, so until someone manages to develop a handheld directed energy weapon the mode of operation will not change very much either. There are few ways to feed ammunition into a pistol, and none as compact as through a hollow handgrip.

It seems likely that advances in handgun design will be evolutionary rather than revolutionary. This does not preclude impressive developments, such as the double-action semi-automatic, which allowed weapons to be brought into action more quickly. The 'repeatable secure striker' built into Fabrique Nationale's Forty-Nine pistol, for example, allows a second attempt to fire a misfiring cartridge without recocking the weapon and improves safety. Other design features becoming common in production pistols include gas ports to vent some propellant, reducing recoil. Modern design and computer modelling processes allow precise calculation of port positions to be made, giving good recoil reduction without a loss in weapon power.

Advanced materials also have their part to play in modern gun design. Stronger weapons are more resistant to abuse and can handle higher chamber pressures, meaning that more powerful ammunition to be used. Advanced materials can also improve handling characteristics while making the weapon more resistant to corrosion, dirt entry and general wear from firing. It may be that future pistols will last far longer before becoming degraded by barrel wear, for example, and function better in filthy conditions.

Parabellum ammunition

The standard 9x19mm round is known as 9mm Parabellum in most regions (from the Latin phrase *Si vis pacem, para bellum*: 'If you seek peace, prepare for war'), but as the 9mm Luger in the USA, after its inventor, Georg Luger.

The ubiquitous 9mm Parabellum round is also very similar in size to .38 and .357 rounds. Adaptor clips are available to allow revolvers chambered for these rounds to fire 9mm Parabellum.

Large-calibre handguns

The .50 Action Express pistol round was first marketed in 1991. It develops almost double the muzzle energy of a .44 Magnum round. Only a few handguns can fire this incredible cartridge, including the Desert Eagle and the Grizzly Magnum automatic pistols, and all still suffer from a fearsome recoil.

Calibre and ammunition

Ammunition also has a part to play. New calibres offering a better balance of recoil and ballistic characteristics will improve the capabilities of standard handguns, while special ammunition types will offer certain advantages such as low probability of ricochet, better energy transfer into the target, or a low chance of overpenetration. This could be particularly important in some specific security applications, for example when used by 'sky marshals' aboard aircraft, where a conventional round might compromise the integrity of a pressurized cabin after missing (or even passing through) a hijacker.

One intriguing idea is the concept of a common rifle and pistol round. Since the demise of black-powder weapons this has been impractical, even though pistol/submachine gun commonality is an industry standard. The established principle that the same round could not be used in a rifle and a handgun was challenged by Fabrique Nationale with their 5.7mm round. The 'Five-seveN' pistol was created to use the same 5.7mm SS190 ammunition developed for use in the P-90 carbine. In the event the ammunition performs poorly in a handgun, but it may be that the concept will lead to other innovations. In the meantime, the project shows that firearms developers are willing to try out new ideas – or new implementations of old ones – in the quest for ever better handguns.

Despite lawsuits blaming manufacturers for misuse of their products, restrictions on ownership and a great deal of bad press, the future of the handgun remains assured. So long as weapons of any kind are required, small portable man-stoppers will remain essential.

Left: The FN Five-Seven pistol is a wholly new design of weapon rather than an evolution of existing pistols. It is built around the 5.7mm cartridge developed for the P90 carbine, also shown here, and includes many innovative ergonomic features.

Right: US soldiers watch Filipino troops with handguns during a live-fire exercise near Manila in 2002. The exercise was part of an attempt to aid Filipino operations against guerrillas believed to be linked to al Qaeda.

15

RIFLES

In the days of black powder, most weapons were smoothbore designs. A 'rifle' was similar to a musket but had a rifled barrel, giving greater accuracy at the expense of slower loading. As the musket faded from history, the meaning gradually changed to its present definition – a longarm with a rifled barrel, firing a long cartridge of smaller calibre to a handgun.

Whenever a rifle is recovered from, or used by, criminals the media tend to refer to it as a 'high-velocity rifle'. This is technically not untrue – rifles propel their ammunition at relatively high velocities compared to a handgun round – but perhaps the term might be more accurately applied to true high-velocity weapons, which can hurl a small projectile at awesome speeds. The average 'plinking' or varmint-shooting rifle develops rather less muzzle energy.

High or low velocity

High velocity is important for two reasons. Firstly, it helps the bullet reach its target: the faster a projectile, the flatter its trajectory. Relatively 'slow' bullets may have to travel in quite a high arc to reach a given range, while faster rounds can be fired virtually straight at the target. This simplifies sighting and reduces the effects of wind or target movement on the shot. A higher-velocity round can also be fired further by using the same high trajectory as its lesser cousins, though there are limits to the ability of most riflemen to hit at extreme ranges.

High velocity also assists in achieving what the bullet was fired to do – disabling or destroying the target. If the projected target is to be small game then a fairly low-velocity rifle is fine: it does not take much to bring down a squirrel, and there is no need for long range if a weapon is to be used mostly in a forest.

On the other hand, if the weapon is intended to bring down a moose or a charging man armed with a sharp implement, then the bullet must arrive with sufficient power to do so. High velocity, coupled with a heavy round, is necessary to achieve an immediate result. This is important for the hunter who does not wish to search for a deer that might have run many hundreds of metres before succumbing to a wound, and vital for the military or law-enforcement shooter who must take down his target before he can shoot or stab.

Left: A soldier dressed in a chemical warfare protection suit takes aim with his SA80 assault rifle. Light, short due to its 'bullpup' configuration and capable of full-automatic fire, the SA80 is ideal for urban or mechanised combat.

Rifle types

Thus, today, the word 'rifle' can refer to a wide range of weapons from single-shot hunting arms to military combat weapons. A few specific terms have been adapted or coined to subdivide the many different types. The mode of operation of these weapons is usually very similar, but their characteristics may vary considerably.

Hunting and 'plinking' rifles often have most in common with their historical ancestors. Whether fed from an internal magazine or a detachable one, and reloaded by mechanical action (e.g. bolt or lever action) or semi-automatic feed, such weapons tend to be conventional in design and would be familiar to a rifleman of 1930 or even 1870. Sniper rifles used by the military and law enforcers are often based on hunting weapons, though some very advanced specialist weapons are available.

Left: Troops debus from their armoured transport. Increased use of vehicles has necessitated shorter rifles than those used by previous generations of infantry, who normally marched to the battle area.

Below: A Yugoslavian sniper looks through the optical sight on his M76. Many modern military rifles are designed for use in highly specialized roles.

Advanced military weapons represent the pinnacle of modern rifle development and are sometimes very different from their ancestors.

The advent of the fully-automatic rifle in the middle of the twentieth century led quickly to the creation of the Assault Rifle, a lightweight weapon capable of firing semi-automatic single shots plus bursts of a controlled length and/or full-automatic fire. Assault rifles are general-purpose military weapons designed for lightness, large ammunition capacity and ease of use by troops travelling in vehicles and fighting in close terrain, such as urban areas. Assault rifles are differentiated from full-auto versions of standard rifles (often termed 'automatic rifles', although the line between the two is often blurry) by their special characteristics.

A good assault rifle must be able to deliver devastating firepower at an instant's notice. Accuracy at 1000 metres (3280 feet) is an advantage but most soldiers cannot hit their target at that range, and combat rarely takes place beyond 300 metres (985 feet), so effectiveness at this shorter 'battle range' is much more important. Reliability is obviously a factor with assault rifles – a hunter can afford to deal with a weapon malfunction but a soldier may not have such a luxury.

Carbines

The term 'carbine' is also applied to many rifle-type weapons, and its use can be confusing. Technically speaking, all modern carbines are by definition rifles (i.e. they are longarms with a rifled barrel) but the term has evolved to apply to a specific subset of rifled longarms, allowing the word 'rifle' to be used for the remainder. Historically, however, a carbine was a short musket-like weapon, usually in pistol calibre, used by cavalrymen.

Right: Sir Colin Campbell's 93rd Highlanders assault a Russian redoubt at the Battle of the Alma. Later in the campaign this regiment, stood in line as a 'thin red streak tipped with steel' and shot apart an assault by Russian cavalry, demonstrating the dominance of infantry firepower.

Today's carbines are rarely chambered for pistol ammunition but use rifle calibres. In general terms, the word carbine often refers to a smaller, lighter version of a standard combat rifle. An example is the Colt Commando, which is a shorter version of the M16 assault rifle.

A carbine, however, may also be a semi-automatic 'civilian' version of an assault rifle or submachine gun, or a pistol fitted with a stock. Some early assault rifles were designated 'carbines' because their compact construction made them so much smaller than the infantry rifles of the day.

Thus the terminology of rifles and carbines can be quite confusing. Lack of precise definitions makes legislation and categorizing of weapons difficult. In the following pages we will use the fairly universal practice of calling a full-sized rifled longarm a 'rifle', subdivided into assault, hunting, sniper and automatic types, and referring to a small, lightweight rifle that does not fit into the assault rifle category as a carbine.

The last days of glory

The wars of the first decades of the nineteenth century were characterized by colourfully clad troops blazing away at one another with muskets or charging home with the sword and bayonet. Visibility was not at that time a death sentence. Indeed, gorgeous uniforms and tall hats made men feel like unstoppable gods who awed the enemy with their appearance. It has been calculated that up to a thousand shots needed to be fired in order to cause one casualty, and with small arms so limited in range that a target 300 metres (985 feet) away might as well be on the Moon, sang-froid in the face of enemy fire was survivable.

The common issue of rifled muskets and, not much later, modern rifles changed all that. By the middle of the nineteenth century an average rifleman had a decent chance of hitting his target at 500 metres (1640 feet), and where the target was a

Fix swords!

The British Rifle Brigade used the long sword bayonet, rather than the shorter spike bayonet, because their Baker rifles were shorter than the standard muskets of the period. The sword provided the reach necessary to bayonet mounted opponents. The Rifle Brigade kept the command 'fix swords!' long after its equipment was standardized with the rest of the British Army.

Left: Sergeant Dore of the 7th New York Militia poses with his Springfield rifle in 1861. The spike bayonet was a fearsome weapon, but it was rapid, accurate rifle fire that now ruled the battlefield.

formed body of infantry or, better yet, cavalry a far greater proportion of shots took effect. The glorious days of massed action were over, and the wars of the mid-nineteenth century would ram home this point with bloody emphasis.

The Crimea

In Europe, the Crimean War of 1854–6 had foreshadowed things to come. The aimed fire of rifled muskets chopped apart dense columns of infantry at the River Alma, while at Sebastopol the 'thin red streak tipped with steel' under Sir Colin Campbell stood in line – not square – and shot down a Russian cavalry charge before it could come into contact. The days of shock action with sword and bayonet were over for ever. The reach of the infantryman was multiplied threefold or more, creating a killing ground that could not be crossed.

The American Civil War

The lesson was there to be learned, but events in Europe seemed far away as the American Civil War broke out and the scramble to raise, train and field troops began. Neither side had a large body of experienced troops or officers since the United States did not then maintain a large standing army. Thus perhaps the reliance on massed action had as much to do with the difficulties of controlling bodies of hastily raised militia as it did with ignorance of military reality.

For whatever reason, the armies of both sides were thrust, almost as innocents, into a maelstrom of evolving military technology, the applications of which were still being determined. Both sides tried to fight an old-style war with new-style weapons, but the devastating firepower provided by rifles such as the Springfield or the Henry and Spencer repeaters made massed action catastrophic. Only unbelievable bravery could permit such slaughter; lesser men would have quit the field or refused to fight at all under those conditions. The American Civil War was the dawn of the modern age of warfare, and its lessons were bought with blood and suffering.

Springfield M1855

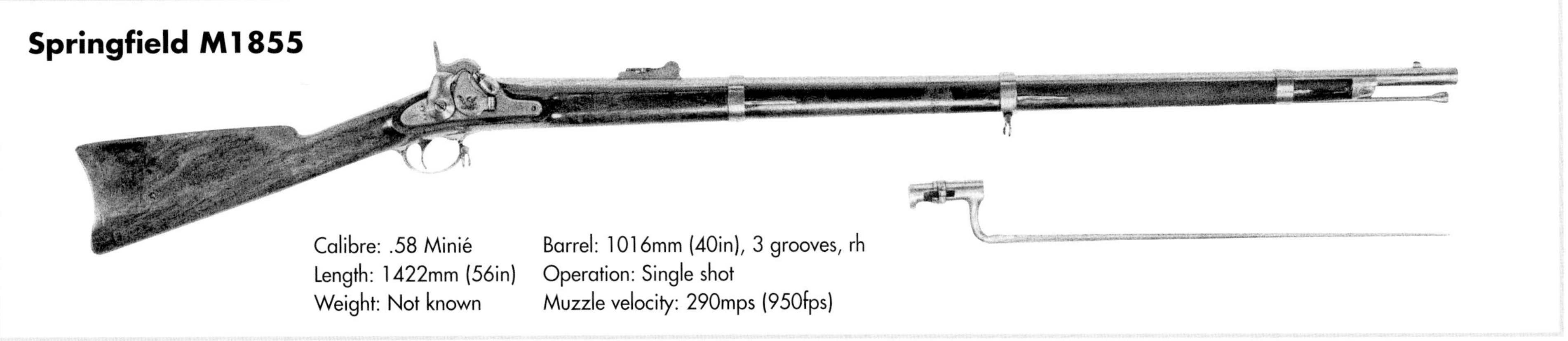

Calibre: .58 Minié
Length: 1422mm (56in)
Weight: Not known
Barrel: 1016mm (40in), 3 grooves, rh
Operation: Single shot
Muzzle velocity: 290mps (950fps)

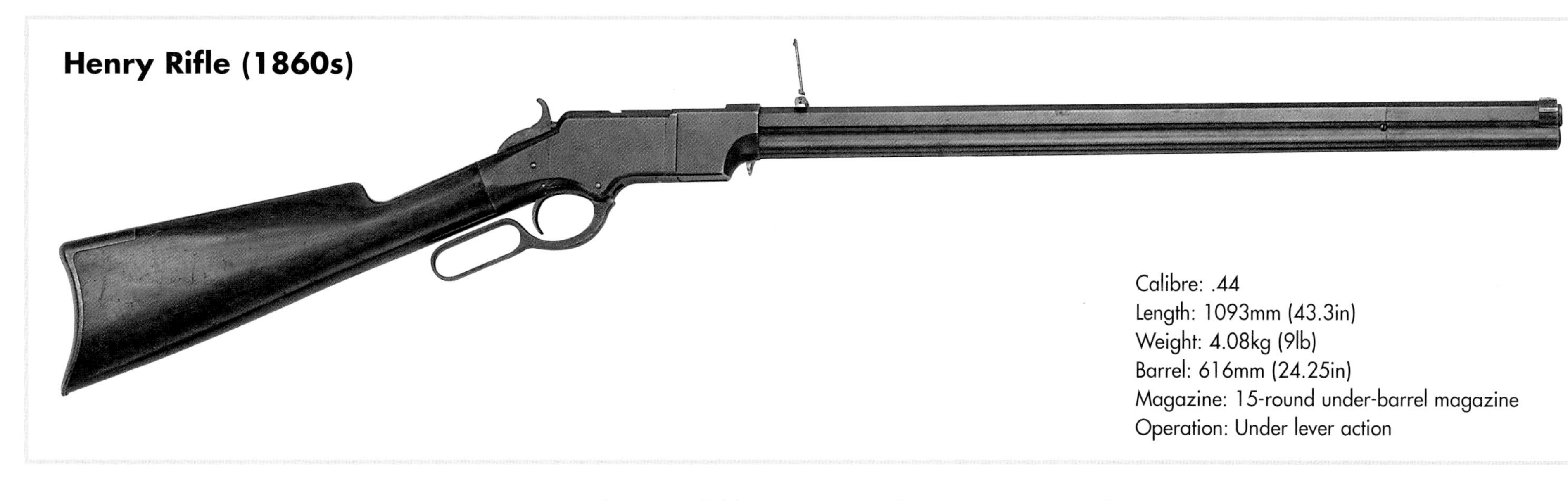

Springfield M1855

The classic infantry weapon of the time was the Model 1855 rifle-musket, known as the 'Springfield' after the armoury in Springfield, Massachusetts, where many were produced. The Springfield was used by both sides. It fired a .58 calibre Minié bullet, named after its French inventor. The Minié bullet was conical and had a hollow base, allowing the propellant gas to expand the base of the round to fill the barrel and grip the rifling. Propellant was black powder, muzzle-loaded and initiated by a percussion cap struck by the weapon's hammer. Theoretically a Minié round could kill a man out to 1000 metres (3280 feet), but at that range accuracy was doubtful, to say the least. Nevertheless the infantry of 1860 could pose a hazard over a very large area when compared to their counterparts of just 40 years before.

The Springfield M1855 was sighted out to 823 metres (2700 feet) and could use a roll of paper caps rather than separate copper caps. It was rather expensive and slow to produce, so many troops went to war with other weapons, including traditional smoothbore muskets that were totally unsuited to this long-range combat environment. In order to speed up production and improve reliability the Union army adopted an updated M1861 version with simpler sights and using the more reliable separate copper percussion cap. A final version, the M1863, featured a stronger hammer for more reliable firing.

In the course of the Civil War the US Army obtained more than 650,000 Springfield rifle-muskets of all types, from more than 20 different contractors. While many other weapons were fielded, the Springfield was the main small arm of the war. Although the Springfield was a very impressive weapon for its time, the quest for greater firepower brought several other rifles to the field of battle, some of them featuring internal magazines and all-in-one cartridges.

Spencer and Henry rifles

The main repeaters of the period were the Spencer and Henry rifles. The Spencer rifle was chambered for .56 and fed by a seven-round internal tube magazine that ran through the butt. Each fired round was ejected, and the next one chambered, by a lever action using the trigger guard. The Spencer's 762mm (30in) barrel was a good 9 inches (230mm) shorter than that of the Springfield.

More than 12,000 Spencer rifles were issued, as opposed to fewer than 2000 Henry rifles. However, greater numbers than this saw action since soldiers on both sides purchased their own weapons in many cases. The Henry rilfe, a .44

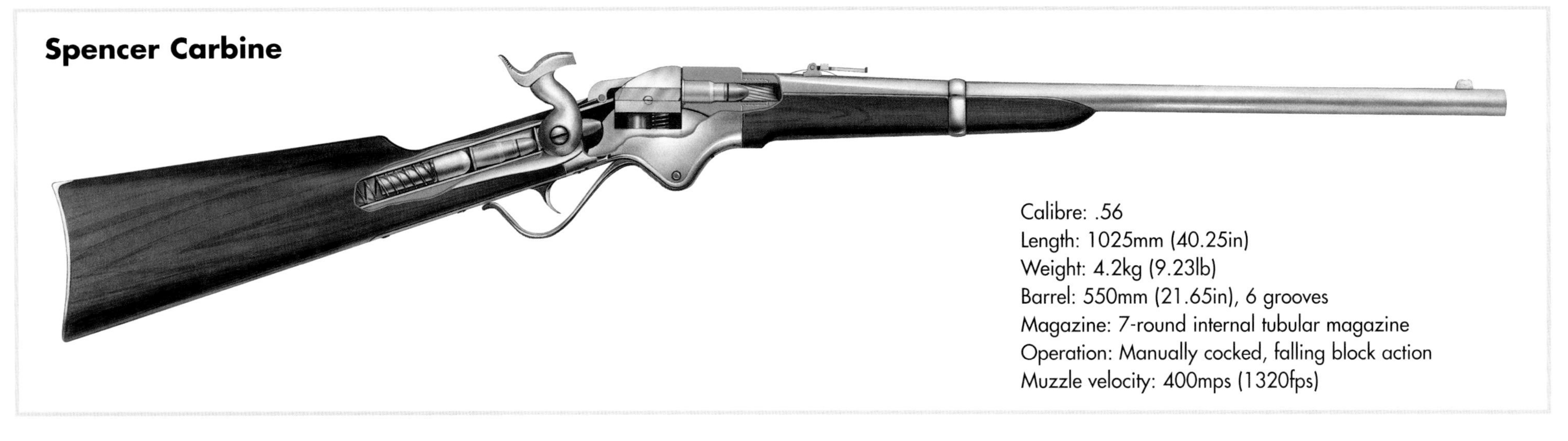

calibre repeater holding 15 cartridges, was operated by a lever on the trigger guard and fed from an under-barrel tube magazine.

Other designs

Many other cartridge weapons were fielded during the Civil War. Some were imported from Europe while others were experimental designs that never really worked out. Among those that did achieve success was the Sharps. Chambered in .52, the single-shot breech-loading carbine was reloaded by lever action using the trigger guard, which opened the breech. The Sharps used a percussion cap to initiate the round, as did many of its contemporaries, so was still limited in its firepower.

Left: A Union cavalry corporal poses with his sabre and Spencer carbine in 1862. Although the dashing sabre was still issued, most Union cavalry fought as mounted infantry, with three men in four skirmishing with their carbines while the other held the horses ready for a rapid redeployment.

Spencer carbine

Magazine-fed carbines offered huge advantages to cavalrymen and mobile raiders of the sort deployed by both sides. Armed with revolvers and repeating carbines, a small band of raiders could strike deep, hard and fast, causing damage out of all proportion to their numbers. The most important such weapons were the Burnside carbine, chambered in .54, of which 55,000 were issued, and the Spencer.

Almost 100,000 Spencer carbines were issued from 1863 onwards. Based on the Spencer rifle, the carbine was fed from a tubular magazine inserted through the butt. Reloading took 10–12 seconds, which, coupled with repeat-fire capability, gave its users a significant advantage over troops armed with single-shot weapons.

Although the cavalry went to war with swords and even lances, it quickly became apparent that firearms were far more effective in combat. Cavalry combats frequently became running gunfights in which whoever could get off the most shots would generally win. Against infantry (and even against other cavalry) the cavalry was most effectively used as mounted and mobile infantry; one man in four held the horses while his companions formed a loose skirmish line and fought with carbines. This unglamorous style of combat was somewhat inefficient, since one-quarter of the unit's firepower was behind the lines, but it proved much better than trying to cross a thousand yards of killing ground to exchange sword strokes.

European conflicts

Despite the bloody lessons of the American Civil War, European powers would make the same mistakes in their wars over the next few years. These wars were also clashes between old and new. On one hand the need for good strategic planning and logistics, and the role of railways in getting troops and supplies to the front, were correctly interpreted by some powers. On the other, soldiers went to war in bright uniforms that made them easy targets, and tried to cross the killing ground with nothing but defiant courage for protection.

The European carnage began in 1864. Disputes over Danish claims to the duchies of Schleswig and Holstein led to war between Denmark and an alliance of Austria and Prussia that ended in a swift defeat for Denmark. The territorial split led to confrontation between Prussia and Austria. Several German states rallied to Austria's side, but it was Prussia that took the initiative.

The resulting clash showed, among other things, the enormous superiority of breech-loading small arms over traditional rifle-muskets. Resolute Austrian counter-attacks were hurled back with massive casualties, mainly due to the accurate and fast shooting of Prussian riflemen armed with the Dreyse 'Needle Gun'.

Dreyse Needle Gun

The 15mm Dreyse Needle Fire Rifle was named after the firing mechanism that initiated its unusual cartridge. The cartridges were composed of an acorn-shaped bullet glued into a paper case, with black powder propellant contained between the lining and outer case, and the primer contained within the cartridge. This was a significant deviation from the usual separate cap arrangement used in many other weapons of the period and it probably resulted in more complete combustion of the propellant than had occured previously.

The Needle Rifle had seen action as early as 1849, during unrest in Dresden, and again during the Prussian campaign in Denmark, but it was in the war with Austria that it truly demonstrated its potential. Almost at a stroke, existing cap-and-ball muzzle loaders became obsolete.

Dreyse Needle Gun

Calibre: 13.6mm
Length: 1100mm (43.25in)
Weight: 4.6kg (10lb)
Barrel: 700mm (27.5in)
Operation: Single-shot, bolt-action, breech-loading
Muzzle velocity: 295mps (960fps)

Bolt-action

The bolt is the metal rod that pushes a round into the chamber and seals it against the propellant gases. When the bolt is opened, a mechanism pushes the spent cartridge out of the chamber.

A bolt or lever-action weapon is a manual repeater. When the operator works the bolt action the chamber is opened, the spent cartridge is ejected and a new round is chambered. No part of this operation occurs automatically; nothing will happen unless the user supplies the power.

Left: French troops at the battle of Sedan. The Franco-Prussian War matched the Chassepot rifles that the soldiers hold here against the Dreyse 'needle gun' of the Prussians.

Casualties in the brief Austro-Prussian War of 1866 ran to four or even five Austrian soldiers to every Prussian. This degree of bloodshed could not be entertained for long and the only reason that Austria was not comprehensively trounced was that Bismarck, the wily Prussian chancellor, decided that further conflict would benefit Russia and France more than it would Prussia. A negotiated settlement soon followed.

One huge advantage of the needle gun was that, although it was a single-shot weapon, as a breech-loader it could be reloaded whilst lying down in cover, something that is almost impossible to achieve with a muzzle-loading weapon. Good staff work, planning and logistics were instrumental in getting the weapons and their users to the right places at the right times. Once there, the Needle Gun's firepower gave them victory.

Chassepot Carbine

Calibre: 11mm
Length: 1175mm (46.25in)
Weight: Not available
Barrel: Not available
Operation: Single shot, bolt action
Muzzle velocity: 410mps (1345fps)

Chassepot

Within four years Prussia was at war again, this time with France. The Franco-Prussian War of 1870 was a clash between two great weapons of the time – the Needle Gun and the French Chassepot rifle. The Chassepot was superior in many ways, including range and accuracy, and was supported by early machine guns. These were, however, badly handled and played little part in the war.

The Chassepot was an excellent weapon, chambered for an 11mm round, and from 1873 onward used a metallic cartridge with the primer

Calibre: .45in
Length: 1310mm (51.5in)
Weight: 4.7kg (10lb 6oz)
Barrel: 850mm (33.25in)
Operation: Single-shot, falling block action
Muzzle velocity: 400mps (1310fps)

situated on the base of the cartridge case. The firing needle (or pin) no longer had to penetrate the whole of the cartridge to initiate firing. As a result it was less likely to be damaged by the firing process, improving reliability. Centre-fire cartridges are still used in modern weapons, and while technical improvements have been made, the principle of operation is not very different today. The Chassepot demonstrated the concept of the centre-fired metal cartridge weapon in that most difficult of environments – in the hands of soldiers committed to battle in large numbers. The development of modern firearms owes a great deal to this historic weapon.

Offensive action

Despite the ever-increasing power of infantry on the defensive, this was the age of 'offensive action' in which commanders believed that, with sufficient resolution, troops could take any position. Unfortunately for the next generation, they were proved more or less correct. Advancing into the teeth of murderous French fire, the Prussian forces were able to take their objectives despite massive casualties, even managing a decisive cavalry charge against positioned infantry.

While the Chassepot rifle was undoubtedly an excellent weapon and the French infantryman was a brave and skilled soldier, these factors were not decisive. Better command, bolder manoeuvring and aggressive spirit allowed the Prussians to dominate their opponents and achieve victory, though at considerable cost. The principle of offensive action was not yet shaken and so, even though the murderous firepower of rifles such as the Chassepot or the Dreyse had been vividly demonstrated, it would take yet more slaughter to drive the message home.

Martini-Henry

While other European states were massacring one another, the British stood aloof, taking care of the affairs of their Empire. Various weapons and calibres were experimented with before the powerful .450 calibre round was settled upon, and a truly great rifle obtained to fire it. This was the Martini-Henry rifle, which served admirably in many corners of the world.

Faced with determined and aggressive local warriors, often in large numbers, the British soldier needed a rifle that could stop the toughest foe in his tracks, and ideally do it at long range. Sighted out to 1325m (1450 yards), the Martini-Henry was highly effective. Its only flaw was that it was a single-shot weapon, but in skilled hands it was capable of 12 rounds per minute.

Lebel M1886

Calibre: 8mm Lebel Mle 1886
Length: 1295mm (50.98in)
Weight: 4.28kg (9.44lb)
Barrel: 800mm (31.5in), 4 grooves, lh
Magazine: 8-round under-barrel tube magazine
Operation: Bolt action
Muzzle velocity: 715mps (2346fps)

Above: The Scots Rifles in camp, circa 1895, with stacks of Lee-Metford (later to become Lee-Enfield) rifles. The soldier's drab, dark-green uniforms show that concealment is now the key to survival on the battlefield.

The .450 cartridge was a good deal smaller than previous ammunition, and ways were sought to further reduce the calibre without compromising stopping power. This meant increasing muzzle velocity, but this was difficult to achieve using black powder. Another problem was that the soft lead bullets of the period could not survive being propelled down the barrel of a rifle any faster than was currently possible.

The answer was discovered by a Swiss artillery officer named Rubin, who demonstrated that a lead bullet 'jacketed' in a harder metal could survive greater velocities. Meanwhile the use of cordite, rather than black powder, produced a more controlled and even explosion. Desiring lighter ammunition, which could be carried in greater quantities, the British Army adopted .303 calibre weapons in 1888. The change in calibre coincided with other innovations: the box magazine and the bolt-action system designed by James Lee.

Lee-Enfield

The combination of these developments made possible in 1891 one of the most important weapons of all time, the Lee-Metford rifle, which after some barrel modifications in 1895 became known as the Lee-Enfield. This weapon, subject to various modifications, was the standard service rifle of the British Army for more than 50 years.

Although the Lee-Enfield had an internal capacity of 10 rounds, it was often used for aimed volley-fire, with the chamber manually reloaded after every shot. This kept the magazine in reserve in case things became desperate. Volley fire of this sort was at the time archaic, as were the linear tactics in use. Against European or American troops the British forces would have been cut to pieces, but in the colonial wars against large forces of poorly armed troops only capable of hand-to-

Left: Long rifles intended for accurate shooting and tipped with bayonets could prove an encumbrance in the close-quarters scrambles of trench warfare.

Rifling and spin

Rifling is simply grooves cut into the inside of the barrel in a spiral shape. As the bullet is pushed up the barrel the grooves make it spin, stabilizing the bullet in flight.

There are all kinds of myths about 'tumbling bullets'. Their origin is the tendency of a rifle round to become unstable in a wound and swap end for end, emerging rear first and creating a nasty exit wound.

hand combat the volley was an effective tactic. The superiority of the Lee-Enfield over its predecessor was demonstrated graphically at the Battle of Omdurman in 1898. Faced with a horde of fanatical dervishes the British troops opened fire with their Lee-Enfields at 2000 metres (6560 feet) and broke the charge at 800 metres (2620 feet). Allied Egyptian troops, armed with Martini rifles, opened fire at 1000 metres (3280 feet) and halted their assailants at half that distance.

As the nineteenth century drew to a close, the modern rifle had truly arrived. Other nations were fielding bolt-action, magazine-fed rifles using jacketed lead cartridges. Despite the graphic lessons of the American, Colonial and European wars, and despite repeated demonstrations that no amount of élan will stop a bullet, the military planners remained firmly wedded to the concept of offensive action. It would take carnage on an previously unimaginable scale to convince them otherwise; an entire generation would pay for the lesson with their lives.

Triumph on the defensive

World War I was said to have been started with a pistol shot – but it was the rifle that fought it. Despite the lessons of the recent wars in Europe and America, the great nations of Europe still believed that offensive action would win the war quickly and decisively.

In the early weeks of the war it seemed that the military planners were right. Battles were fluid affairs of rapid advance and retreat, in which cavalry played a useful part with sabre and lance. The first casualty of the war was caused by a cavalry sabre wielded by an officer of the 4th Dragoon Guards, while a private of the same regiment fired the first shot from his rifle. Both occurred during a cavalry skirmish in the town of Mons and seemed to suggest that rapid and aggressive attacks would drive the enemy from the field.

Yet despite a rapid German advance in the early weeks, the war rapidly settled down into a slogging match fought with artillery, rifle and machine gun across a few hundred metres of trench lines. Conditions in the trenches were appalling. Men might be killed by artillery fragments, bullets or gas, or collapse under the mental strain of daily life in such conditions. The filth and mud of the trenches was hard on men and harder still on weapons. Yet despite these conditions soldiers and their weapons were able to survive and fight.

Lebel M1886 rifle

The French army went to war armed with the excellent but heavy Lebel M1886 rifle. Descended from an earlier design but incorporating many new features, the Lebel was prone to malfunction if the bolt action became clogged with dirt – an entirely likely occurrence. Despite this the Lebel gave good service. Its eight-round magazine offered sustained, rapid firepower when necessary, although the practice of holding the magazine in reserve and loading single rounds into the breech was still in force. The heavy 8mm round offered good stopping power, and the weapon's use of smokeless powder meant that the firer's position was not so readily discerned by the enemy, while in turn he retained a clear view of advancing enemies.

Mauser Gewehr 1898

Calibre: 7.92mm Mauser M98
Length: 1255mm (49.4in)
Weight: 4.14kg (9.13lb)
Barrel: 740mm (29.14in), 4 grooves, rh
Magazine: 5-round integral box magazine
Operation: Bolt action
Muzzle velocity: 870mps (2855fps)

Mauser Gewehr 1898

The German army was built upon lessons learned by the Prussians. It had an excellent general staff and the importance of logistics was firmly grasped. These two factors were important in the rapid advances of the early war, but equally vital was the weapon in the hands of the infantryman: the recently-introduced Mauser Gewehr 1898.

Chambered for 7.92mm ammunition, the Mauser 98 was a very well-made, reliable rifle with a strong bolt action, although its five-round integral magazine offered less sustained firepower than the Lebel. Accuracy and stopping power were a little better, even though the Mauser was only marginally lighter. The Mauser 98 also saw action in World War II and was the basis of the KAR 98 rifle that became the standard German infantry arm of the 1940s.

Springfield M1903

The United States came late to the Great War, entering at a time when the pattern was well established. The American contribution was impressive in terms of numbers of troops, and equally so in terms of quality of equipment. The Springfield Model 1903 rifle was one such excellent tool. Shorter than the Lee-Enfield with which British troops were equipped, the Springfield was just as accurate and its .30 calibre round hit hard. The M1906 (30-06) round used by this rifle is still in use and remains well respected.

The Springfield 03 rifle was handy enough for use at close quarters, almost falling into 'carbine' dimensions, but despite this it was accurate out to beyond 1000 metres (3280 feet). Fitted with a Weaver telescopic sight, the Springfield saw use as a sniper rifle until the end of the Vietnam War. A five-round internal magazine and reliable bolt action made for sustained rapid fire. A number of varients were introduced during the Springfield

Springfield M1903

Calibre: .30in M1906
Length: 1097mm (43.19in)
Weight: 3.94kg (8.68lb)
Barrel: 610mm (24in), 4 grooves, rh
Magazine: 5-round integral box magazine
Operation: Bolt action
Muzzle velocity: 853mps (2800fps)

M1903's long service history. The weapon was in production until 1965 and deserves its place in history as a truly great rifle.

SMLE Mk II

British troops were fortunate to have the Lee-Enfield rifle available for the Great War. Chambered for .303 calibre amunition and fed from a 10-round box magazine, the Lee-Enfield Mk II was noticeably lighter and nearly 300mm (6in) shorter than the Lebel rifle, though its accuracy was just as good. A smooth, fast bolt action allowed a rapid rate of fire.

The Short Magazine Lee Enfield (known to some enthusiasts as the 'Smellie' to this day) was first issued in 1903 and was in turn developed from the Lee-Enfield Mk I of 1895. The latter was designed in response to the availability of cordite. SMLE variants continued in British service for years and surviving examples of this rugged weapon can still found in use around the world today.

Mosin-Nagant

The Russian army fought with determination and courage in the Great War, despite the increasingly desperate situation at home, until everything fell apart in 1917. As revolution swept through Russia the troops at the front 'voted for peace with their feet'. Many took part in the power struggles waged at home during the Revolution and after.

The foremost weapon of the soldiers of Russia, both revolutionaries and counter-revolutionaries, was the Mosin-Nagant Rifle, which dated from the 1890s. Like most Russian weapons it was capable of functioning in truly horrible conditions, which are normal in Russia, and was thus an ideal weapon for the trenches of World War I.

Chambered in 7.62mm, the bolt-action Mosin-Nagant had a non-detachable five-round box magazine and was effective out to 1000 metres (3280 feet). One of the longest rifles then in common service, the Mosin-Nagant was dependable enough to become the standard service

Below: A World War II US Marine takes aim with his M1903 rifle, which has been turned into a sniping weapon by the addition of an optical sight. Although its design was almost fifty years old at this point, the M1903 remained an accurate, reliable weapon.

Mosin-Nagant M1938 Carbine

Calibre: 7.62mm Mosin-Nagant
Length: 1016mm (40in)
Weight: 3.47kg (7.6lb)
Barrel: 508mm (7.6in)
Magazine: 5-round integral box magazine
Operation: Bolt action
Muzzle velocity: 766mps (2514fps)

rifle of the Soviet Army for many years. Shorter, 'carbine' versions were also produced, of which the M1891/30 served well in World War II.

Although bolt-action rifles were not ideal for close-quarters fighting in the trenches, for the main work of infantry at that time – shooting at the fleeting targets offered by entrenched infantry or repelling massed assaults across the wire and mud of no-man's land – they were excellent weapons. An attack into the teeth of such firepower, even without artillery and machine guns, was guaranteed to result in huge casualties. Most attacks became a bloody shambles before they were properly underway.

Various means of breaking the trench deadlock were tried, ranging from massive brute force assaults to subtle infiltration. New weapons were deployed including poison gas, armoured vehicles and personal automatic weapons, and so the next generation of warfare was ushered in. The necessity that drove this wave of technological invention was the invincibility of steady infantry on the defensive, armed with a good rifle.

Rapid fire

Good troops armed with bolt-action rifles such as the SMLE could deploy such rapid fire that some attackers mistakenly thought they were facing machine-guns. Fire could be delivered with such accuracy that the killing zone began hundreds of metres away – often further than the nearest enemy positions.

Below right: Russian troops dug in during World War I. Their Mosin-Nagant 1891 rifles are tipped with unusually long spike bayonets. The difficulty of using such a clumsy weapon at close quarters in a trench is obvious.

Enter the self-loaders

Wars are not won by defending, so some means had to be found to overcome the defensive power of enemy infantry. Experience had shown that it was possible to get troops into an enemy position, but once there they needed a great deal of firepower in order to overcome the defenders who might well outnumber the surviving assault troops. Other developments, such as armoured vehicles, made it possible to conduct fast-moving offensive operations once again.

As infantry became more mobile, lighter and handier weapons that were able to offer the individual rifleman greater firepower became desirable. Most armies continued to equip the bulk of their infantry with bolt-action rifles, but these became lighter and shorter while a proportion of infantrymen were issued self-loading or fully automatic rifles.

The ability to shoot several times without pausing to work a bolt, or to spray an area with automatic fire, was of critical importance during the urban scrambles of World War II, but the weapons in use had their origins in the trench deadlock of the preceding war.

M1 'Garand'

The US M1 'Garand' Rifle is a classic example of the early self-loaders. Closely resembling the M1903 Springfield, the M1 was introduced in 1936 and was chambered for the powerful .30-06 round in standard use by US troops. Rather than manual bolt action, the M1 was automatically reloaded by gas pressure created by the previous round. It was fed by an internal magazine holding an eight-round 'clip', which had to be loaded into the weapon full. It was not possible to conduct tactical reloading by adding extra rounds to a partially fired clip.

Designed by John C. Garand (by whose name it is frequently known) the M1 was effective out to about 500 metres (1,640 feet), which is quite enough for a battle rifle in the hands of an ordinary infantryman. It was heavy but robust and gave good service throughout its 23-year production life.

Although outwardly it seemed little different from the previous generation of bolt-action rifles, the M1 was in truth a huge leap ahead in weapons technology, allowing every infantryman to shoot as fast as he could pull the trigger. This was a double-edged sword, since inexperienced or poorly trained troops could waste a lot of ammunition to no real effect under the stress of combat, but in close-quarters fighting the self-loader was greatly superior to a bolt-action weapon. This was proven many times over in urban, jungle and hedgerow actions.

Right: A US soldier comes under fire on Okinawa during World War II. His M1 Garand self-loading rifle affords more rapid firepower than a bolt-action rifle, and on his back is the infantryman's best friend – an entrenching tool.

M1 'Garand'

Calibre: .30-06 US
Length: 1103mm (43.5in)
Weight: 4.37kg (9.5lb)
Barrel: 610mm (24in), 4 grooves, rh
Magazine: 8-round integral box magazine
Operation: Gas
Muzzle velocity: 853mps (2800fps)

M1 Carbine

The M1 Carbine was developed for use by troops who were not expected to become involved in infantry fighting but needed a fairly effective weapon just in case. The M1 Carbine fired a short .30 cartridge similar in power to a pistol round, although with its longer barrel it was effective out to about 300 metres (985 feet). Issued to artillerymen, officers and vehicle crews, the rifle was fed by a 10- or 30-round detachable box magazine.

Although the weapon did not really know what it was supposed to be – carbine or overgrown submachine gun – and lacked stopping power, it proved popular with the troops, perhaps because neither it nor its ammunition was particularly heavy. Variants with folding stocks or full-automatic capability were produced and in total more than six million M1 carbines of all types were produced between 1941 and 1945.

The practice of issuing a carbine or submachine gun to troops not expected to take part in normal infantry fighting persisted until quite recently. Most modern assault rifles, however, are sufficiently light and handy for a common weapon to be issued to all troops.

SKS Carbine

The benefits of self-loading were not lost on the Soviets, who captured large quantities of 7.62mm short ammunition from the retreating Germans and wanted something from which to fire them. The result was the SKS carbine, designed by Simonov and fielded in 1956, a year before the classic Kalashnikov AK-47.

The SKS was a fairly conventional-looking short rifle/carbine fed from a 10-round detachable magazine. Capable of semi-automatic fire only, it was overshadowed by the Kalashnikov and did not find much favour in the Soviet Union. The Simonov had an effective range of about 400 metres (1312 feet), quite enough under battle conditions, and carried a folding bayonet under the muzzle in case it might possibly be useful from time to time.

Compared to the AK47, which is obviously a modern rifle, the SKS looks very dated. Even so, its robust construction, coupled with the fact that it is a workmanlike weapon capable of doing its job under adverse conditions, ensured that the SKS was taken up by several nations despite its Soviet inventors' lack of interest.

M1 Carbine

Calibre: .30 Carbine
Length: 905mm (35.7in)
Weight: 2.5kg (5.47lb)
Barrel: 457mm (18in), 4 grooves, rh
Magazine: 15- or 30-round detachable box magazine
Operation: Gas
Muzzle velocity: 595mps (1950fps)

Calibre: 7.62mm Soviet M1943
Length: 1022mm (40.2in)
Weight: 3.86kg (8.5lb)
Barrel: 520mm (20.47in), 4 grooves, rh
Magazine: 10-round detachable box magazine
Operation: Gas
Muzzle velocity: 735mps (2410fps)

Iron sights and optical sights

Iron sights consist of a U-shaped notch at the rear of the weapon and a pillar with a 'bead' at the top at the muzzle. Placing the bead over the target and lining it up in the notch aligns the weapon for a shot. Most allow for the rear notch to be adjusted to a preset range.

Many modern weapons can use an 'optical' sight (one that includes lenses and integral sighting aids). Most have some magnification built-in, but are not as powerful as a true telescopic sight.

L1A1 SLR / FN FAL

The classic self-loading rifle of the post-war period is the FN FAL, which entered service in the British Army in 1954 as the L1A1 Self-Loading Rifle, or SLR. In British service the rifle was capable of semi-automatic fire only, although full-auto versions were employed by other militaries. During the Falklands War of 1982 both sides were equipped with the FN FAL – Argentine forces had fully automatic versions, while the British achieved a comparable rate of fire at need by vigorous use of the trigger finger.

Chambered for 7.62mm NATO ammunition and fed from a 20-round magazine, the SLR is accurate out to 800 metres (2625 feet) or more and has excellent stopping power. It is a fairly difficult weapon to handle and requires well-trained troops to make best use of it. In good hands, however, its performance was sufficiently good for it to remain the standard British army rifle for 30 years; even after it was replaced in the mid-1980s by the SA80, the L1A1 was still in use with some special forces units. Variants of the FN FAL include a heavy barrel version (with a bipod) capable of full-automatic fire for squad support and 'paratrooper' versions with shortened barrel and folding or skeletonized stocks.

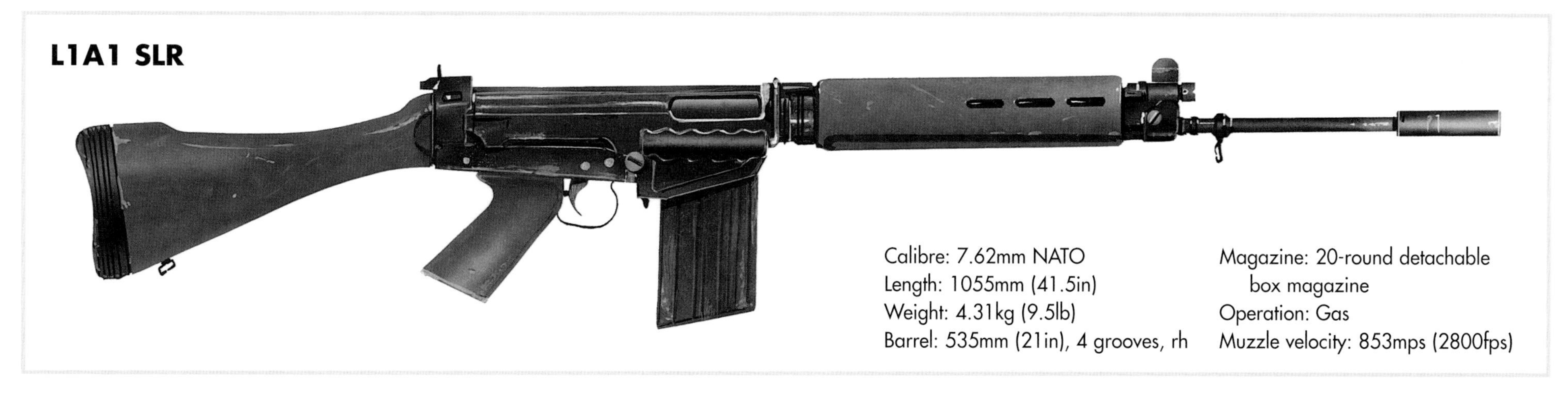

Calibre: 7.62mm NATO
Length: 1055mm (41.5in)
Weight: 4.31kg (9.5lb)
Barrel: 535mm (21in), 4 grooves, rh
Magazine: 20-round detachable box magazine
Operation: Gas
Muzzle velocity: 853mps (2800fps)

Left: Although the British Army makes use of specialist sniping weapons, this Royal Marine sniper in the Falklands War is armed with the regular L1A1 SLR. The device atop the weapon is a night sight, cased for protection.

Supersonic noise

Rifle rounds travel very fast indeed. Even if the noise of the propellant is suppressed, a supersonic bullet will still cause a level of noise that may be unacceptable for certain applications. Subsonic ammunition does not hit as hard or have such a long range, but it is less likely to give the firer away.

Automatic rifles

The machine gun had proven its worth several times over by the time US troops reached the trenches of the Great War, but machine guns were bulky and heavy. They were excellent for supporting attacks or beating them off, but advancing infantry would quickly lose the benefit of automatic support fire as they outdistanced their machine gun-armed supports.

BAR

John Browning saw the advantage of a machine gun that could keep up with infantry, and in 1917 he designed the Browning Automatic Rifle (BAR). Chambered for .30-06, the same ammunition used in standard infantry rifles, the BAR was fed by a 20-round detachable box magazine and could fire on full-automatic or single shots as a self-loader.

Although a BAR could burn through its entire magazine very quickly at 350 or 550 rounds per minute, the firepower it offered in a package only twice as heavy as an infantryman's rifle made it popular with the troops. The standard BAR came equipped with a bipod, although this was often removed to save weight. It served in both World Wars and was not withdrawn until 1957. Even then it was retained for special applications, including VIP protection, for many years afterwards.

The BAR was significant for many reasons, not least because it proved the concept of the squad support weapon. It was observed in World War II that when a unit came under fire, it was generally the squad automatic weapon – often a BAR – that first returned fire, with riflemen joining in. To this day many armies build their infantry squads around a light machine gun referred to as the 'squad automatic weapon' or 'squad support weapon' (SAW or SSW). Doctrine in many forces has it that the SSW is the main offensive power of the unit and the riflemen are there to protect it.

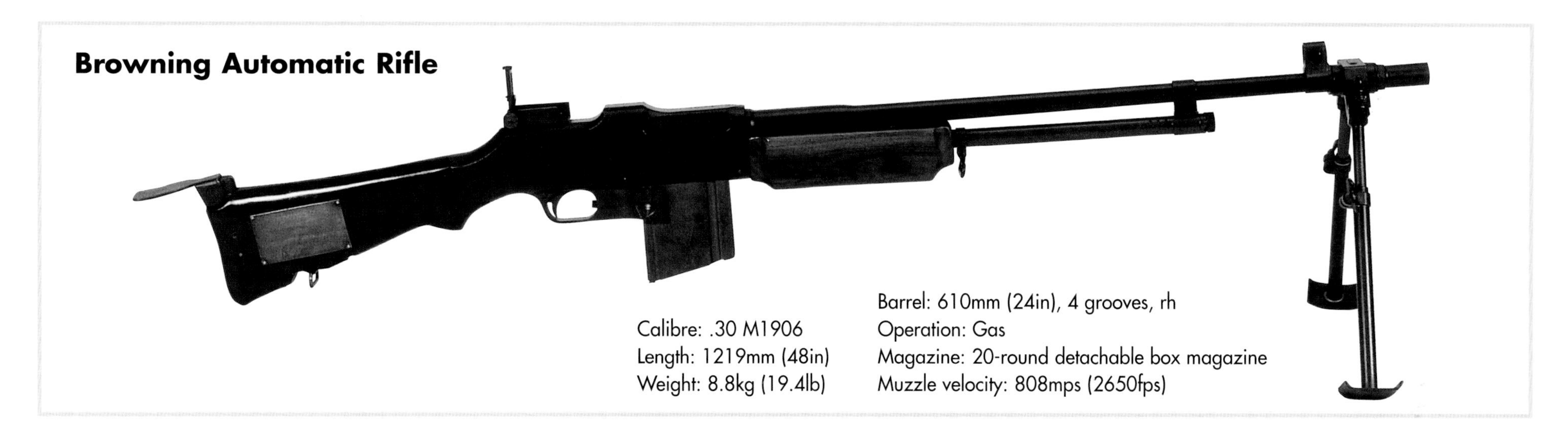

Browning Automatic Rifle

Calibre: .30 M1906
Length: 1219mm (48in)
Weight: 8.8kg (19.4lb)
Barrel: 610mm (24in), 4 grooves, rh
Operation: Gas
Magazine: 20-round detachable box magazine
Muzzle velocity: 808mps (2650fps)

M14 and Mini-14

Developed in the 1950s from the highly successful M1 Garand, the M14 is often referred to as a carbine. It is essentially an M1 reworked to use the 7.62x51mm round that was becoming the standard NATO rifle ammunition. The M14 was, like its predecessor, a tough and reliable weapon but it was arguably obsolete before it entered service.

The M14 was capable of full-automatic fire but at 750 rounds per minute would get through its 20-round magazine very quickly. Although it was accurate out to 800 metres (2625 feet) the weapon was less than controllable when firing full-auto, and some examples were built as semi-automatics. Production ran from 1957 to 1968, and the M14 turned out to be more popular than it was good.

When compared with contemporary automatic rifles, or even the AK-47 of a decade earlier, the M14 is shown up for what it is – an old-style weapon timidly creeping into the age of assault rifles where its contemporaries were striding boldly ahead. Nevertheless, the M14 saw combat in Vietnam and elsewhere and if it was not very good, neither was it particularly bad. It was simply a slight evolution of existing technologies in a time when revolutions were taking place. An accurized version was used as the basis of the semi-automatic M21 sniper rifle, and gave excellent military service, so perhaps the M14 was merely a little late arriving on the scene. A far better (and smaller) version of the M14 rifle, the Ruger Mini-14, is chambered for 5.56x45mm, the other standard NATO rifle-calibre round. Available in full- or

M14

Calibre: 7.62mm NATO
Length: 1117mm (44in)
Weight: 3.88kg (8.55lb)
Barrel: 558mm (22in), 4 grooves, rh
Magazine: 20-round detachable box magazine
Operation: Gas
Muzzle velocity: 595mps (1950fps)

semi-automatic versions, the Mini-14 has found favour with civilian and law enforcement users as well as making some military sales. Much more controllable in the lighter calibre, the Mini-14 is a quality weapon and remains popular.

FG42

The German need for improved firepower in World War II was answered by various means, including submachine guns and a number of automatic rifles. The Fallschirmjäger 42 (FG42) was one such weapon. Developed specifically for parachute troops who needed to overcome their opponents quickly, the FG42 was chambered for 7.92x33mm and fed from a 20-round box magazine. The barrel incorporated a bipod to allow the weapon to be used for support fire.

The FG42 was unusual in that its magazine was side-mounted and it was one of the first weapons to use a plastic stock, although later in the war wooden ones were fitted due to plastic shortages. The sharply raked pistol grip was also a foretaste of things to come. Previously the stock of a rifle included the handgrip: the FG42 used a revolutionary pistol grip and in-line stock arrangement that has since become standard the world over. The FG42 was an advanced weapon for its time, but difficult to produce. In spite of various simplifications to its manufacture over the course of war, only around 7000 were made by 1945.

FG42

Calibre: 7.92mm
Length: 940mm (37in)
Weight: 4.53kg (9.99lb)
Barrel: 502mm (19.76in), 4 grooves, rh
Magazine: 20-round detachable box magazine
Operation: Gas
Muzzle velocity: 761mps (2500fps)

StG 44

Although originally named the MP43 (MP stood for Maschinenpistole), the weapon that became known as the Sturmgewehr 44 (StG 44) was a rifle, and can be considered the first true assault rifle. Chambered for the same short 7.92mm ammunition as the FG42, the StG 44 was an excellent weapon. With 30 rounds available in the detachable magazine and a sensible rate of fire (500 rounds per minute), the StG 44 was heavy but handy at close quarters and easy to control under automatic fire. Its 300 metre (985 feet) effective range was entirely adequate for infantry combat.

Although designed more than 60 years ago, the StG 44 looks like a modern assault rifle. Indeed its name, Sturmgewehr, first gave rise to the phrase 'assault rifle'. Since the end of the war the rifle has been used by a number of nations outside Germany, and has inspired a generation of similar weapons.

StG 44

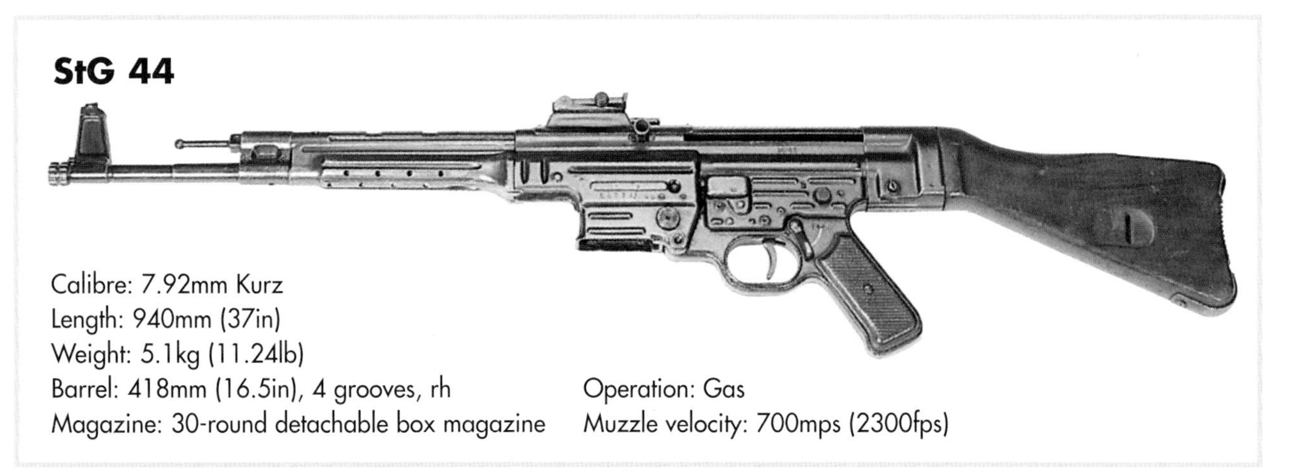

Calibre: 7.92mm Kurz
Length: 940mm (37in)
Weight: 5.1kg (11.24lb)
Barrel: 418mm (16.5in), 4 grooves, rh
Magazine: 30-round detachable box magazine
Operation: Gas
Muzzle velocity: 700mps (2300fps)

AK-47

Although others, including Tokarev, inventor of the standard Russian pistol, were experimenting with automatic rifles, it was the design team led by Mikhail Kalashnikov that created the definitive Soviet assault rifle. Designated Avtomat Kalashnikov 47, or AK-47, this was one of the most important firearms ever introduced. The AK-47 owes much of its design to the German StG 44. Typically of Russian weapons, the AK-47 was designed to be reliable first and accurate second. Its 7.62x39mm cartridge is underpowered by NATO standards but remains effective out to between 300–400 metres (985–1310 feet), which is further than the average soldier can hit anything with a rifle anyway.

The Kalashnikov rifle is unusual for several reasons. The cocking handle is on the right-hand side of the weapon, so that the user has to reach over the top to ready his rifle. The selector is also something of an acquired taste. Operating it produces the distinctive 'Kalash Klack', and unlike most weapons it is not arranged as safe/semi-auto/full auto but safe/full/semi. One advantage is that selecting full-automatic fire is a very deliberate action. Soldiers needing to bring their weapon into action quickly tend to ram the selector all the way home. This can lead to the first, hurried, shot blasting off the entire magazine leaving the soldier with an empty weapon and perhaps endangering comrades. In the same situation an AK-47 user will fire only a single round.

The AK-47 and its successors are almost unbelievably rugged weapons. Examples have been buried in stashes for extended periods and had their woodwork virtually eaten away by termites, yet still functioned reliably afterwards.

Several variants, licensed versions and blatant copies of the Kalashnikov AK-47 have been fielded, usually by nations falling within the Soviet sphere of influence. The quality of such weapons varies from excellent to extremely poor. What they all have in common is the core of the AK-47's appeal – its accuracy is modest at best, range is adequate and it is not the most user-friendly of weapons. Recoil is unpleasant, to say the least. But when the trigger is pulled the weapon will fire under virtually any conditions. To the soldier going in harm's way this makes the Kalashnikov a very fine rifle indeed.

Right: Iraqi policemen hold AK-47s aloft during a parade in Baghdad in 2003. The parade was in response to US attempts to gain a UN resolution against Saddam Hussein.

Left: US Marines armed with M16 rifles make good use of a sandbagged position during peacekeeping operations in Beirut in 1983. Sand or earth absorbs bullet energy without creating secondary fragmentation, providing excellent protection from small arms fire.

M16

The distinctly mediocre M14 demonstrated that the assault rifle concept was worth pursuing, but US forces really needed something better. Eugene Stoner provided the answer in the M16 assault rifle. This weapon began life as the AR-10, chambered for NATO 7.62mm ammunition. Trials of a 5.56mm version, the AR-15, showed it to be more suitable and it went into production as the M16, manufactured under licence by Colt.

M16A2

Calibre: 5.56mm M193
Length: 990mm (39in)
Weight: 2.86kg (6.3lb)
Barrel: 508mm (20in), 6 grooves, rh
Magazine: 30-round detachable box magazine
Operation: Gas
Muzzle velocity: 1000mps (3280fps)

Right: The M16 was introduced during the Vietnam War as a rifle that never needed cleaning. Experience quickly showed otherwise, however. Despite its teething troubles, however, the M16's light weight and low recoil were distinct advantages in jungle warfare.

First impressions of the M16 suggested an excellent weapon with classic assault rifle lines: a pistol grip and in-line stock made it look far more modern than the M14. The rifle's early service in Vietnam, however, was beset with teething troubles. The M16, it was discovered, was an excellent weapon when kept clean, but had a tendency to fouling.

The M16A1 eliminated many of the early faults and better propellant reduced the fouling problem. The result was a rifle that lived up to its early promise. Fairly short and handy, and light by rifle standards, the M16A1 gave years of sterling service.

An updated version, the M16A2, is the current US service rifle. The A2 was designed to fire improved 5.56mm ammunition and is limited to three-round bursts rather than full-automatic fire. A heavier barrel adds to the weapon's overall weight, which is also increased by a generally heavier and more robust construction. This may have been a response to problems with plastic components that became brittle in cold conditions, creating a danger that they might break off if struck sharply on the sort of objects soldiers regularly encounter, such as walls and vehicle hulls.

The M16 has been in production since 1959 and remains an industry standard in the assault rifle world. Indeed, many competing rifles are designed to take 30-round M16 magazines and even when this massively successful weapon is phased out of US inventories it will continue to influence the construction of other assault rifles. If the StG 44 may be considered the ancestor of all modern assault rifles, then the M16 is the stern, white-haired patriarch who currently heads the family.

Heckler & Koch G3

During the 1940s Mauser designed a delayed-blowback feed system that used rollers to delay the movement of the bolt backwards until gas pressure in the chamber had dropped to a safe level. This system was used as the basis for several weapons, of which the Heckler & Koch G3 was the most successful. While the G3 never achieved the household name status of the M16 or AK-47, it was taken up by more than 50 armed forces and influenced the development of a whole generation of firearms. Fed from a 20-round magazine, the G3 used 7.62x51mm ammunition, which led to it falling out of favour as the world moved to smaller calibres. A 5.56mm version never really caught on even though the G3 itself is an excellent design.

Nevertheless, the G3 had an honourable combat history and deserves recognition as a seminal assault rifle. A sniper version (G3SG1), which features a bipod and telescopic sight, became popular as a police sniper weapon.

Heckler & Koch G3

Calibre: 7.62mm NATO
Length: 1025mm (40.35in)
Weight: 4.4kg (9.7lb)
Barrel: 450mm (17.71in), 4 grooves, rh
Magazine: 20-round detachable box magazine
Operation: Delayed blowback
Muzzle velocity: 800mps (2625fps)

CETME Model 58

In between Mauser's initial work and the H&K G3 came the CETME, developed by Spanish engineers. Originally chambered for 7.62mm, the CETME Model 58 went into production in several versions, capable of firing 7.62mm and later 5.56mm ammunition. Although it remained in service with the Spanish and other armed forces for many years, the CETME never really caught on. It did, however, prove the concept of roller-delayed blowback operation as later used in the G3.

The advantages of delayed-blowback operation are considerable. Gas pressure in the chamber just after firing pushes the bolt back to open the breech and eject the spent round before chambering the next. Just after firing, however, the pressure is high enough to be dangerous, especially when vented right next to the user's head. A heavy bolt provides enough delay (due to inertia) to allow the gas pressure to drop a little, but this makes for a somewhat heavy weapon. In addition, blowback-operated weapons normally fire from an open bolt, which reduces accuracy.

One way to deal with this problem is to use gas operation, whereby the bolt is moved not by direct pressure on it but by a piston and spring arrangement, which is in turn operated by gas pressure. This allows the weapon to fire from a 'closed' bolt, but adds weight and complexity.

The roller-locking delayed blowback system uses a pair of metal rollers that block the passage of the firing pin until they are pushed into recesses by the lock-piece. This only occurs when the round is chambered and the bolt closed. Upon firing, the bolt is held in place by the rollers until they are unlocked by a shaped cam path. The bolt is then freed to move backwards, reloading and recocking the weapon. A return spring pushes the bolt back into place, relocking the rollers ready for the next shot. The unlocking delay is minuscule but sufficient to ensure safe levels of gas pressure in the chamber.

While the CETME never achieved worldwide fame it has seen widespread service and has been more influential in terms of modern rifle design than many more famous rifles.

Stalk and kill: sniper rifles

The average infantryman is likely to engage his enemies at ranges under 300 metres (985 feet) and often much closer. He must be able to leap in and out of vehicles with his weapon ready for use, to

Left: Derived from a German design, the CETME Model 58 was adopted by the Spanish military as its standard service rifle. Originally chambered for a light cartridge, later versions adopted the standard 7.62mm NATO round.

assault positions and take cover in awkward places. What he needs more than anything else is a weapon that will deliver maximum firepower at close range under desperate conditions.

Not so the sniper. Snipers, whether law enforcers or soldiers, operate by stealth and concealment, often moving at agonizingly slow speeds to reach a firing position undetected. It takes a very special individual to do the work of the sniper, and if he is to be effective he needs the best tools. Early sniping rifles were either hunting weapons or standard combat rifles fitted with a telescopic sight. The need for specialist weapons, however, soon became apparent and some fine examples entered service.

CETME Model 58

Calibre: 7.62mm NATO
Length: 1015mm (40in)
Weight: 4.4kg (9.7lb)
Barrel: 450mm (17.72in)
Magazine:20- or 30- round box
Operation: Delayed blowback
Cyclic rate of fire: 550–600 rpm

CLASSIC ASSAULT RIFLES: M16 VERSUS AK-47

The M16 and the AK-47 both date from the early years of the assault rifle, and both have seen many improvements over the years. Although broadly similar in concept, they emphasize very different approaches to assault rifle design. The M16 is a small-calibre rifle accurate out to a very long range and requires a well-trained shooter to make the best use of it. The weapon uses much plastic in its construction. This was a departure from normal construction methods when the M16 was introduced and helps keep the weight of the weapon down, even though early versions sometimes became brittle in cold conditions.

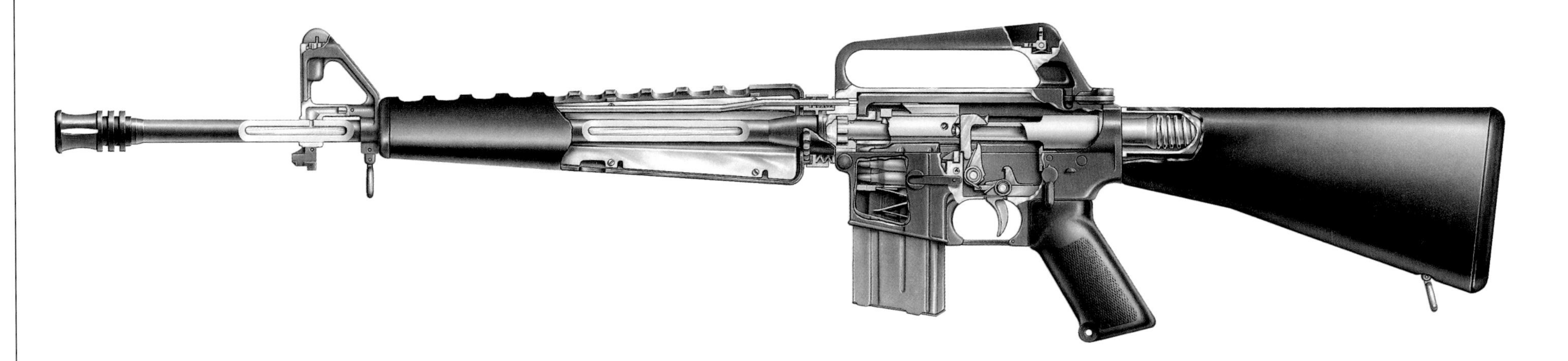

STRENGTHS

- Lightweight
- Accurate at long range
- Low recoil

WEAKNESSES

- Early versions very susceptible to dirty conditions
- Plastic stock could become brittle in cold conditions
- Some doubt as to stopping power of 5.56mm round

M16A1

Calibre: 5.56mm M193
Length: 990mm (39in)
Weight: 2.86kg (6.3lb)
Barrel: 508mm (20in), 6 grooves, rh
Magazine: 30-round detachable box magazine
Operation: Gas
Cyclic rate of fire: 800rpm
Muzzle velocity: 1000mps (3280ftps)

Although it was in theory a very fine rifle, the M16 tended to jam in dirty conditions. Many of its faults were compensated for in the A1 version, and by the time the A3 appeared the M16 had become a very fine weapon indeed. The AK-47, on the other hand, is intended to be used and abused by vast numbers of poorly trained conscript soldiers, and is very tolerant of environmental conditions. Updated as the AKM and AK-74, the basic AK-47 remained true to this original concept. Heavy, cheap and rather crude, the Kalashnikov family nevertheless has some very convincing strengths.

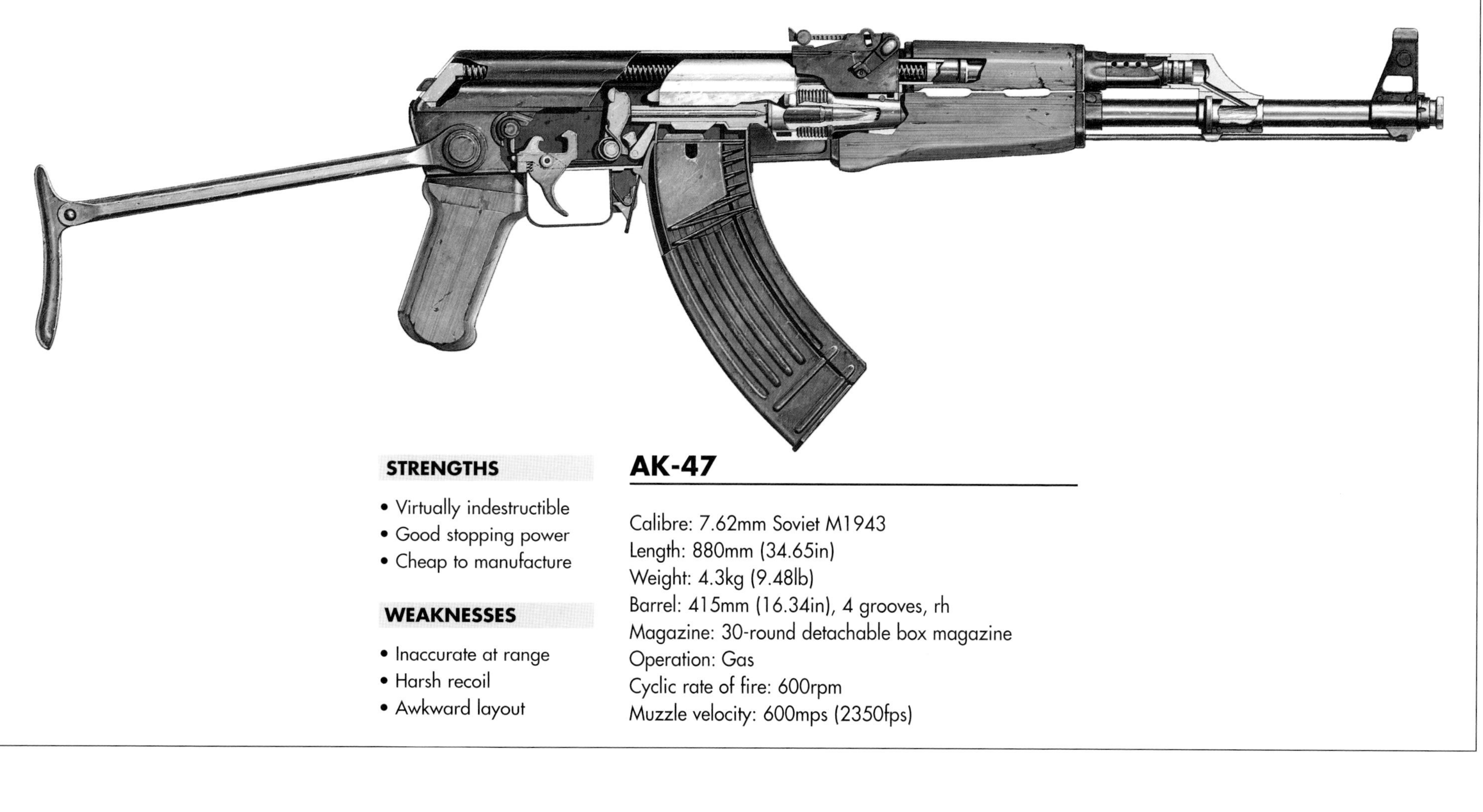

STRENGTHS

- Virtually indestructible
- Good stopping power
- Cheap to manufacture

WEAKNESSES

- Inaccurate at range
- Harsh recoil
- Awkward layout

AK-47

Calibre: 7.62mm Soviet M1943
Length: 880mm (34.65in)
Weight: 4.3kg (9.48lb)
Barrel: 415mm (16.34in), 4 grooves, rh
Magazine: 30-round detachable box magazine
Operation: Gas
Cyclic rate of fire: 600rpm
Muzzle velocity: 600mps (2350fps)

Model 85

The Parker Hale Model 85 rifle can be considered a fine example of the 'conventional' sniper weapon. Based on a hunting rifle, the Model 85 is a bolt-action weapon fed from a 10-round magazine and chambered in 7.62mm NATO. A range of sights can be fitted and the rifle is designed to be adjusted to suit the user perfectly.

There is little innovative or unusual about the Model 85, but it is a well-designed and well-produced representative of the conventional rifles normally used for sniping worldwide, against which more unusual weapons may be measured.

M21

Many sniping weapons are obviously descended from standard battle rifles. One example is the M21, which is basically an M14 constructed to the highest standards and, like specialist versions of many military systems, has outlived in service the weapon on which it is based. A semi-automatic rifle fed by a 20-round magazine, the M21 is not capable of awesomely long shots but is a reliable, effective weapon for most of the tasks a military sniper may be called upon to accomplish. Outside of the USA, the M21 was also adopted by the Israeli defence force.

Galil Sniper

Another sniping weapon that shows its origins is the Galil Sniper. Like the M21, the Galil Sniper is based on a service rifle, in this case the Galil assault rifle in service with the Israeli Defence Force. The Galil Sniper has a heavier barrel than its cousin, with a bipod fitted. It also includes an adjustable stock and a Nimrod x6 telescopic sight. Its designers put reliability and ruggedness above super-accuracy, and in so doing created a very workmanlike weapon that, while not the most accurate of sniping rifles, can do the job under the most difficult of conditions.

SVD Dragunov

Unlike some other armed forces, the Russian army has always placed a high value on snipers. The SVD (Snaiperskaya Vintovka Dragunova), or Dragunov, rifle is an excellent tool in the right hands. Built around the standard AK-47 action, the SVD is chambered for 7.62x54mm ammunition that is not compatible with standard infantry rifles. With its long, heavy barrel the semi-automatic SVD is accurate out to 800 metres (2625 feet). Fairly light for a sniping weapon, the SVD is nevertheless as rugged as all Russian equipment.

PSG1

Much more futuristic in appearance, but actually descended from a design of the 1940s, the Heckler & Koch PSG1 (Präzisionsschützengewehr) is based on the G3 assault rifle. It has a heavy barrel and is chambered for 7.62xNATO ammunition. A semi-automatic weapon fed from 5- or 20-round magazines, the PSG1 provides excellent accuracy at ranges of up to 600 metres (1972 feet), making it suitable for most battlefield sniping tasks. Law-enforcement snipers often shoot from under 100 metres (328 feet), so achieving a one-shot kill with a PSG1 is not a problem for a police marksman.

Walther WA 2000

While the preceding weapons are all suitable for military operations, the WA 2000 from Walther is really too delicate to survive the rough-and-tumble

Right: A US Army sniper armed with the M21 version of the M14 rifle (itself an updated version of the M1 Garand).

Snipers

The longest ever confirmed kill by a sniper was at 2377 metres (7799 feet). This incredible shot was made in Vietnam by Gunnery Sgt Carlos Hathcock of the US Marine Corps, using a .50 calibre machine gun fitted with a scope. Not many years later, .50 calibre sniping rifles made their debut.

Galil Sniper

Calibre: 7.62mm NATO
Weight: 6.4kg (14.11lb)
Barrel: 508mm (20in) without muzzle brake, 4 grooves, rh
Magazine: 20-round box magazine
Operation: Gas, self-loading
Muzzle velocity: 815mps (2675fps)
Length: 1115mm (43.89in) stock extended; 840mm (33in) stock folded

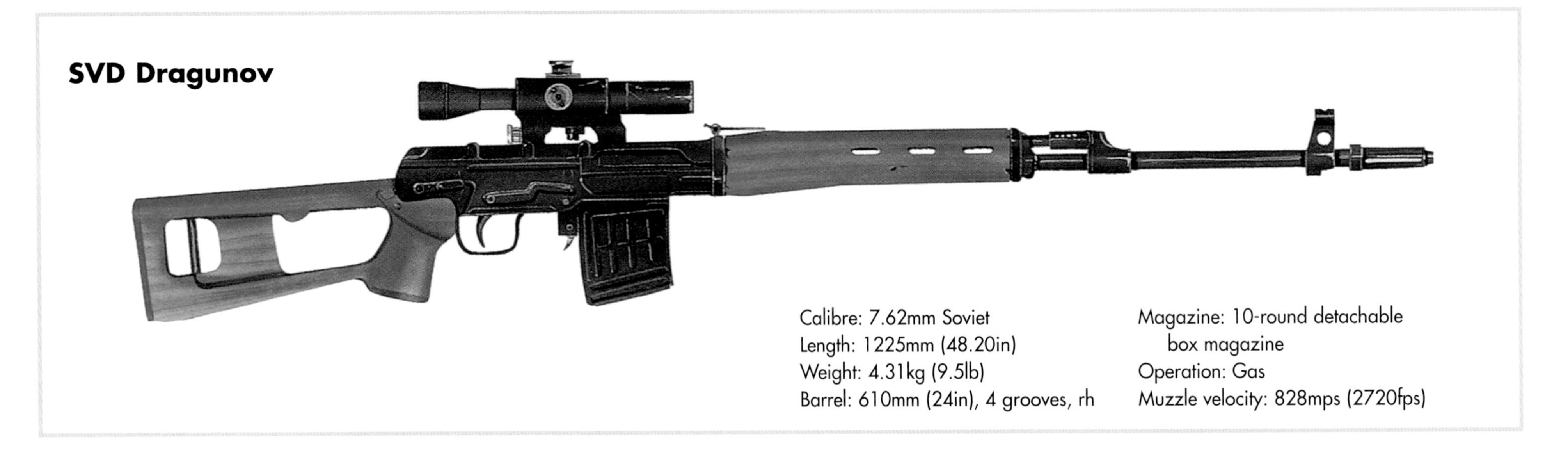

Calibre: 7.62mm Soviet
Length: 1225mm (48.20in)
Weight: 4.31kg (9.5lb)
Barrel: 610mm (24in), 4 grooves, rh
Magazine: 10-round detachable box magazine
Operation: Gas
Muzzle velocity: 828mps (2720fps)

of the field. For counter-terrorist and law enforcement applications, however, it is a truly excellent weapon – and comes with a price tag to match. It is accurate out to 1000 metres (3280 feet), although it will normally be used at much closer ranges.

The WA 2000 is fed from a six-round box magazine located behind the trigger assembly in what is known as the 'bullpup' arrangement. It is chambered for .300 Winchester Magnum, one of the most powerful and accurate rounds available. The standard telescopic sight is the Schmidt and Bender x2.5 to x10, although alternatives can be fitted. Operation is semi-automatic.

The design of the weapon is notably unusual. The barrel is clamped to the weapon body at the front but floats free for most of its length to reduce vibration interference. The barrel itself is externally fluted for strength, vibration reduction and to improve cooling, and is directly in line with the firer's shoulder to reduce muzzle climb.

Barrett 82A1 Light Fifty

The venerable .50 calibre machine gun remains an excellent battlefield weapon and its huge bullet is prodigiously effective. It would, however, be totally impractical to create a battle rifle for the average soldier based on that round, since the weight and recoil of such a weapon would be prohibitive. However, a. 50 calibre (12.7mm) bullet, fired from a suitably monstrous rifle, offers the marksman increased range and enormous destructive power.

A number of .50 calibre sniping weapons have been marketed, of which the Barrett 82A1 was selected for issue to small numbers of US Army snipers. An initial order of 300 weapons achieved considerable success in the first Gulf War of 1991. The massive round was found to be useful against 'material' targets such as helicopters, light vehicles and aircraft as well as more conventional personnel targets. The current world record for a sniper kill was achieved with a .50 calibre weapon.

The 82A1 rifle is a formidable beast weighing 14.7 kilograms (32.41 pounds), more than four times as much as an M16, and is half as long again as a standard battle rifle. It is fed from an 11-round detachable box magazine and has an integral bipod. This is not a weapon that the average soldier can run about with; it is also a very expensive piece of equipment. But in the hands of a skilled sniper a single rifle of this type can cause utter havoc, disrupting enemy operations and communications from beyond the reach of effective retaliation.

Advanced assault rifles

The post-war period saw the emergence of such classic assault rifles as the AK-47 and M16, but in any field of technological development there is always room for an evolutionary or even revolutionary idea.

Barrett 82A1 Light Fifty

Calibre: .50 Browning
Length: 1549mm (60.98in)
Weight: 14.7kg (32.41lb)
Barrel: 838mm (33in), 8 grooves, rh
Magazine: 11-round box magazine
Operation: Short-recoil, semi-automatic
Muzzle velocity: 843mps (2800fps)

AKM

Evolution can be seen in action when the Kalashnikov family of rifles is examined. The AK-47 was an excellent rifle, but it had its quirks and drawbacks. Among these was a flaw with its receiver. This is the main section of the weapon containing trigger and feed mechanisms, plus the firing chamber, and is thus the vital heart of a successful rifle. The AK-47 receiver was originally of stamped steel construction which, while cheap, could create reliability problems if – as happened too often for AK users' liking – quality was low.

Experiments with machined receivers, beginning in 1951, were successful but made the weapon too expensive to be constructed and fielded in the vast numbers required. The solution was to revert to a stamped metal receiver but to impose higher quality requirements. The result was the 1959 AKM ('Modernized') assault rifle.

The AKM incorporated other improvements. Muzzle climb was reduced by a redesigned muzzle that deflected some gas upwards, in effect creating a primitive muzzle brake. The AKM retained the hard-hitting if somewhat short-ranged 7.62x39mm chambering and was an enormous success. Indeed, today it is the commonest version of what is already one of the world's most widely used weapons. The AKM can be distinguished from the AK-47 by a recess above the magazine housing.

Right: Cheap, crude but reliable, the AK-74 has become a symbol of unrest and conflict worldwide. It is tough enough to survive rough handling by untrained militia and gunmen such as this Mujahideen fighter in Afghanistan.

PRECISION RIFLES: HECKLER & KOCH PSG1 VERSUS

For precision shooting and sniping, a suitably accurate weapon is essential. This is especially true in hostage-rescue situations where an instant kill is vital or where collateral casualties must be avoided, or when shooting at small targets over extremely long ranges. The best sniper rifles are precision instruments capable of astonishing accuracy, but some may be too precise for some roles. Military snipers often have to lug their weapons over many miles of hostile terrain; not all rifles are tolerant of this kind of abuse; 'Prima Donna' weapons are little use in the field, but may be excellent for law enforcement sniping.

STRENGTHS

- Proven design based on a rugged military weapon
- Can use standard NATO ammunition
- Large capacity magazine available

WEAKNESSES

- Not as accurate as WA 2000
- Traditional layout
- More than 300mm (11.8in) longer than WA 2000

PSG1

Calibre: 7.62mm NATO
Length: 1208mm (47.56in)
Weight: 8.1kg (17.86lb)
Barrel: 650mm (25.6in), 4 grooves, rh
Magazine: 5- or 20-round detachable box magazine
Operation: Roller-locked delayed blowback
Muzzle velocity: 815mps (2675fps)

WALTHER WA 2000

With 30 years of development behind it, the PSG1 is a well-tried military rifle with an impressive pedigree. It uses H&K's standard roller-locking delayed blowback semi-automatic feed and can take a 5- or 20- round magazine, using standard NATO 7.62mm rounds rather than match-grade ammunition at need. The WA 2000, on the other hand, was developed purely as a sniping weapon. Its Bullpup design takes advantage of straight-through recoil absorption. Chambered for .300 Winchester Magnum, the WA 2000 needs constant attention to maintain its phenomenal accuracy, making it unsuitable for military use.

STRENGTHS

- Incredibly accurate
- Bullpup configuration
- Powerful cartridge

WEAKNESSES

- Intolerant of abuse
- Very expensive
- Ammunition supply may be an issue in the field

WA 2000

Calibre: .30 Winchester Magnum
Length: 905mm (35.63in)
Weight: 8.31kg (18.32lb) loaded, with telescopic sight
Barrel: 650mm (25.59in)
Magazine: 6-round detachable box magazine
Operation: Gas
Muzzle velocity: 800mps (2624fps)

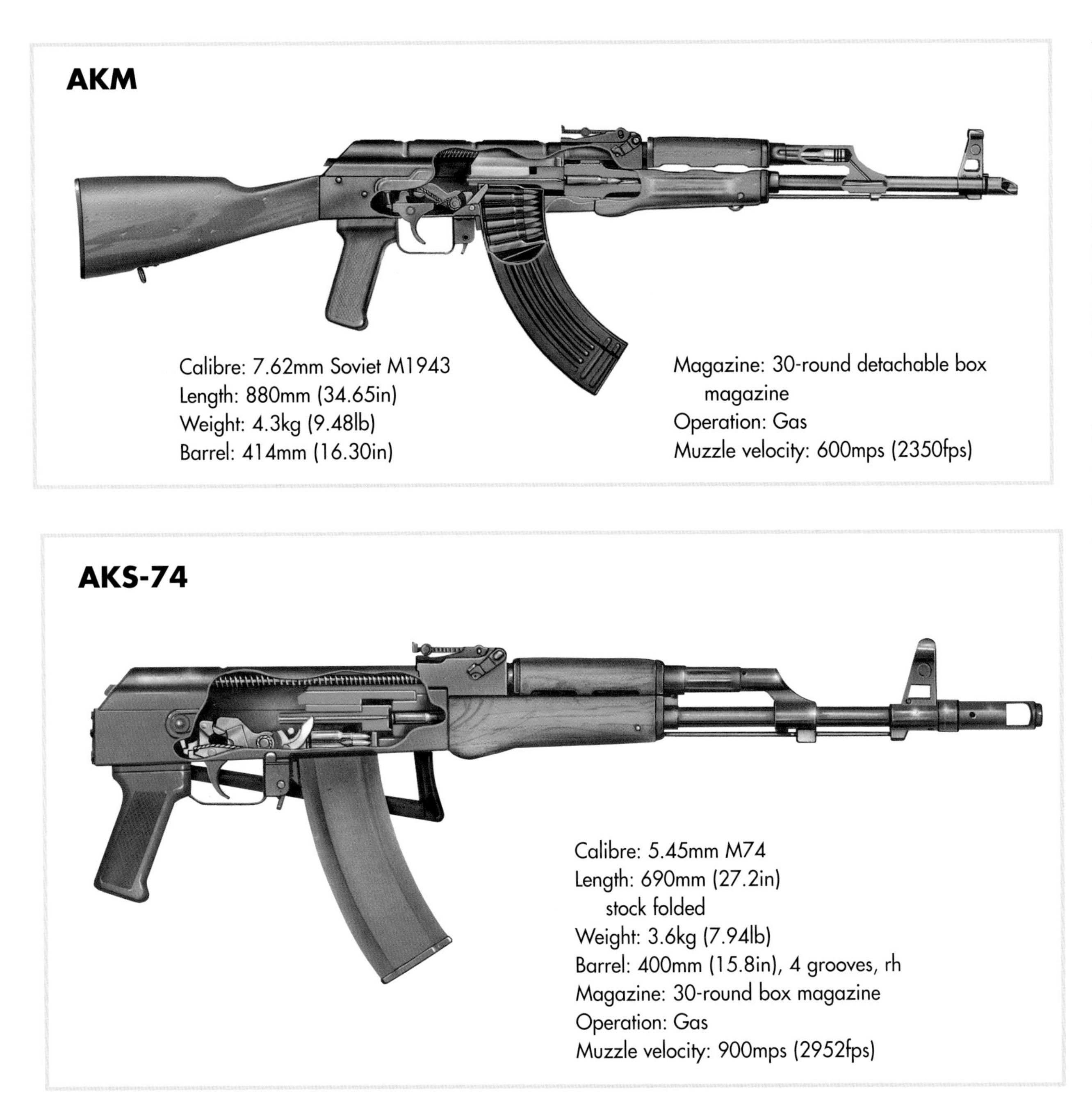

AKM

Calibre: 7.62mm Soviet M1943
Length: 880mm (34.65in)
Weight: 4.3kg (9.48lb)
Barrel: 414mm (16.30in)
Magazine: 30-round detachable box magazine
Operation: Gas
Muzzle velocity: 600mps (2350fps)

AKS-74

Calibre: 5.45mm M74
Length: 690mm (27.2in) stock folded
Weight: 3.6kg (7.94lb)
Barrel: 400mm (15.8in), 4 grooves, rh
Magazine: 30-round box magazine
Operation: Gas
Muzzle velocity: 900mps (2952fps)

AK-74 and variants

By the 1970s armed forces worldwide were moving towards smaller-calibre, higher-velocity rifles. The Soviet Union and her Warsaw Pact allies embraced smaller calibres in the form of a 5.45mm round rather than the 5.56mm ammunition that became standard in the West. Since the Soviets already possessed an excellent service rifle in the AKM, all that was necessary was to modify it to fire 5.45mm. The result was the AK-74.

Slight modifications were made to the basic AK design, such as a more prominent muzzle brake that reduces felt recoil (already reduced because of the smaller round) to almost nothing. The AK-74 replaced the AKM in Soviet army service. Many surplus AKMs also found their way overseas at excellent prices, accounting for much of the weapon's popularity.

AKSU

Several versions of the AK-74 are produced. These include the AKS-74 (or AKSU), which features a folding stock to turn it effectively into a rifle-calibre submachine gun. Its shortness makes it a useful weapon for airborne forces, vehicle crews and troops engaged in urban fighting. Its impressive muzzle flash is a drawback and full-automatic fire can be somewhat random, but the AKSU remains an effective close-quarters weapon.

AK 101 & AK 103

Kalashnikov also manufactures AK rifles that use ammunition other than the Russian armed forces' standard 5.45mm. These include the AK 101 and the AK 103, which take 5.56x45mm NATO and

Above: Egyptian troops armed with AKMs during the 1973 Yom Kippur War – the variant is recognisable by its angled muzzle attachment. The AK family of rifles has achieved massive export success and Kalashnikovs of one type or another can now be found wherever there is conflict.

7.62x39mm ammunition, respectively. Large stockpiles of the latter still exist in former Warsaw Pact nations. These weapons have all the features of the AK series – reliability and ease of use being most prominent – and make them available to users worldwide. AK weapons are sufficiently well respected that, despite historical wariness of all things Russian, many US citizens favour AK weapons for home security.

It is estimated that more than 30 million AK assault rifles have been manufactured, not counting 'relatives' such as the Vektor. The reason for this success is that, while the AKM and its cousins may not be particularly good rifles, they are definitely excellent weapons. They shoot when the trigger is pulled, can hit a target out to a perfectly usable range, and they are likely to put that target out of action if it is hit. For most users this is all that is needed and the AK series does it on a budget.

Galil ARM, AR or SAR

The AK series has a number of indirect descendents. Arguably the best of these is the Galil ARM used by the Israeli armed forces. Based on the Valmet, a Finnish design that was in turn derived from the Kalashnikov, the Galil is available in several versions. The standard is the ARM, which has a built-in bipod to allow it to be used in the light machine gun role. The AR has no bipod or carrying handle, and the SAR has a short barrel. All versions are available with either a fixed or folding stock. The Galil Sniper is based on the standard Galil rifle, and is just as robust as the infantry version. Originally the Galil was chambered for 7.62x51mm, the same calibre as the FN FAL rifles then in use with the Israeli Defence Force. Today the 5.56mm version is more common, in keeping with the international move towards lighter calibres.

The standard Galil magazine holds 35 rounds rather than the more common 30. This can make using the rifle while prone problematic. A 50-round magazine is also available for support fire.

Vektor R4

South Africa was for a long time subject to an international arms embargo, which led to the development of an impressive arms industry. One of its products was the Vektor family of rifles, which was based on the Israeli Galil and included many of that weapon's best features. The fitting of

a bottle opener, for example, may seem incongruous, but it does prevent soldiers from damaging their weapons by using handy projections to open bottles. The R4 is larger and stronger than the Galil despite being around the same weight, largely thanks to greater use of high-impact nylon and glass fibre in the construction.

The Vektor is chambered for 5.56x45mm and fed from 35- or 50-round magazines, like the Galil. The standard version is the R4. The R5 is a carbine version and the R6 is shorter still.

Valmet M76

One of the first AK-47 derivatives was produced by Finland. Designed from the outset to be used in arctic conditions, the Valmet M76 uses the basic Kalashnikov action but benefits from modern materials and construction techniques. 7.62x39mm and 5.56x45mm versions are available, as are different butt configurations. The Valmet can have a folding or fixed stock. The latter is available as a conventional version or, as the M76T variant, with a distinctive steel tube.

The Valmet can be fed from 15-, 20- or 30-round magazines. The trigger guard is easily detachable for use with heavy Arctic clothing. The M78 squad support variant has a heavy barrel and a bipod but is otherwise very similar to the M76. The Valmet is, like all the Kalashnikov derivatives, rugged and soldier-proof, even under very cold or icy conditions.

SAR 80

There are also derivatives and variants of the M16 on the market, of which the SAR 80 is one of the best. Developed by Chartered Industries of Singapore in conjunction with the British firm Sterling Armaments, the SAR 80 is cheap to manufacture yet has the best features of the M16. The straight line from muzzle to stock aids controllability, while the user can select from semi-automatic, three-round burst or full-automatic fire. The SAR 80 can fire rifle grenades without modification and uses the standard 30-round M16 magazine. It is chambered for 5.56x45mm and is therefore compatible with the existing equipment of many nations. Although the rifle has not achieved 'classic' status, this weapon does perhaps deserve to.

Heckler & Koch G36

The excellent H&K G3 also spawned several descendants, ranging from full-sized rifles to submachine guns. Unlike most of the others, the G36 does not use the roller-locking delayed blowback system of the G3. The G36 is a gas-operated assault rifle with an integral bipod and has been designed as part of a family of weapons built around a common receiver. The G36K is a shorter 'carbine' variant of the G36 intended for use by vehicle crews and in close-quarters situations. The MG36 is a light support weapon. There is also a smaller G36C close assault model for special forces use.

Families of weapons constructed this way have been fielded before. In the 1960s Eugene Stoner developed a similar weapon system, based around a common receiver, which could be built as a carbine, rifle or light machine gun as necessary. Such an approach offers advantages in flexibility, but more importantly in terms of spares and maintenance. The ability to purchase a single weapon system that can fill several niches in the inventory is attractive to many armed forces and it seems likely that the G36 family will see widespread success.

INSAS

Most modern rifles are in some way related to the AK-47, G3 or M16. The Indian INSAS assault rifle has all three in its family tree, and combines their best features to produce a fine weapon. The INSAS is gas-operated and cannot fire on full-automatic, being restricted to single shots or three-round bursts, a capability its designers felt to be of more use. Accurate out to 800 metres (2625 feet), the INSAS is reliable and dependable, and perhaps represents the ultimate development of the conventional assault rifle.

SIG SG540

The Swiss firm SIG is well known for producing quality weapons, although they are often expensive. The rotating-bolt, gas-operated SIG SG540 is one such high-quality weapon. Although it is not a particularly innovative design, the SIG SG540 stands as an example of an adaptable and reliable conventional assault rifle. Chambered in 5.56mm NATO, the SG540 is fed from a 20- or 30-round magazine and can launch rifle grenades without additional equipment. It is accurate out to beyond 800 metres (2625 feet) and can make a decent sniper weapon with the addition of a suitable sight. Variants of the SIG SG540 are available in 7.62mm calibre.

Urban warriors – the Bullpups

For troops who must scramble in and out of vehicles or battle through close urban terrain, a short overall weapon length is highly desirable. For this and other reasons, many nations have chosen to arm some of their soldiers with submachine guns. The close-in firepower of a light, handy automatic weapon is undeniable, but submachine guns use low-powered pistol cartridges and have a short effective range. The average soldier may be fighting house-to-house one day and shooting at enemies 500 metres (1640 feet) away the next – a task for which a submachine gun is useless. Obviously, the SMG is not an ideal weapon for general infantry issue.

Assault rifles offer most of the advantages of submachine guns, such as lightness and firepower, and indeed have at times threatened the SMG with extinction. A rifle, however, needs a fairly long barrel to make it accurate, as well as a shoulder stock to assist the user in aiming. The conventional assault rifle is about as short as it can usefully be, and is certainly more handy than a 1900-vintage infantry rifle, but a rifle that could fit the same barrel length into a shorter overall package would give its users many advantages.

One answer was to fit a folding or detachable stock, allowing the weapon to be converted into a rifle-calibre submachine gun. Another solution, which did not require any alteration to the weapon from one situation to the next, was the 'Bullpup' configuration. Instead of the conventional assault rifle arrangement of grip-trigger-assembly-feed mechanism-barrel, Bullpup weapons are fed from behind the trigger assembly, through the stock.

A rifle stock is 'dead' volume, so placing the magazine well there was a stroke of genius. Placing the chamber so far back along the weapon's length

H&K G36

Calibre: 5.56mm NATO
Length: 758mm (29.8in) stock folded
Weight: 3.4kg (7.49lb)
Barrel: 480mm (18.9in), 6 grooves, rh
Magazine: 30-round detachable box magazine
Operation: Gas
Muzzle velocity: Not available

SIG SG540

Calibre: 5.56mm NATO
Length: 950mm (37in)
Weight: 3.26kg (7.19lb)
Operation: Gas, rotating bolt
Barrel: 460mm (18in), 6 grooves, rh
Magazine: 20- or 30-round box magazine
Muzzle velocity: 980mps (3215fps)

Steyr-Mannlicher AUG

Calibre: 5.56mm M198 or NATO
Length: 790mm (31.1in)
Weight: 3.6kg (7.93lb)
Barrel: 508mm (20in), 6 grooves, rh
Magazine: 30- or 42-round detachable box magazine
Operation: Gas
Muzzle velocity: 970mps (3182fps)

meant that a full-length barrel could run over the handgrip, starting well behind it, whereas a conventional weapon's barrel started in front of it. This allowed the same barrel length to be fitted into a weapon of much shorter overall length.

EM-2

The first Bullpup weapon was developed just after World War II. Designated the EM-2, this highly innovative weapon was chambered for a special 7mm round and fed by a 20-round magazine behind the trigger assembly. The EM-2 was a fine weapon. Light and well-balanced, it offered battle rifle accuracy in a short package, making it ideal for urban or mechanized combat.

The Bullpup configuration does have some drawbacks. When, many years later, the British Army adopted a Bullpup rifle it was found that many drill evolutions were not well suited to such a short weapon. More seriously, the position of the ejection port on a Bullpup weapon is such that it cannot be fired left-handed. Shooting from the left side of a position of cover can also be problematical, since ejected cartridge cases will rebound and strike the firer in the head.

Despite such issues, the EM-2 was good enough for the British Army to agree to trials – and liked what it saw. The weapon was accepted for service as the Rifle, Automatic, 7mm, No 9 Mk1. The EM-2, however, never entered service. Britain's allies, notably the USA, were standardizing ammunition at that time, and settled on the 7.62x51mm round. The British Army adopted the FN FAL instead.

Having come so close to revolutionizing the combat rifle world, the EM-2 has slipped into an obscurity that it truly does not deserve. Not many years later, rifles based on the same principles would become common and well respected, but at its inception the first of the Bullpups was a weapon far ahead of its time.

Space-age weaponry

The AUG looked like something from a science-fiction film and soon featured in several movies. During the 1980s quite a number of starship crew broke out their high-tech rifles to battle alien monsters, while more than one modern-day hero encountered experimental assault rifles in the hands of the bad guys.

Steyr-Mannlicher AUG

One of the most radical-appearing rifles of recent times is the Steyr-Mannlicher AUG (Armee Universal Gewehr), which became the weapon of choice in the 1980s for film-makers needing to depict futuristic weaponry on a budget. At the same time, however, the AUG was familiar to Austrian troops, who found it to be a truly excellent weapon. Although it looks spindly and somewhat fragile, the AUG is a robust and reliable weapon with a clear plastic magazine (holding 30 or 42 rounds) that allows the user to tell at a glance how much ammunition is left.

The AUG, which is normally chambered in 5.56x45mm, is constructed on a modular basis. Different barrel lengths are available and the receiver is also used as the basis of a 9mm submachine gun for use by paratroops. The weapon is also very accurate in both assault rifle and submachine gun configurations, and the vertical

Calibre: 5.56mm NATO or Type France
Length: 757mm (29.8in)
Weight: 3.61kg (7.96lb)
Barrel: 488mm (19.21in), 3 grooves, rh
Magazine: 25-round detachable box magazine
Operation: Gas
Muzzle velocity: 960mps (3150fps)

Above: The French FAMAS assault rifle is a classic example of the modern Bullpup assault rifle. Its small size makes it handy inside buildings and vehicles yet its accuracy at range is good enough for open combat.

foregrip is useful in 'from-the-hip' shooting, for example during fluid urban fighting or close assault.

FAMAS

Another excellent Bullpup, although very different in appearance to the AUG, is the French FAMAS. Short even by Bullpup standards, the FAMAS has a robust, businesslike appearance. Sometimes nicknamed 'Le Clarion' ('Bugle' or 'Trumpet'), after its shape, the FAMAS is chambered for 5.56mm NATO ammunition and can take the M16 magazine without modification.

The FAMAS is a very good rifle, accurate out to 400 metres (1312 feet). The trigger, however, is somewhat light and the rate of fire on full-automatic rather high, resulting in heavy ammunition expenditure unless the user is very careful.

SA80 (L85A1)

The debut of the SA80, or Enfield Individual Weapon L85A1, was not auspicious. Adopted by the British Army to replace ageing SLRs, the Bullpup-configuration SA80 was an excellent weapon on paper, and really very good in early trials. Once in service, however, it was found to suffer from a number of faults – some quite serious.

Reliability was found to be less than ideal if the weapon became dirty – something that tends to happen in service use. Other design faults included a tendency for the cocking handle to come off in the user's hand, rendering the weapon useless. When carrying the rifle across the body, a standard position, it was possible to activate the magazine release accidentally, perhaps leaving a full magazine behind. Not only is this a liability should the weapon need to be brought into action quickly, it could also result in live ammunition getting into the wrong hands.

Development

Most of these defects were resolved by slight engineering tweaks, and gradually the SA80 began to fulfil its promise. Like other Bullpups it is light, short, accurate and comfortable to fire. The 30-round magazine is identical to the standard M16 magazine and the rifle take a grenade launcher attachment under the barrel. Other good points include an optical sight fitted as standard. The advantages of the SUSAT (Sight Unit, Small Arm,

Above: The SUSAT optical sight of the SA80 rifle, seen here in the hands of a British Royal Marine, not only provides enhanced accuracy at range but also magnification, increasing infantry reconnaissance capabilities.

Trilux) over iron sights are considerable, not least because it gives each soldier access to, in effect, a magnifying telescope.

Automatic fire

The debate over whether the SA80's ability to use full-automatic fire is a good thing or not still continues. Critics point out that the British Army managed without autofire for many years, in many combat environments, and suggest that full-automatic operation encourages irresponsible shooting. Others contend that a well-trained soldier will make the best use of the tools he has available: rapid firepower is a useful capability that allows all troops (rather than just the squad support gunner) to suppress enemy positions and increases effectiveness in close-quarters urban fighting.

While this debate will likely remain unresolved for many years, the SA80 has developed from a promising but unreliable weapon into a good modern combat weapon. Variants on the standard SA80 include a squad support weapon and a carbine, which has an even shorter overall length due to a shorter barrel. Effective range is reduced by about 100 metres (328 feet), to 300 metres (985 feet), but this is counterbalanced by the weapon's suitability for vehicle crews and for combat in confined spaces.

The Bullpup-configuration assault rifle has become an industry standard in the past few years. Its drawbacks are overwhelmed by the advantages of such a short, handy weapon in today's crowded battle environment. The Bullpup has earned its place in the modern military inventory and it will take something very impressive to displace it.

Carbines and PDWs

The word 'carbine' has been defined in many ways. not all of them particularly useful. A good working definition is that a carbine is a small, light firearm with a long barrel, intended for two-handed use. The term is often applied to military weapons that have been adapted to civilian use, such as submachine guns converted to semi-automatic fire or even pistols with extended barrels and shoulder stocks fitted. However, carbines are simply small rifles. Thus while a carbine need not necessarily be chambered in a rifle calibre, most are.

Trooping the Colour

The introduction of the Bullpup-configuration SA80 caused consternation for the regiments tasked with performing the spectacular displays for which the British Army is famous, such as Trooping the Colour on Horse Guards Parade. Many drill evolutions were found to be impossible to perform with such a short weapon.

Colt M4 Commando

The Colt M4, or Commando, or XM177E2 – the correct designation is Colt M16A2 Commando, although the name is rarely used – is a carbine version of the M16 assault rifle. The lineage is obvious from general lines, although the M4's stock and barrel shroud are distinctive. Parts are interchangeable with those of the M16 (over 80 per cent of the parts are identical) and the carbine can mount a 40mm grenade launcher in the same manner as the parent rifle.

Although the M16A2 and the original M4 are limited to burst fire, the M4A1 Commando is capable of full-automatic. The weapon is accurate to 400 metres (1312 feet), thanks to improvements in its sights. As the name suggests, the Commando is popular with special forces and security personnel, who appreciate the heavyweight firepower. It is not noticeably shorter than the M16, however, since the shorter barrel produces a very large muzzle flash, requiring the fitting of a long flash hider.

Left: The Colt Commando is, as its name suggests, popular with special forces units. It was used as the testbed for the US Army 'Land Warrior' project, a programme intended to enhance infantry capabilities by creating a modular, integrated fighting system with computerised navigation, communications, weapons and sighting systems.

Calico M950

Although chambered in .22LR or 9mm Parabellum, both pistol calibres, the Calico M950 is really more of a carbine-type weapon. Shaped like a large handgun with a curious cylinder (the magazine) on top, the Calico has enough barrel shrouding to allow a two-handed grip more suited to a submachine gun or rifle than a pistol; some variants have a canted foregrip. The M950's long barrel allows accurate fire out to about 60 metres (197 feet), which is more normally seen with submachine guns than handguns, and the 50- or 100-round helical feed magazine offers impressive, semi-automatic only, firepower.

The basic M950 at present falls between several stools. It is too big to be a pistol but, lacking a stock or autofire capability, it is clearly not a submachine gun or conventional carbine. Just because it refuses to be neatly pigeonholed, however, does not mean that the M950 is not a useful weapon. Weighing less than a large-frame Magnum revolver, it offers a lot of firepower in a

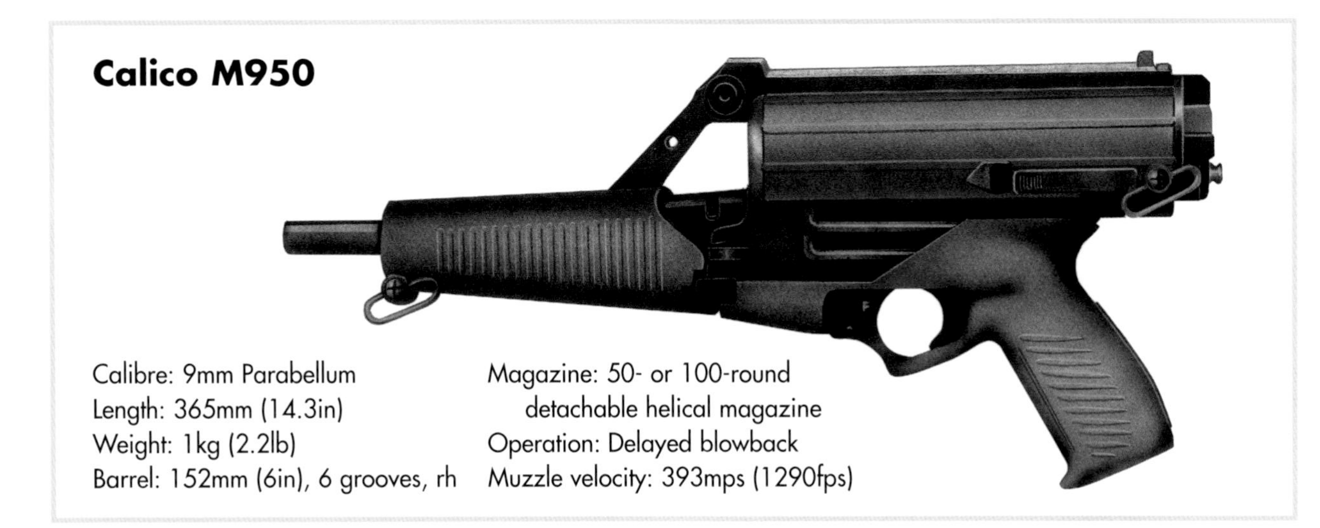

Calico M950

Calibre: 9mm Parabellum
Length: 365mm (14.3in)
Weight: 1kg (2.2lb)
Barrel: 152mm (6in), 6 grooves, rh
Magazine: 50- or 100-round detachable helical magazine
Operation: Delayed blowback
Muzzle velocity: 393mps (1290fps)

small package. Whether or not the concept will catch on remains to be seen, but the M950 is a fascinating experiment that might lead to even more innovative weapons.

Calico M950 variants

A true carbine version, the Liberty 100 (or Liberty 50 in the case of the 50-round variant), is available. This is effectively a 9mm M950 with a fixed stock and is semi-automatic only. The Calico M960A is a submachine gun version. Fed by either the 50- or 100-round magazine, the M960A has an 'assault' foregrip, minimal stock and a muzzle brake/flash hider. This version, while somewhat odd in appearance, is the easiest of the variants to classify: it is a true submachine gun with a huge magazine capacity that offers very impressive firepower.

Ruggedness as standard

Modern rifles are designed to take huge amounts of abuse and keep on working. During tests on the Steyr AUG, an example was run over several times by a truck. The optical sight was broken in the process, but the weapon continued to function.

FN P90

Like the Calico M950, the Fabrique Nationale P90 can be classified in various ways. Some call it a submachine gun, some a carbine. Its makers term it a Personal Defence Weapon, and cite its role as a defensive weapon for personnel whose duties do not normally include small arms combat, such as vehicle crews and artillerymen. Thus in its intended role, as well as its general size and appearance, the FN P90 seems to be a carbine.

The reasoning behind this very unusual-looking weapon is that handguns and submachine guns firing pistol ammunition lack both range and damage potential, especially against body armour. FN wished to create a weapon that fulfilled these requirements while remaining light and easy to carry, but took the unusual route of developing a new ammunition calibre for it to use.

The 'Five-Seven' round

The 5.7x28mm round developed by Fabrique Nationale is also used in FN's 'Five-Seven' handgun, although its performance in the P90 is better. The round was designed to defeat body armour and standard military helmets at 50–100 metres (165–330 feet).

The P90 is designed for ambidextrous use, with cocking handles on each side and the selector below the trigger. The weapon is capable of both semi- and full-automatic fire and is fed from a 50-round magazine. The weapon's feed mechanism is unusual in that rounds are held pointing at right angles to the breech and are fed over a ramp that aligns them before chambering.

The Personal Defence Weapon concept has received a certain amount of attention in recent years, and it may be that the P90 is the forerunner of a whole generation of similar weapons. Certainly Fabrique Nationale's most recent FN 2000 bullpup design features many of the P90's most innovative ergonomic features.

The future of the rifle

Rifles are too useful to go away. Even if directed energy weapons (such as lasers) were to become workable as small arms in the near future, the relative simplicity of shooting a projectile at the target would keep the rifle in service. This does not mean, however, that new ideas cannot be applied to the basic assault rifle concept.

Shared ammunition

The idea of pistol and carbine in the same calibre is not new – Napoleonic cavalrymen carried pistols and carbines that shared ammunition – but it has been out of favour for many decades. Perhaps the P90 will successfully challenge that situation.

Heckler & Koch G11

These new ideas fall into two categories: what the rifle is able to do, and how it is to do it. One experiment into new and better ways to do the same job is the Heckler & Koch G11. Strange in appearance, the G11 does not use conventional cartridges like almost all other weapons. Instead its ammunition is 'caseless', requiring no ejection mechanism since everything comes out of the muzzle when the weapon is fired.

The G11's 4.7x33mm caseless ammunition consists of a block of propellant with primer and bullet embedded in it. Ejection problems account for most weapon jams and malfunctions, so the G11 gains reliability advantages immediately. The smaller ammunition allows a 50-round magazine to be used without adding any bulk.

The G11 can fire on full-automatic at 600 rounds per minute or in three-round bursts. In the latter mode, all three rounds are fired in a single recoil cycle and at an equivalent cyclic rate of 2200 rounds per minute. This awesome rate of fire ensures that weapon movement due to recoil or other factors scarcely affects the grouping of a burst. At lower rates of fire, a burst may be scattered by barrel vibration or muzzle climb. The

FN P90

Calibre: 5.7mm FN
Length: 400mm (15.75in)
Weight: 2.8kg (6.17lb)
Barrel: 263mm (7.75in), 6 grooves, rh
Magazine: 50-round detachable box magazine
Operation: Blowback
Muzzle velocity: 850mps (2800fps)

Heckler & Koch G11

Calibre: 4.7mm DM11 caseless
Length: 752.5mm (29.62in)
Weight: 3.80kg (8.38lb)
Barrel: 537.5mm (21.16in), 6 grooves, polygonal, rh
Magazine: 50-round detachable box magazine
Operation: Gas
Muzzle velocity: 930mps (3050fps)

OICW

Calibre: 5.56mm NATO and 20x85mm High Explosive
Length: 890mm (35.04in)
Weight: 5.5kg (12.13lb) empty; 6.8kg (15lb) loaded
Barrel: 250mm (9.84in) for 5.56mm rifle; 460mm (18.11in) for 20mm launcher
Magazine: 20- or 30-round box for 5.56mm rifle; 6-round box 20mm launcher.
Operation: Gas-operated, rotating bolt

Tactical reloading

It may be logical and tidy-minded to reload only when the magazine is empty, but it is always better to have a full magazine. Troops trained to use tactical reloading will remove any part-fired magazine and replace it with a full one at the first opportunity.

Some riflemen like to put a tracer round at the bottom of a magazine. These rounds have a small incendiary charge in their base so that the firer can correct his aim. Placed near the bottom of the magazine, it will also remind him when he is close to running out of ammo.

G11 is accurate out to 500 metres (1640 feet) and includes an optical sight as standard. Like other Bullpup configuration weapons, the Heckler & Koch G11 is short and handy, and its weight is about average for an assault rifle.

Despite the engineering challenges presented by the development of caseless ammunition and a suitable feed system, the G11 does its job and does it well. It has been adopted by German special forces, but has not entered mainstream service. This is as much due to the high cost as anything else. It may be that caseless ammunition is the future of small arms, or the G11 is an aberration; time will tell. The G11 has undoubtedly demonstrated a new way of doing what rifles already do, offering some advantages and some intriguing possibilities for the future. Whatever else it may be, though, the G11 is a fine combat rifle whose rather outlandish appearance at least serves to distinguish it from more conventional weapons.

OICW (XM29)

Where the G11 found a new way to do the same job, the OICW (Objective Infantry Combat Weapon) is intended to give the battle rifle a whole new set of capabilities. Developed by Alliant Techsystems and Heckler & Koch, the OICW (also designated XM29, suggesting that its service designation will be M29) combines a 5.56mm-calibre rifle based on the H&K G36 with a 20mm weapon that gives infantry personnel extra firepower.

The XM29 also includes a laser rangefinder and internal electronics that allow a 20mm round to be fused to a distance found by the laser. This allows soldiers to 'shoot around corners' by detonating a 20mm shell over or beside cover used by enemy personnel. If it can be made to work under battle conditions, the OICW will allow each infantryman to take on some of the roles of support weapons, doing away with the need for specialists equipped with grenade launchers, or at least ensuring that, if a 'hard' target or one needing indirect fire is encountered, there is a suitable weapon available to every member of the squad.

The Objective Infantry Combat Weapon is a bold and futuristic weapon system. At present it is very heavy and its size is likely to present some problems. However, the real question is whether

Right: An Iraqi militiaman armed with a Kalashnikov rifle in the holy city of Najaf, 2004. Cheap, hard-wearing, and easy-to-maintain assault rifles such as the Kalashnikov are likely to remain popular for many years to come.

the electronics can be made reliable enough to function for years in the sort of environments encountered by combat rifles.

Revolution or convention?

Various experiments have been undertaken to make rifles more effective. These include many attempts to create improved ammunition, requiring the design of new weapons to fire it. Flechette weapons, capable of firing a very small-calibre dart in a similar manner to Armour-Piercing Fin-Stabilized Discarding Sabot (APFSDS) antitank ammunition, have been tried, as have duplex and triplex rounds, in which a rifle round contains two or three separate projectiles rather than a single larger one.

Highly unusual technologies are also under development, including electromagnetically launched projectile weapons and even directed energy weapons (lasers and microwave weapons). Despite occasional rumours of foreign projects, working 'ray guns' and handheld rail guns (linear magnetic accelerators) are a long way off. The power requirements alone present massive technological obstacles. The electrically fired Metalstorm system offers some possibilities, but so far workable small arms using this promising technology have not been introduced.

It is therefore likely that conventional rifles will continue to dominate for many years to come. Most weapon users need something that shoots when the trigger is pulled and can hit what it is aimed at out to a couple of hundred metres. They also need a weapon that can be maintained and repaired in the field with basic tools, that does not require constant delicate care and is not prohibitively expensive.

Thus while the future may well hold super-capable advanced conventional weapons such as the OICW, and even higher-tech systems such as electromagnetic accelerator or directed-energy weapons, these will at best dominate the top end of the spectrum. For civilians considering a weapon for home security, law enforcers, hunters or the soldiers of less developed nations, the future of the rifle lies in cheap, well-made, idiot-proof weapons of no great capability and using tried and tested technology. Unexciting as such weapons may be, they do their job and will continue to do so for many years to come.

SUBMACHINE GUNS

From the trench warfare of World War I to hostage rescue and special operations today, there has long been a role for a close assault weapon capable of delivering close-range firepower without compromising speed or manoeuverability. Submachine guns and machine pistols combine compact size, ease of use and substantial, controllable firepower.

For the most part, firearms are intended to allow the user to deal with attackers and enemies at a distance. There are times, however, when combat occurs at extremely short ranges. Under these conditions a rifle, even a short assault rifle, is not always the ideal weapon.

Trench warfare in World War I demonstrated a need for a new class of firearm, the close assault weapon. Such a weapon had to be capable of quickly disposing of multiple enemies while not getting in the way. During a stealthy approach to the enemy position, a mad rush across broken terrain or the wild scramble of a hand-to-hand fight, a rifle was more a liability than an asset, so many troops left theirs behind and armed themselves with knives (or detached bayonets), clubs and revolvers if close combat was expected. These expedients worked well enough, but something better was desirable.

Left: The 9mm Heckler & Koch MP5, a popular weapon with special forces units. The MP5 is capable of semi-automatic fire, three-round bursts and 800rpm full-automatic fire.

An assortment of 'trench brooms' were fielded during the close fighting that took place in World War I, ranging from shotguns to light automatic weapons. The latter were generally preferred by Stormtroopers since they offered a measure of suppressive firepower at a moderate range as well as the ability to disable enemy personnel quickly.

Machine pistols and SMGs

Machine pistols had been around for a few years at this point, but they were not very effective. For one thing, the recoil of very rapid automatic fire tended to cause the muzzle to climb uncontrollably. Thus it was decided that something larger and more controllable – perhaps holding more ammunition too – might be a better idea.

Although these larger weapons retained the 'machine pistol' label, they were not strictly pistols but weapons more akin to a carbine, requiring the firer to use both hands to operate properly. Smaller than a machine gun, but similar in operation, they became known as submachine guns, and so they are called to this day.

Until the end of World War II close assault weapons of this type tended to be fairly bulky and could in most cases be more accurately described as automatic carbines chambered for pistol ammunition. Design, however, was to diverge in the years that followed.

While some manufacturers continued to produce carbine-like weapons, others marketed submachine guns that were more like semi-automatic pistols in configuration. The classic example is the Uzi submachine gun. Fed through the butt, the Uzi looks like an overgrown pistol whereas, for example, the MP5 clearly shows its 'carbine' heritage. Both approaches have their merits and flaws, and there are excellent weapons in both groups.

Less effective is the 'assault pistol', a full-automatic version of a handgun that suffers from all the same problems as its ancestors of 100 years ago. Too light to handle automatic fire, assault pistols are probably less effective than a decent handgun. They represent the extreme end of the small automatic weapon scale, a region where further miniaturization is pointless since it merely marginalizes the utility of the weapon even further.

A good close assault weapon must be short and light, allowing rapid mobility through difficult terrain. It must be capable of being brought into action quickly and decisively, delivering sufficient firepower to deal with any threat encountered. It must also be accurate out to a reasonable distance, in case the close assault troops or other users are forced to engage at more than pistol range.

As a rule, close assault weapons are intended to be used for the same situations where a handgun could be employed, but offer significant advantages over sidearms. If long-range combat is anticipated, a rifle or carbine is a better option, although a submachine gun is more use than a pistol.

Submachine guns in the World Wars

In the latter stages of the Great War it was obvious that massed infantry assaults were not going to break the deadlock. While technological means were being tried elsewhere, the German High Command chose to place their faith in infantry of a special kind, the Stormtroopers (*Stosstruppen*). Forming units of the best men available and arming them for close combat, the Germans hoped to achieve a decisive success by new tactics.

The tactical approach was, in hindsight, obvious. Instead of hurling vast numbers of troops at heavily defended objectives, small units would instead

Left: World War II British troops armed with Thompson submachine guns. Submachine guns were a popular alternative to full-sized rifles which were too cumbersome for the paratroopers' usual close assault role.

infiltrate enemy positions, overrunning weak points and bypassing centres of opposition. The troops spearheading the assault would use surprise, speed and firepower to overwhelm their enemies and move on to cause havoc in the enemy's rear, while follow-up forces secured their gains. The concept was a foot-powered version of the armoured *Blitzkrieg* of World War II and many conflicts since.

The Stormtroopers achieved a number of impressive successes, although they were too few and too late to alter the course of the war. They used pistols, grenades, carbines and flamethrowers in their assaults, but the most important weapon in their arsenal was the machine pistol.

Bergmann MP18

Developed by Hugo Schmeisser, the Bergmann MP18 was introduced in 1918 and proved extremely effective in the hands of the Stormtroopers. Fed from a box magazine holding 20 or 32 rounds, or a 32-round 'snail drum' magazine, the MP18 had a wooden stock and clearly shows its 'automatic carbine' heritage. Chambered for 9mm Parabellum, the weapon was highly effective at close quarters in a trench assault. Its dimensions are similar to those of a modern assault rifle, and its 70 metre (230 feet) effective range was quite acceptable given its intended role. The distinctive drilled barrel shroud is designed to assist in cooling and was a feature of many automatic weapons in years to come.

Post-war restrictions on automatic weapons meant that the German army was not permitted to issue the MP18, although police units were permitted to possess it. Simple, straightforward and

Bergmann MP18

Calibre: 9mm Parabellum
Length: 815mm (32.09in)
Weight: 4.19kg (9.25lb)
Barrel: 196mm (7.75in), 6 grooves, rh
Magazine: 32-round 'snail' or 20- or 32-round detachable box magazine
Operation: Blowback
Cyclic rate of fire: 450rpm
Muzzle velocity: 395mps (1295fps)

Pistole Mitraglitrice Vilar-Perosa M15

Calibre: 9mm Glisenti
Length: 533mm (21in)
Weight: 6.25kg (14.37lb)
Barrel: 318mm (12.5in), 6 grooves, rh
Magazine: 2x25-round box magazine
Operation: Delayed blowback
Cyclic rate of fire: 1200rpm
Muzzle velocity: 365mps (1200fps)

Personal defence

Submachine guns are not the only weapons to use pistol cartridges. In the 1880s a device was marketed to counter the threat of being garrotted from behind. It consisted of a pistol cartridge held at the back of the belt and fired by a hand-held lanyard.

An even more ridiculous device was designed for the use of explorers. It comprised a pistol mechanism built into a pith helmet and fired by biting on a tube running down to the mouth. Presumably the helmet had to be securely fastened by its chinstrap!

reliable, the MP18 and a developed version, the MP28, went back into production under the Nazi rearmament programme, and gave good service in World War II. Production ceased in 1945, but the design had by then influenced many other weapons.

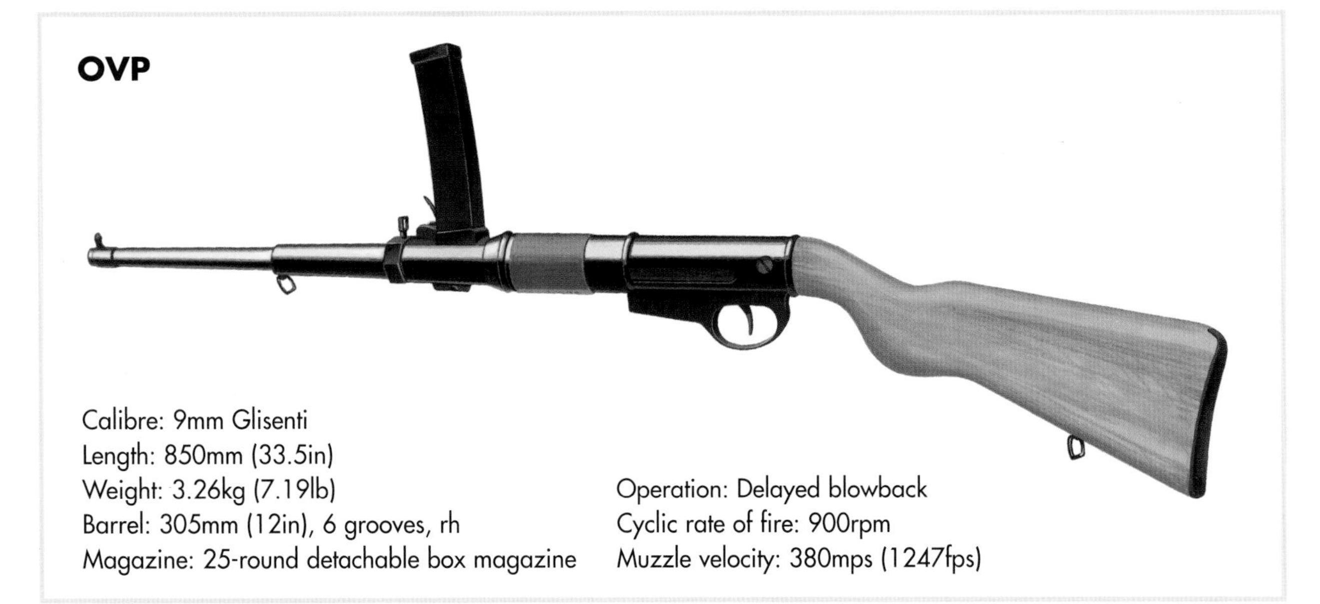

OVP

Calibre: 9mm Glisenti
Length: 850mm (33.5in)
Weight: 3.26kg (7.19lb)
Barrel: 305mm (12in), 6 grooves, rh
Magazine: 25-round detachable box magazine
Operation: Delayed blowback
Cyclic rate of fire: 900rpm
Muzzle velocity: 380mps (1247fps)

Pistole Mitraglitrice Vilar-Perosa M15

Other experimental light automatic weapons of the period included the Pistole Mitraglitrice Vilar-Perosa M15, a weapon that was more influential than effective. Less than 550mm (21.5 inches) long, shorter than a Mini-Uzi, the M15 was a double-barrelled weapon chambered in 9mm and fed from above by two 25-round magazines. It was designed as a support weapon and could be used with a bipod or suspended on straps for 'assault' firing. The light bolt resulted in the M15 firing at 1200 rounds per minute, an extremely high rate of fire that would empty both magazines in an instant. It was less than handy to use, making it a rather poor submachine gun, but these were early days.

OVP

Developed from the M15, the OVP submachine gun was a short-lived weapon that more closely approximated a useful submachine gun. Essentially half an M15, with a wooden stock and conventional trigger assembly to turn it into a carbine-like weapon, the OVP offered full-auto or semi-automatic operation and was effective to beyond 100 metres (328 feet). As primitive as it might look, the OVP was a reasonable weapon and, for its time, quite innovative.

Thompson M1921/28

Perhaps the most well-known submachine gun of all time, the Thompson submachine gun was designed by a US army general in recognition of the need for a pistol-calibre close assault weapon for trench warfare. Initially gaining notoriety in the Prohibition era as the weapon of choice for gangsters and the law-enforcement officers who battled them, the Thompson was a fine and reliable weapon, firing a .45 ACP cartridge that hit hard out to 120 metres (394 feet) or more. Firing at 700 rounds per minute, with recoil reduced to a controllable level by a Cutts Compensator on the barrel, the Thompson spoke with authority.

Versions of the Thompson included one with a canted foregrip for 'assault' fire (this is the version normally recognized as the 'gangster gun') and a more conventional rifle-type foregrip. Box magazines were available holding 18, 20 or 30 rounds as well as the characteristic drum holding

Left: Looking every inch the 1920s gangster, Winston Churchill poses with a Thompson SMG. The pugnacious wartime Prime Minister approved of the Thompson's firepower and its ability to stop any enemy in his tracks.

50 or 100 rounds. The original Thompson (M1921) was followed by the M1928 model, which incorporated some minor modifications including a rate of fire reduced from 800 to 700 rounds per minute. The M1928 was the first Thompson taken up by a military user (the US Marine Corps). A version developed for more rapid manufacture, designated the M1 (and later M1A1) went into production in 1942.

The Thompson gave good service in World War II and afterward, arming Marines and paratroopers as well as infantrymen. Although production ceased in the 1960s it is still popular with enthusiasts, especially in the US, and sometimes surfaces in modern conflicts. Examples were observed in use in the early 1990s during troubles in the former Yugoslavia.

Suomi KP/-31

The submachine gun concept underwent rapid development between the two World Wars. Some designers explored blind alleys while others produced mediocre, over-complex and generally less than useful weapons. Some weapons, however, were destined to influence some of the finest examples of the type ever to be constructed.

The Finnish designer Aimo Johannes Lahti got it right with the Suomi KP/-31. Choosing the 9mm Parabellum round to build his weapon around, he came up with a carbine-type SMG fed by a 20- or 50-round box magazine or a 71-round drum. The box was divided into two columns, creating a shorter magazine than on some other SMGS.

Capable of engaging targets at a range more normally associated with rifles – claims of a 300 metres (985 feet) effective range are not uncommon – the KP/-31 delivered 900 rounds per minute and was reliable under combat conditions. It remained in production until 1944 and in service for 10 years more. Overseas buyers came from as far afield as South America, and the design influenced a series of Soviet weapons that included one of the best SMGs of all time. This was the PPSh-41, which not only incorporated design lessons from the KP/-31 but used a 71-round drum magazine.

MP38

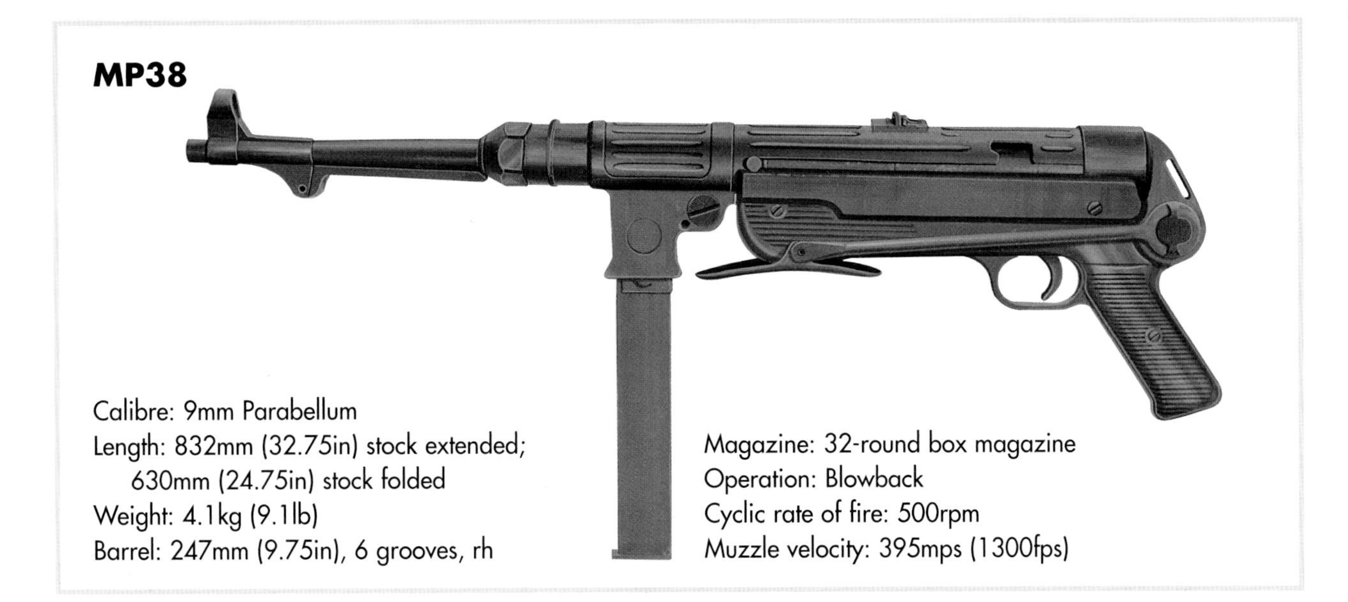

Calibre: 9mm Parabellum
Length: 832mm (32.75in) stock extended; 630mm (24.75in) stock folded
Weight: 4.1kg (9.1lb)
Barrel: 247mm (9.75in), 6 grooves, rh
Magazine: 32-round box magazine
Operation: Blowback
Cyclic rate of fire: 500rpm
Muzzle velocity: 395mps (1300fps)

Lanchester

Calibre: 9mm Parabellum
Length: 850mm (33.5in)
Weight: 4.34kg (9.56lb)
Barrel: 203mm (8in), 6 grooves, rh
Magazine: 50-round box magazine
Operation: Blowback
Cyclic rate of fire: 600rpm
Muzzle velocity: 380mps (1247fps)

Star SI35

One weapon that was very good in principle but did not prove to be a success was the Star SI35, a submachine gun developed in Spain. This weapon had some very interesting features. Its bolt, for example, was locked open when the magazine became empty, which became common with assault rifles much later. The rate of fire was also selectable between 300 and 700 rounds per minute.

Capable of taking 10-, 30- or 40-round magazines of 9x23mm ammunition and accurate out to 50 metres (164 feet), the SI35 was a good weapon but turned out to be too complex to manufacture in large numbers. Initial interest waned and the weapon passed into obscurity as a creditable also-ran.

Erma MPE or EMP

The German firm Erma is most famous for the MP38 and MP40 SMGs, but in the early 1930s they produced the forerunner of those weapons, which was very good in its own right. The gun was produced by Berthold Geipel GmbH from 1934, when it bcame named the EMP or MPE (the name is derived from 'Erma Maschinenpistole').

The EMP had a wooden rifle-type stock with a vertical foregrip built in and was fed from the side by a 20- or 32-round magazine. Chambered for 9mm Parabellum, the MPE pioneered the telescoping return spring casing concept that later featured in the MP38 design. The weapon saw service in Central and South America and in the Spanish Civil War.

Right: The Lanchester submachine gun was popular with the Royal Navy since it made an ideal weapon for boarding parties. Here armed guards escort captured U-boat crewmen ashore in Canada.

MP38 and MP40

One of the most distinctive weapons ever designed, the German MP38 arrived on the scene just in time for World War II, and proved to be ideal for the rapid armoured advances and bitter urban fighting that characterized that conflict. Chambered for 9mm Parabellum and fed by a 32-round magazine that also served as a foregrip, the MP38 was accurate out to 70 metres (230 feet) and, with a rate of fire of 500 round per minute, struck a balance between firepower and controllability.

The folding minimal stock extended the weapon's length to that of a carbine; folded, it was less than 650mm (25.6 inches) in length, making it ideal for close-quarters fighting and rapid exits from vehicles. Production was cheap, using stamped metal rather than machining, but reliability was good despite a tendency to fire when dropped or hit against something solid.

A developed version, the MP38/40, addressed the accidental discharge problem but was superseded by the MP40. This weapon was almost identical to the MP38 but was made even cheaper to manufacture by use of sub-assemblies and standardized manufacturing procedures. More than a million MP40s were constructed during World War II.

Both the MP38 and MP40 have become known as the 'Schmeisser', even though they were actually designed by Heinrich Vollmer of Erfurt Maschinenwerk (Erma).

Lanchester

The side-loading, carbine-like submachine gun continued to be popular after the end of World War I. Some were almost copies of the MP18. One fine example is the British Lanchester, designed by George Lanchester of the Sterling Armament Company. The Lanchester used the furniture of a Short Magazine Lee-Enfield rifle and, unusually for a submachine gun, had a bayonet fitting. Another peculiarity was the magazine fitting, which was made of solid brass to help reduce corrosion.

The Lanchester was chambered in 9mm Parabellum and fed from a 50-round magazine, offering impressive firepower. Although it was a very fine weapon, it was never issued in vast numbers due to cost.

Sten Mk II

While the Lanchester was a beautiful and excellent weapon, the Sten was a typical wartime expedient. Looking as if it had been thrown together from scrap metal, the Sten was in fact an effective weapon, if occasionally unreliable due to feed problems. More than two million Mk IIs were manufactured, some of them by British schoolboys in metalwork classes.

With its small size and good firepower, the Sten was as effective as it was ugly, and several versions were introduced to service. None could be said to be visually appealing, and all retained the problematic feed system. While there is no doubting the lethality of the Sten gun at close range, its effectiveness fell off sharply at range. Old soldiers talk of seeing Sten rounds bouncing off greatcoat-clad enemy personnel at 75 metres (246 feet).The Sten, however, was there when it was needed and in sufficient numbers to make a real difference. Its name comes from the initials of the designers, Shepherd and Turpin, plus the first two letters of the Enfield factory where it was developed.

Owen

Another wartime expedient, the Owen submachine gun was a peculiar-looking piece of engineering. Threatened with Japanese invasion and unable to obtain suitable weapons from hard-pressed Britain,

Left: The Sten gun looked like a collection of scrap metal, but it was available in vast numbers when guns were desperately needed. This Sten, in the hands of a British paratrooper, is also fitted with a small spike bayonet.

the Australian government fielded the Owen. One of the very few top-loading submachine guns ever designed, the Owen actually worked very well and remained in service until the mid-1960s.

Chambered for 9mm Parabellum and fed from a 33-round magazine, the Owen was accurate out to about 70 metres (230 feet) and showed itself to be a reliable and effective weapon.

Patchett Mk 1

Similar in some ways to the Sten gun, although aesthetically much more pleasing, was the Patchett SMG. Designed by George Patchett of the Sterling Armament Company, the Patchett Mk 1 was a 9mm side-fed design with a rate of fire of 550 rounds per minute. The Patchett could accept Sten magazines and saw action with airborne troops at Arnhem in 1944. Well put together and effective in combat, the Mk 1 Patchett was replaced by the Mk 2, which is better known as the excellent Sterling submachine gun.

Austen

Another effort to create something better than the Sten, but which was not much more expensive, was the Australian Austen SMG. Combining features of the MP40 and the Sten, the Austen was a robust and effective weapon chambered for 9mm Parabellum. The 28-round magazine fed from the side, above a canted foregrip. With a length of only 550mm (21.5 inches) with the metal stock folded, the Austen was very handy at close quarters but was edged out by the more reliable Owen.

Owen

Calibre: 9mm Parabellum
Length: 813mm (32in)
Weight: 4.21kg (9.28lb)
Barrel: 247mm (9.75in), 7 grooves, rh
Magazine: 33-round detachable box magazine
Operation: Blowback
Cyclic rate of fire: 700rpm
Muzzle velocity: 380mps (1247fps)

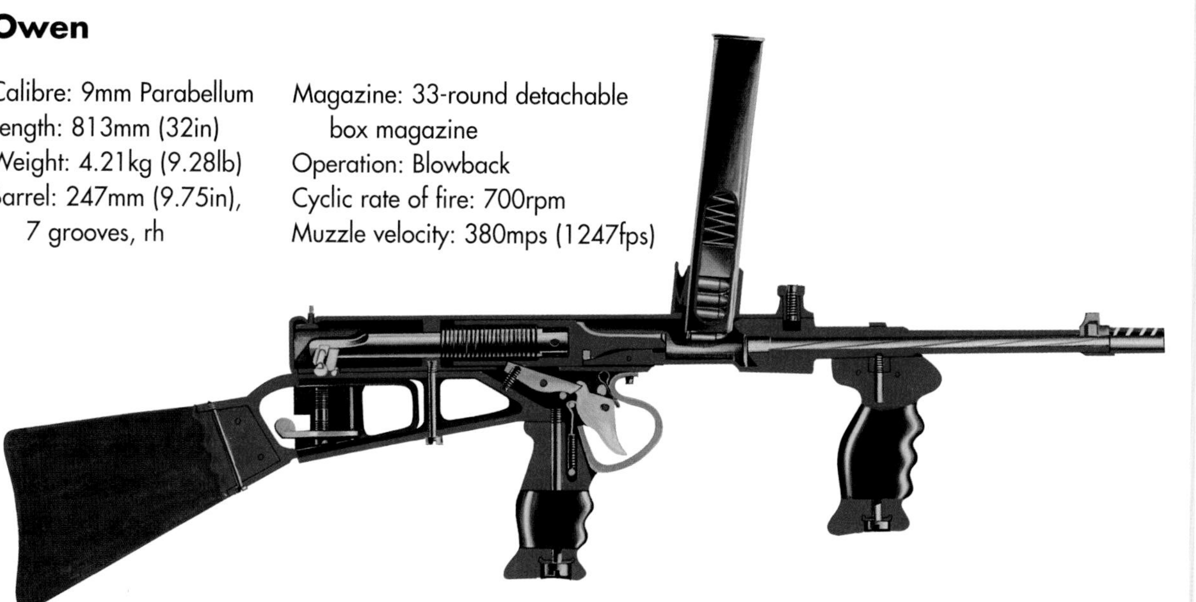

Patchett Mk 1

Calibre: 9mm Parabellum
Length: 685mm (27in)
Weight: 2.7kg (6lb)
Barrel: 195mm (7.75in), 6 grooves, rh
Magazine: 32-round detachable box magazine
Operation: Blowback
Cyclic rate of fire: 550rpm
Muzzle velocity: 395mps (1295fps)

MAS 38

French wartime armament production included the MAS 38 submachine gun, which was unusual for several reasons. The bolt was able to travel unusually far, being returned to position by a very long spring situated in the butt. The barrel and stock were offset slightly, giving the weapon a 'broken' appearance but helping to control recoil, which was not great anyway owing to the low power of the 7.65mm round used by the weapon.

The MAS 38 was manufactured for the French Army during the early years of World War II and by the Vichy regime after June 1940. It remained in production for a few years after the war, but was effectively killed by ammunition standardization agreements. The 7.65mm Long round had never found favour outside France, so overseas sales did not materialize.

Beretta Model 1938/42

Beretta met the challenge of wartime weapon production by adapting their 1938A SMG for mass-production on a huge scale. The result was the Model 1938/42, a carbine-style submachine gun with wooden furniture. The 34-round magazine, feeding from underneath, looks incongruously small on what is really quite a long weapon compared to modern SMGs. The 1938/42 was manufactured in large numbers but still retained the excellent performance of its predecessor. One useful modification in view of Italy's military experience in North Africa was a special dust jacket covering the bolt, intended to prevent fouling from sand. The balance between furnishing enough weapons and producing good ones is difficult to achieve, and the 1938/42 stands as an example of how it can be done.

Beretta Model 1938/42

Calibre: 9mm Parabellum
Length: 798mm (31.4in)
Weight: 2.72kg (6lb)
Barrel: 198mm (7.79in), 6 grooves, rh
Magazine: 34-round detachable box magazine
Operation: Blowback
Cyclic rate of fire: 550rpm
Muzzle velocity: 395mps (1295fps)

M3A1

Another weapon intended for cheap mass-production, the M3A1 submachine gun (also known as the 'grease gun', after its shape), was designed from the outset to be turned out in huge numbers. Using pressed steel components it was quick and cheap to construct, and presented little in the way of engineering challenges for its manufacturer, General Motors. The M3A1 was available in either 9mm or .45 calibre and featured a folding metal stock and 30-round magazine. Rate of fire was low for a submachine gun, only 450 rounds per minute. Although not the best weapon ever fielded, the M3A1 was available in large numbers and served its purpose at a time when large numbers of troops needed adequate weapons immediately rather than good ones eventually.

PPD-34/38 and PPD-40

As World War II approached, the Soviet Army's search for a truly world-class submachine gun saw the introduction of the PPD series, the PPD-34/38 and, later, the PPD-40. Based heavily on the Bergmann MP18 and 28 designs, and influenced by the Finnish Suomi SMG, the PPD-34/38 was a carbine-type SMG fed by either a 25-round curved magazine or a 71-round drum.

Accurate to 100 metres (328 feet) and firing 7.62x25mm pistol rounds at 800 rounds per minute, the PPD-34/38 was a fine weapon but suffered from expensive production methods. Although the results were good, the large numbers needed were not possible. Despite this, the weapon

M3A1

Calibre: .45 ACP or 9mm Parabellum
Length: 762mm (30in) stock extended; 577mm (22.75in) stock folded
Weight: 3.7kg (8.15lb)
Barrel: 203mm (8in), 4 grooves, rh
Magazine: 30-round detachable box magazine
Operation: Blowback
Cyclic rate of fire: 450rpm
Muzzle velocity: 275mps (900fps)

was manufactured from 1934 to 1940, at which point it was replaced by the PPD-40.

The PPD-40 was similar in performance and appearance to its predecessor, but had a simplified construction process and was consequently cheaper. It was, however, not cheap enough and was eclipsed by the PPSh-41.

PPSh-41

Developed from the PPD-34/38 and the PPD-40, the PPSh-41 finally met the Soviet Army's requirements. Forever the symbol of World War II Soviet infantrymen, the PPSh-41 was constructed from stamped-metal parts and was designed for speed of manufacture. Vast numbers of submachine guns were needed to arm Soviet soldiers fighting

Drum magazines

The PPSh-41 drum magazine copies that on the Finnish Suomi Model 51. Not long after, the Finns copied the Russian PPS-43 SMG to create their Konepistooli M44.

Right: A Soviet soldier dressed in a white snow suit waits in ambush with his PPSh-41during the winter of 1942.

WORLD WAR II SUBMACHINE GUNS: PPSH-41 VERSUS

Several classic light automatic weapons earned their laurels in World War II, among them the Russian PPSh-41 and the Thompson. Each was, in its way, an excellent submachine gun with many fine qualities, and there are some striking similarities between these guns even though they were developed a world apart. The Thompson was designed 'from the ground up' and could take either box magazines or large-capacity drums of powerful .45 ACP ammunition. With a Cutts Compensator built into the muzzle, the Thompson's powerful recoil was controllable; some users found it useful to turn the weapon sideways and allow

STRENGTHS

- Extremely reliable
- Cheap and quick to produce
- Light recoil

WEAKNESSES

- Weak 7.62x25mm cartridge
- No foregrip
- Bulky with drum magazine attached

PPSH-41

Calibre: 7.62mm M1930
Length: 838mm (33in)
Weight: 3.64kg (8lb)
Barrel: 266mm (10.5in), 4 grooves, rh
Magazine: 35-round detachable box; 71-round drum magazine
Operation: Blowback
Cyclic rate of fire: 900rpm
Muzzle velocity: 490mps (1600fps)

THOMPSON M1928

recoil to 'fan' the bullet stream. Unlike the Thompson, the PPSh-41 drew on earlier designs and incorporated many of the lessons learned from its predecessors. It fired a little faster than the Thompson but had no foregrip; the user's left hand gripped the magazine or drum to stabilize the weapon. The PPSh-41 was designed to be thrown together in cottage workshops and cities under siege and could be produced far more quickly and cheaply than the Thompson. Yet it was also a reliable and popular weapon that, like the Thompson, served for many years after the war ended.

Thompson M1928

Calibre: .45 M1911
Length: 857mm (33.75in)
Weight: 4.88kg (10.75lb)
Barrel: 266mm (10.5in), 6 grooves, rh
Magazine: 18-, 20- or 30-round detachable box magazine; 50- or 100-round drum magazine
Operation: Delayed blowback
Cyclic rate of fire: 700rpm
Muzzle velocity: 280mps (920fps)

STRENGTHS

- Powerful .45 ACP round
- Massive ammunition supply
- Excellent craftsmanship

WEAKNESSES

- Heavy recoil
- Expensive and laborious to produce
- Bulky with drum magazine attached

Left: Guards Corporal A.M. Samikin of the 1st Ukrainian Front advances through a suburban garden during the battle for Berlin in 1945. The soldier is armed with the crude but businesslike PPS-43 submachine gun, the Soviet equivalent of the British Sten gun.

the Nazi invasion. The barrel was chrome-lined to reduce wear, but in all other ways the PPSh-41 was a wartime expedient: when the need was most desperate, two PPSh-41 barrels could be made by cutting a Mosin-Nagant rifle in two.

Like the PPD series, the PPSh-41 was chambered for 7.62x25mm and fed by a 71-round drum or a curved box magazine (in this case holding 35 rounds). Accurate to 120 metres (394 feet) and reliable under even the awful conditions of the Russian homeland, the PPSh-41 was capable of delivering 900 rounds per minute and was popular with soldiers of both sides. Large numbers were also used by Soviet partisans. Five million were produced by Soviet Russia, and more when the weapon was adopted by North Korea. Examples were seen in combat in the 1970s, and there were occasional sightings even later.

PPS-42/43

Another example of Russian expediency, the PPS-42 and -43 never achieved the fame of the PPSh-41, but show what can be achieved with very limited materials. Invented during the siege of Leningrad during 1942, the PPS-42 was flung together using stamped metal. While certainly crude, it turned out to be an effective weapon and went into production to arm Soviet Army units after the siege was lifted.

The PPS-42 and its slightly improved derivative, the PPS-43, were chambered for 7.62x25mm and fed from a 35-round magazine, firing at 650 rounds per minute. The folding stock made the weapons very useful for vehicle crews. Despite its rather desperate origins the PPS-43 remained in production after the war (more than a million were eventually constructed) and served through the Korean War.

Type 100

Jungle warfare is an environment in which the submachine gun can excel. Long-range rifle engagements are a difficult proposition, and even manipulating a long rifle presents problems in thick vegetation. This, coupled with the advantages of automatic weapons during island assaults, should have made the Japanese strong proponents of the SMG concept during World War II. In the event, however, they fielded only one SMG – and a fairly poor one at that.

The Type 100 was a side-fed, carbine-type weapon with some positive features. The barrel was chrome-lined to resist corrosion and a muzzle brake was fitted to help control recoil. For paratroops the normal fixed wooden stock was replaced with a folding version. A 30-round curved magazine fed from the side and the weapon was reasonably accurate out to about 70 metres (230 feet), which was adequate for assaults and jungle fighting.

Despite these features the original Type 100 did not perform well. Its 8mm ammunition lacked stopping power and was prone to feed problems, and in 1943 production was curtailed. An improved version, designated Type 100/44, was fielded from 1944. This somewhat better weapon had a higher rate of fire (800 as opposed to 450 rounds per minute) but was not available in sufficient numbers to make much difference.

The Type 100's primary significance was that its performance clearly demonstrated the superiority of its hard-hitting, reliable battlefield opponent, the American Thompson submachine gun.

Type 100

Calibre: 8mm Nambu
Length: 890mm (35in)
Weight: 3.83kg (8.44lb)
Barrel: 228mm (9in), 6 grooves, rh
Magazine: 30-round box magazine
Operation: Blowback
Cyclic rate of fire: 450rpm
Muzzle velocity: 335mps (1100fps)

Wartime expedients

Weapons such as the British Sten and the Soviet PPS submachine guns were designed to be thrown together hastily in large numbers – in both cases to resist invasion. Considering their origins, these were really very good weapons, although long-term durability was never a major priority.

When the war began to turn against Germany, cheap and simple weapons based on the Sten gun were turned out in their thousands to arm German militias for the final defence of the homeland.

Post-war developments

By the end of World War II, the machine pistol was moving towards a weapon that might be recognized as the modern SMG.

Designs had thus far followed a fairly conventional automatic-carbine approach, but that was about to change. Large conflicts were relatively few, but the armed forces of the great powers became involved in a large number of 'brush-fire wars', some of which were very different from the massive conflicts that had provided the most recent combat experience. Urban fighting, jungle engagements and similar close-quarters combat provided the submachine gun with a new proving ground.

In addition, international terrorism became increasingly common in the second half of the twentieth century. Concealable light automatic weapons were useful to the terrorist and the counter-terrorist alike. A new generation of submachine guns was born. Some continued to use the 'carbine' arrangement, while others harked back to the days of the full-automatic pistol.

Open bolt

Most submachine guns fire from an 'open bolt'. The bolt is not locked to the chamber at the moment of firing, although obviously it is in contact and seals the chamber. Firing from an open bolt is less accurate than a closed (locked to the chamber) bolt.

These new machine pistols offered a number of advantages. Small and light, they could dump a lot of ammunition into the target very quickly, making for a rapid takedown or an equally effective threat. Weapons like the Uzi and the MAC10, fed through the butt, have advantages similar to a Bullpup assault rifle – length can be kept to a minimum despite a respectably long barrel. Such weapons are also easy to reload, since one hand (holding the magazine) can easily find the other (wrapped around the magazine well). This can be important in dark or stressful situations.

Samopal CZ23 series

Among the earliest butt-fed machine pistols was the Czech M48A, known since 1950 as the CZ23, 24, 25 and 26. The different designations denote slight variations on a common weapon. The M48A pioneered the wraparound bolt, an arrangement whereby the tubular bolt encloses the end of the barrel when the weapon is ready to fire. This allows for a shorter weapon, which was further facilitated by feeding the magazine through the handgrip.

Chambered variously for 9mm Parabellum and 7.62x25mm ammunition, the M48A served (under its later designations) for more than a decade and still turns up occasionally in 'unofficial' hands. The basic weapon is only 450mm (17.7 inches) long. It was available with a wooden stock (CZ23 and 24) or a folding metal stock (CZ25 and 26). This weapon is relatively unknown, but it was the basis for a much more famous, and quite similar, family of SMGs.

IMI Uzi

Possibly the most famous post-war submachine gun, thanks to Hollywood and a reputed popularity with gangsters, the Israeli Arms Uzi is based on the earlier CZ23 series. It is 470mm (18.5mm) long with the metal stock folded and delivers 9mm Parabellum at a cyclic rate of 600 rounds per minute from 20-, 32- or 40-round magazines. The magazine is inserted through the handgrip, allowing for fast hand-finds-hand reloading.

Despite being created as an expedient at a time when Israel needed weapons fast and had little manufacturing capability, the pressed steel Uzi is remarkably reliable and is accurate out to 200 metres (656 feet). This is due to its long barrel – 260mm (10.2 inches) as compared to 225mm (8.85 inches) on the standard MP5. Despite this the Uzi is shorter than its German competitor, demonstrating the advantages of its configuration.

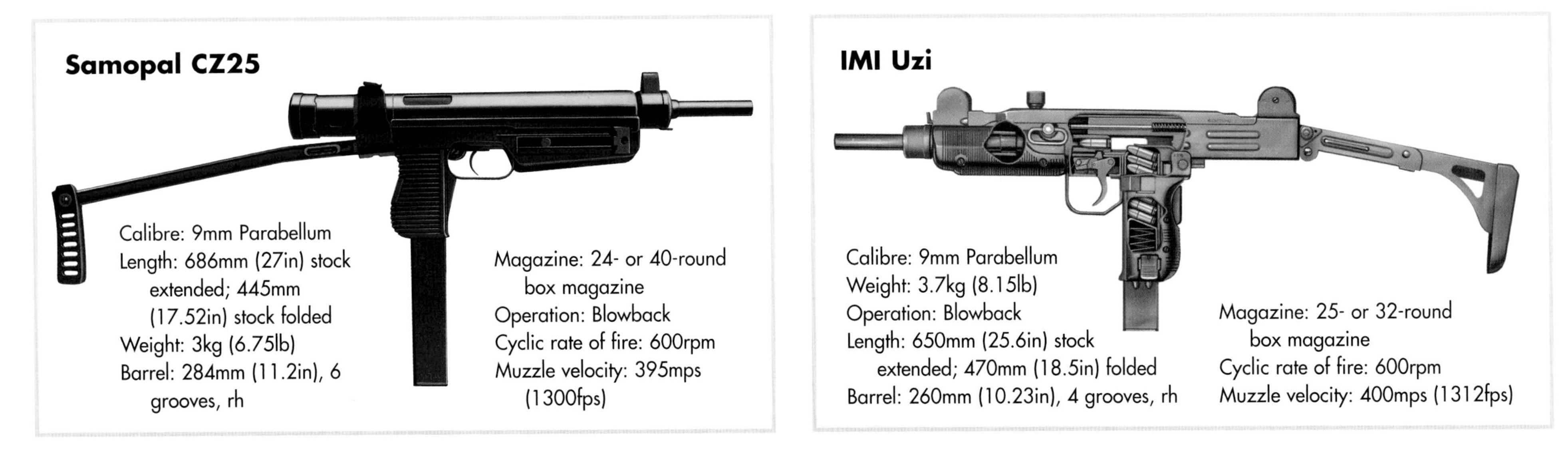

Samopal CZ25

Calibre: 9mm Parabellum
Length: 686mm (27in) stock extended; 445mm (17.52in) stock folded
Weight: 3kg (6.75lb)
Barrel: 284mm (11.2in), 6 grooves, rh
Magazine: 24- or 40-round box magazine
Operation: Blowback
Cyclic rate of fire: 600rpm
Muzzle velocity: 395mps (1300fps)

IMI Uzi

Calibre: 9mm Parabellum
Weight: 3.7kg (8.15lb)
Operation: Blowback
Length: 650mm (25.6in) stock extended; 470mm (18.5in) folded
Barrel: 260mm (10.23in), 4 grooves, rh
Magazine: 25- or 32-round box magazine
Cyclic rate of fire: 600rpm
Muzzle velocity: 400mps (1312fps)

Smaller versions

Uzi submachine guns have been purchased by more than 25 overseas military forces as well as by vast numbers of private users. Other versions include the Mini-Uzi and the even smaller Micro-Uzi. The smaller Uzis are lighter than the full-size version with a lighter bolt resulting in a higher rate of fire (the Mini-Uzi has a cyclic rate of 950 rounds per minute and the Micro-Uzi reaches more than 1200 rounds per minute). The smaller versions also have a much shorter range. They are popular with terrorists, criminals and the agencies that exist to defend against them.

Samopal Skorpion

Taking a slightly different approach to the short-SMG concept, the Czech designers at Samopal produced the VZ61 Skorpion machine pistol. With its distinctive stock folded over the top of the weapon, the Skorpion has dimensions similar to a typical handgun. It was designed for issue to Czech vehicle crews and other military personnel not expected to be placed in direct combat situations. Fed from a 7-, 10- or 20-round magazine situated in front of the trigger assembly, the Skorpion uses .32 ACP (7.65x17mm) pistol ammunition. Variants are available chambered for other ammunition, such as 9mm Makarov, 9mm Short and other light calibres.

The bolt in such a small weapon is necessarily light, and this leads to a very high cyclic rate. To bring this down to an acceptable level (850 rounds per minute), the designers built in a spring-loaded weight in the butt. This reduces the rate of fire, but the movement of the weight adds further instability to a weapon that already suffers from serious muzzle climb. The Skorpion is therefore most useful at very close range where its ferocious firepower can be used to spray a target. While the weapon can shoot accurately on semi-automatic, its cartridge is underpowered for combat applications.

Ingram MAC10

The Ingram MAC10 (or M10) also uses a pistol-type configuration. A square, blocky weapon, the MAC10 has been in service since the 1970s. It is normally chambered for 9mm Parabellum but .45 ACP and .380 ACP versions are also available. Fed through the handgrip by a 20- or 32-round magazine, the MAC10 is capable of delivering 1000 rounds per minute out to a range of around 70 metres (230 feet).

With the stock folded and a short, 20-round 'carry' magazine loaded, the MAC10 is a light and portable weapon that has found favour with criminals worldwide. At one time it was also popular with law enforcement agencies, although it has since been edged out by the MP5.

The MAC11 variant uses .380 ACP ammunition and a Sionics suppressor on the barrel to create an effective silenced submachine gun. The Ingram is back in production today as the Cobray M11.

Star Z-84

The 'Uzi' configuration is followed by other very good machine pistols, not all of which are mere copies. The Star Z-84, for example, looks a lot like an Uzi and has similar stamped-steel construction. It was developed independently, however, and has found favour with Spanish security and special forces personnel.

The Z-84 has no external moving parts and is highly resistant to water. In addition to these advantages it can take a variety of 9mm Parabellum rounds, including hollow-point and semi-jacketed ammunition. Its cyclic rate is a controllable 600 rounds per minute, although this can still empty a 25-round magazine very quickly.

Steyr MPi 69

A similar weapon, the Steyr MPi 69 originally incorporated some very unusual features, although later versions are more conventional. A 9mm weapon fed from a 25- or 32-round magazine, the MPi 69 originally had no cocking lever but was cocked by pulling on the sling. This feature was replaced by a more standard system on the MPi 81 that followed, but the selector remained.

Instead of the more common safe/semi/full-auto three-position safety/selector found on most machine pistols and SMGs, the MPi 69 has a trigger lock safety. Selecting between full-auto and single shots is by trigger pressure. This means that any attempt to bring the weapon into action quickly is likely to result in autofire, which may or may not be a bad thing, depending on the circumstances.

Some authorities believe that a small machine pistol is a better sidearm than a handgun since it has advantages of range and firepower. This is certainly the thinking behind issuing vehicle crews with VZ61 Skorpions instead of handguns. There is a lot of merit in this line of thought, since a Micro-Uzi or MAC10 fitted with a short magazine is not much heavier or more bulky than a handgun. However, miniaturizing submachine guns is subject to diminishing returns; at some point the weapon becomes nothing more than a handgun capable of automatic fire. As we have already seen, most such 'assault pistols' are of marginal use at best. It is possible, however, that the concept may be making a revival in the form of Individual Defence Weapons.

Modern submachine guns

The submachine gun of conventional layout was also subject to important developments in the post-war years. Early versions clearly show their lineage, but some of the light automatics introduced in the 1960s and 1970s were among the finest ever made. Many of them are still around today.

Madsen M50

Drawing on such successful designs as the PPS, Sten and M3 SMGs, the Danish Madsen M45 was not itself a great weapon, but it was followed by developed versions, the most successful of which was the M50. A simple blowback-operated weapon using a 32-round magazine situated well forward, the Madsen was a very serviceable weapon that was easy to maintain yet accurate to around 150 metres (492 feet). Equipped with a folding stock as standard, this weapon perhaps represents the ultimate development of the cheap World War II-style SMG.

Sterling L2

Another development of a wartime design, the Sterling L2 equipped the British Army for decades and gave excellent service in all corners of the world. Urban patrols equipped with a mix of semi-automatic FN FAL rifles and Sterling submachine guns offered a balance between long and short range effectiveness and were highly successful in Cyprus and elsewhere.

Although it shares much of its appearance with early pressed-steel weapons such as the Sten, the Sterling is in fact mostly constructed from

Above: Lieutenant Scrager of the Lancashire Regiment stands guard with a Sterling L2 while an injured suspect is carried to a truck during terrorist attacks in Aden, 1964

Right: Armed with a Sterling L2 and an early Self-Loading Rifle, British paratroopers from the 3rd Battalion Parachute Regiment keep watch along a potential enemy supply route during the Radfan Crisis, Aden, 1964.

Madsen M50

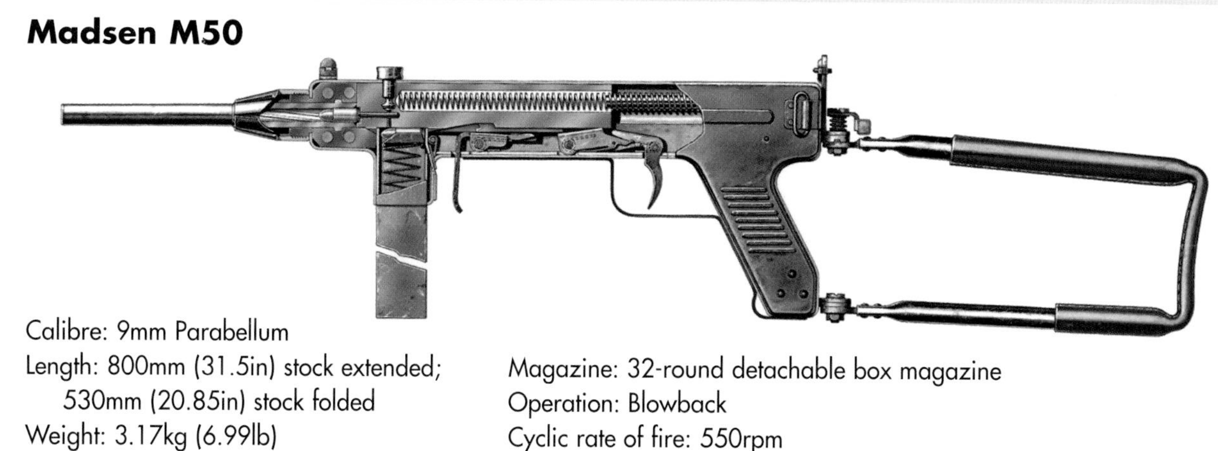

Calibre: 9mm Parabellum
Length: 800mm (31.5in) stock extended; 530mm (20.85in) stock folded
Weight: 3.17kg (6.99lb)
Barrel: 197mm (7.75in), 4 grooves, rh
Magazine: 32-round detachable box magazine
Operation: Blowback
Cyclic rate of fire: 550rpm
Muzzle velocity: 380mps (1274fps)

machined parts and has shown itself to be reliable under all manner of conditions. Fed from the side by a 34-round curved magazine and chambered for 9mm Parabellum, the Sterling is accurate out to 150 metres (492 feet) but clearly shows its obsolescence when set alongside the Uzi, which has a 260mm (10.2 inches) barrel as compared to 198mm (7.8 inches) on the Sterling, despite a similar overall length.

It may be dated, but the Sterling remains a fine weapon. Its role in the British Army has disappeared with the adoption of the SA80 assault rifle, but examples still serve worldwide and are manufactured under licence in India. A silenced version, the L34A1, has been used by special forces personnel.

MAT-49

Based on wartime designs and designed to replace the assortment of weapons then in service, the French MAT-49 SMG is no longer in French military service but is used by some overseas forces. A simple 9mm weapon vaguely reminiscent of a Thompson with a wire stock, the MAT-49 can deliver 9mm Parabellum from a 20- or 32-round magazine at 400 rounds per minute. It was highly effective during various French colonial wars in the immediate post-war period.

Unusual features of this weapon include a wraparound barrel rather than bolt – the bolt enters the rear of the chamber – and the ability of the magazine to fold forward and lie under the barrel for stowage in tight spaces, such as vehicles.

Walther MP-K and MP-L

Predating the Heckler & Koch MP5, the 9mm Walther MP-K and MP-L are almost identical. Both have a futuristic, businesslike appearance despite their age. The main difference between the models is in barrel length – 257mm (10.12 inches) on the larger L and 171mm (6.7 inches) on the K version. Both have a folding wire stock and use the same 32-round magazine.

Left: Stylish and effective, the Beretta Model 12 achieved considerable export success and entered service with Italian security forces. It is very clearly designed for urban defensive and assault applications.

Firing at 550 rounds per minute, the MP-K and L were adopted by police units in Germany and other nations including Brazil and Colombia. Although they have been replaced in German hands by the MP5, these weapons showed the shape of things to come.

Beretta Model 12

Like the MP-K, the Beretta Model 12 is fed from a centrally positioned magazine, in this case holding 20, 30 or 40 rounds of 9mm Parabellum. Available with a metal or wooden stock, the Model 12 was developed in the 1950s but remains an excellent weapon for urban combat and VIP protection. It has proven itself to be tough and reliable in Europe, Asia, Africa and South America and has been licensed for overseas production.

The Model 12 has both a conventional safety and a trigger-like grip device below the trigger guard, preventing accidental discharge if the weapon is not properly held. Engineering is – typically of Beretta – very good, even though this weapon uses many metal stampings rather than machined parts. This was something of a departure for Beretta, but seems to have worked out well.

The wraparound bolt allows a relatively long 203mm (7.9-inch) barrel on a 416mm (16.3 inch) weapon, and the two pistol grips are ideal for close-range point-and-shoot from the hip – a likely scenario when facing a sudden attack on a VIP.

Above: An MP5 fitted with a torch to aid searching and reaction shooting. H&K manufacture a range of other accessories for their weapons, including laser pointers.

Below: Another very useful MP5 accessory: a double magazine clip. This device allows faster reloading since the full magazine is in hand the instant the empty one is detached.

Heckler & Koch MP5A3

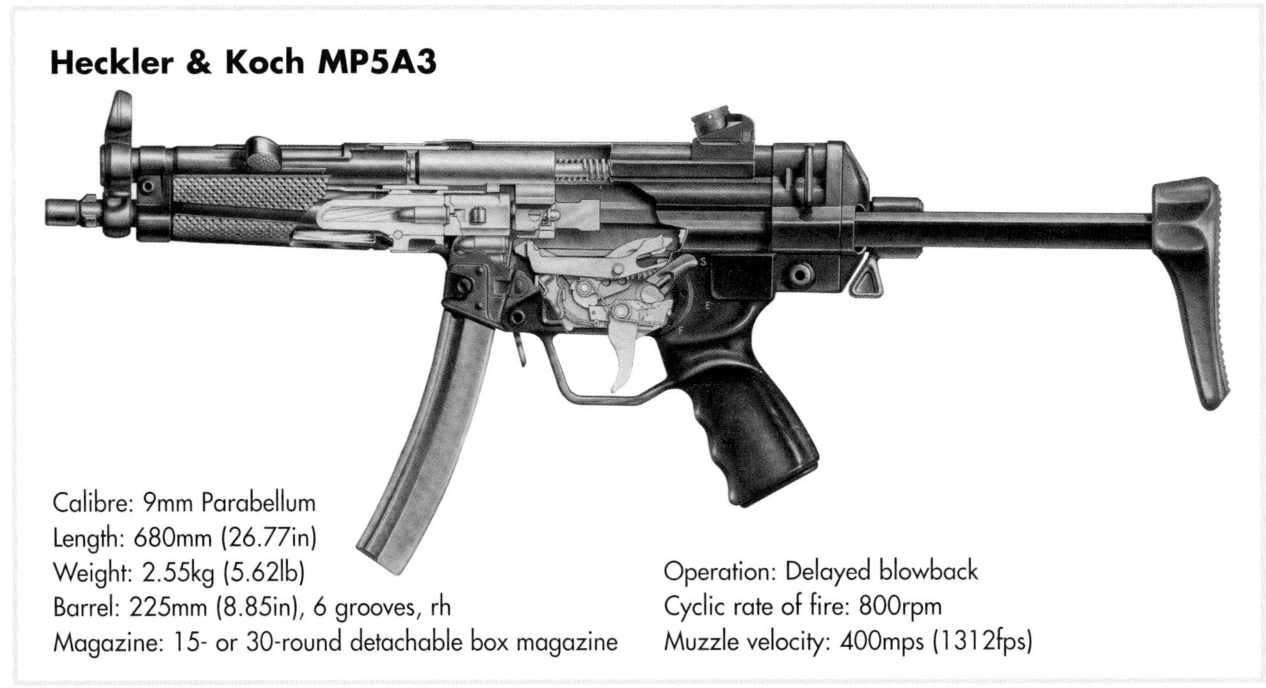

Calibre: 9mm Parabellum
Length: 680mm (26.77in)
Weight: 2.55kg (5.62lb)
Barrel: 225mm (8.85in), 6 grooves, rh
Magazine: 15- or 30-round detachable box magazine
Operation: Delayed blowback
Cyclic rate of fire: 800rpm
Muzzle velocity: 400mps (1312fps)

H&K MP5 series

The highly successful MP5 family from Heckler & Koch perhaps represents the epitome of the conventional submachine gun. Based on the roller-locking delayed blowback action of the MG42 machine gun, the MP5 shares some aspects of its appearance as well as its mechanism with H&K's assault rifles. The standard MP5 has a 225mm (8.86 inches) barrel and is fed from in front of the trigger assembly by a 15- or 30-round magazine. Like many assault rifles, design is straight-through to the stock (solid plastic on the A2 version and folding metal on the A3) improving the weapon's already excellent accuracy.

Despite its ultramodern and stylish appearance, the MP5 has been manufactured since 1965, and many slight variations and sub-models have been produced. Modern MP5s are capable of semi-automatic fire, three-round bursts or full-auto at 800 rounds per minute.

MP5s are popular with special forces and hostage rescue units, who must often fight at close range with the risk of hitting hostages or bystanders. Accuracy is essential, as well as firepower, if collateral casualties are to be avoided. The MP5 has been used in such high-profile assaults as the siege of the Iranian Embassy in London in 1982, and shown itself to be an excellent choice for the role.

MP5 variants are available chambered for 10mm and .40 Smith & Wesson, although most still use

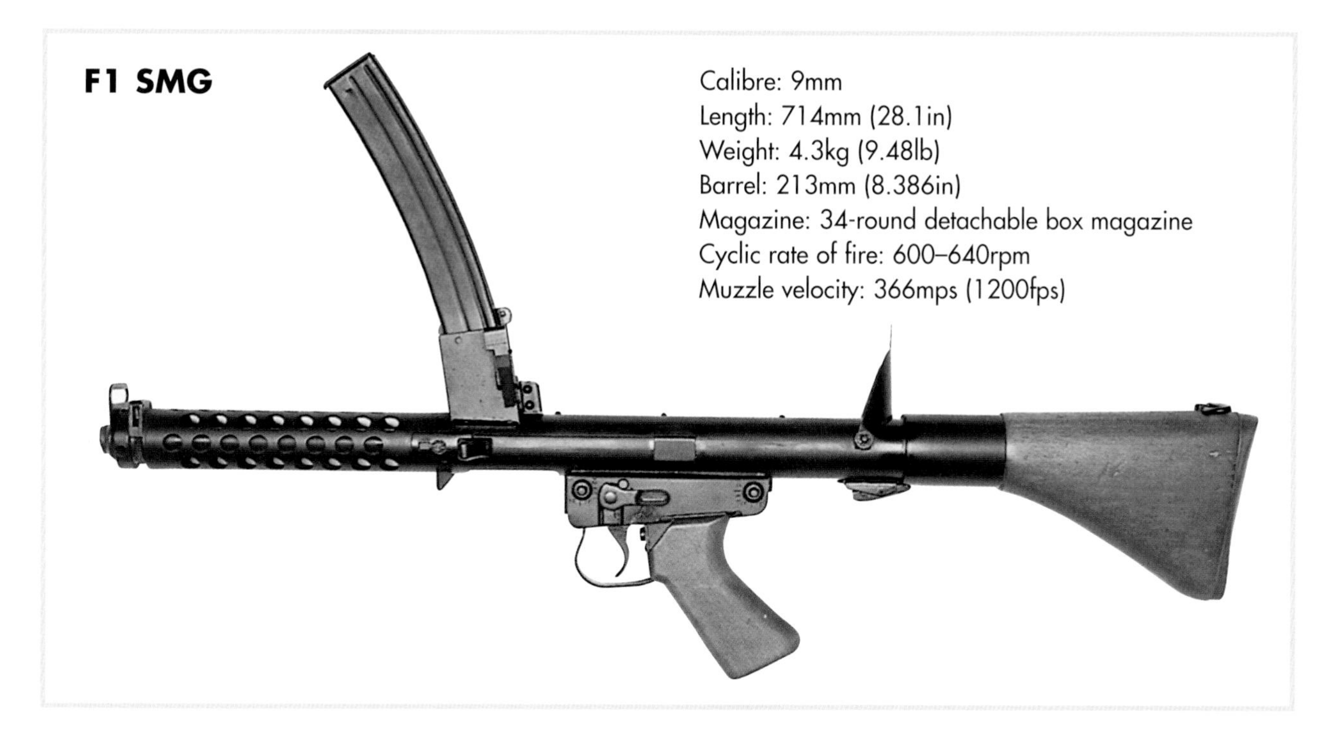

9mm Parabellum. The commonest variant is the MP5K, a short, stockless version with minimal sights and a foregrip. Designed for close-quarters work, the MP5K is excellent for the role of VIP protection, since it can easily concealed.

The MP5SD variant uses a standard 9mm Parabellum round with an integral suppressor to create an almost silent weapon capable of full-automatic or, in some cases, burst fire.

A weapon this good comes with a corresponding price tag, so the MP5 has not entered mainstream military service. It remains a firm favourite of military and police special units, however, and is likely to remain so.

Hostage rescue

The Heckler & Koch MP5 won its spurs in hostage-rescue operations in 1977 (an airliner in Mogadishu) and 1980 (the Iranian Embassy in London) when special anti-terrorist troops effected the dramatic rescue of hostages. It has become the standard weapon for such units.

Unusual SMG layouts

The conventional SMG has been around for a good many years, and there is a reason why this configuration is used by most weapons – it works, and works well. Occasionally, however, a weapon emerges that challenges the conventional way of doing things. Not all such weapons are successful, but experimentation continues.

F1 SMG

An example of one such unusual layout is found on the F1 submachine gun. Derived from the Australian Owen SMG of World War II, it replaced the Owen gun in Australian army service. The F1 somewhat resembles a Sterling with a top-loading magazine. Strange and unwieldy as this configuration may appear, the result is a friendly and well-balanced weapon. The F1 can take a bayonet, which is uncommon in SMGs and probably not all that effective.

The F1 delivers 9mm Parabellum from a 34-round magazine at between 600 and 650 rounds per minute. Prototype F1s (then designated X3) were used by Australian troops fighting in Vietnam, and proved to be reliable and effective despite the dreadful conditions of the Mekong Delta.

Top-loading submachine guns remain essentially an Australian experiment and have never really caught on. However, there is a submachine gun version of the Calico M950 that feeds from the top, albeit in a very different manner, so perhaps the top-loader is not quite ready to pass into history.

Steyr AUG 9 Para

Short and handy as the Steyr AUG assault rifle may be, the designers decided that airborne troops needed something even smaller. The result was the AUG 9 Para, essentially a cut-down assault rifle chambered for 9mm Parabellum.

The AUG Para retains all the best features of the AUG rifle including its general construction – most parts are interchangeable – and the clear plastic

Left: This Washington DC police officer holds a Colt SMG; essentially a cut-down Colt Commando chambered for 9mm (note how the magazine is smaller than the well). The under-barrel flashlight is useful in low-light urban areas.

magazines. The weapon is 665mm (26 inches) long yet retains a respectable barrel length owing to its Bullpup layout. This leads to good accuracy at a reasonable battle range of 200 metres (656 feet), especially in conjunction with the optical sight that comes as standard on the whole AUG family.

Although it is definitely a submachine gun in terms of calibre, role and size, the AUG Para still retains its rifle heritage. As a result it is not as easy to carry as some SMGs of the same length; this is a battlefield weapon rather than a security SMG. Whether or not the concept of a cut-down assault rifle in SMG calibre will catch on remains an open question. It could be argued that weapons such as the H&K P90 are very similar in concept; somewhere between a baby rifle and an overgrown submachine gun. There does seem to be a need for such weapons, so perhaps others will follow suit.

Colt SMG

Colt also manufactures a cut-down assault rifle, the Colt SMG. Like the Commando, which is essentially a carbine version of the M16 rifle, the SMG is based on the assault rifle. However, it is shorter and chambered for 9mm Parabellum; 20- and 32-round magazines are available.

Although the Colt SMG looks like a 'toy' version of the M16, it is actually a very useable light automatic weapon and has been adopted by the US Drug Enforcement Agency. One advantage of cut-down assault rifles is that they are constructed to handle relatively powerful rifle cartridges. When firing lighter 9mm ammunition, less recoil is felt than with a purpose-built submachine gun. This reduces muzzle climb and, in turn, increases accuracy. However accurate a weapon may be on the bench, the ability of the user to hit what he is aiming at with a weapon that is jumping about all over the place is severely diminished. Cut-down rifles may be bulky but they do absorb recoil well.

AKSU

Some makers choose to create cut-down versions of their assault rifles and call them submachine guns, even though they retain assault-rifle chambering. Exactly where the line between an automatic carbine and a SMG actually lies is a difficult question; different observers may use different interpretations based on role, ammunition, length or general configuration. The opposite is also true – some submachine guns, chambered for pistol ammunition, could nevertheless be considered to be carbine-type weapons.

One weapon right on the line between submachine gun and assault rifle is the Kalashnikov AKSU. Essentially a shortened AK-74 rifle with a folding metal stock, the AKSU is built around the same receiver and is chambered in 5.45mm like its parent rifle. The weapon, however, is intended for the submachine gun role and has served with vehicle crews and airborne forces, for example during the invasion of Afghanistan.

Its overall length is only 420mm (16.5 inches), well within SMG dimensions, but this is achieved mainly by shortening the barrel, which reduces accuracy and causes automatic fire to spray about in a fairly random manner despite the muzzle brake. The 30-round magazine protrudes almost as far as the barrel, but the weapon is still a more concealable than a full-sized AK-74. Within common combat ranges, out to about 200 metres (656 feet), the AKSU is perfectly serviceable as a rifle, although less effective than its larger cousin. In close combat, it possesses most of the advantages of an SMG while retaining the punch of a rifle cartridge.

These four weapons represent aberrations in submachine gun design; experiments that explored new avenues or showed why other weapons did not follow these principles. For the most part, the modern submachine gun follows established principles but includes evolutionary developments in terms of construction, ergonomics and response to perceived needs among the potential users. The results are indeed very impressive.

The next generation emerges

For those concerned with protecting themselves or others from assault, or who may have to deal with armed criminals at less than battlefield ranges, the SMG is the weapon of choice.

Jatimatic

Recent years have seen the emergence of a new generation of light automatics tailored to the needs of the security user. One such is the Jatimatic, designed in Finland and constructed cheaply from pressed steel components. The gun weighs less than 2 kilograms (4.4 pounds) even when fitted with a 20-round magazine. It has no stock, nor provision for one – this is a close-in weapon and a very fine one.

Like the French MAS 38, the Jatimatic has a 'broken' appearance. In this case the barrel appears to be bent upwards where it emerges from the housing. This is because the bolt travels at an upwards angle, making the weapon more controllable under 650 rounds per minute autofire. A fold-down foregrip allows close-in 'assault position' firing under good control.

Another slightly unusual feature is the selective trigger action. Single shots are fired by pulling the trigger, with greater pressure resulting in full-automatic fire. Magazines holding 20 and 40 rounds are available.

The Jatimatic never achieved much international success despite the fact that it is a very good security weapon. Competition is fierce in that market, and quality does not always equate to success.

Spectre

Another excellent security weapon, the Spectre also makes a good visual deterrent. Its futuristic appearance belies the fact that it was designed around 20 years ago. Just 580mm (22.8 inches) long, the foregrip and stockless arrangement suit it best to close-in work. The Spectre has achieved considerable success with security agencies and looks set to continue in service for some time.

The Spectre has several important features. It is a double-action weapon, so can be brought into action by simply pulling the trigger, even if uncocked. In the few desperate seconds of a security emergency, this may be a life-saving factor. It is also useful from a safety point of view. With

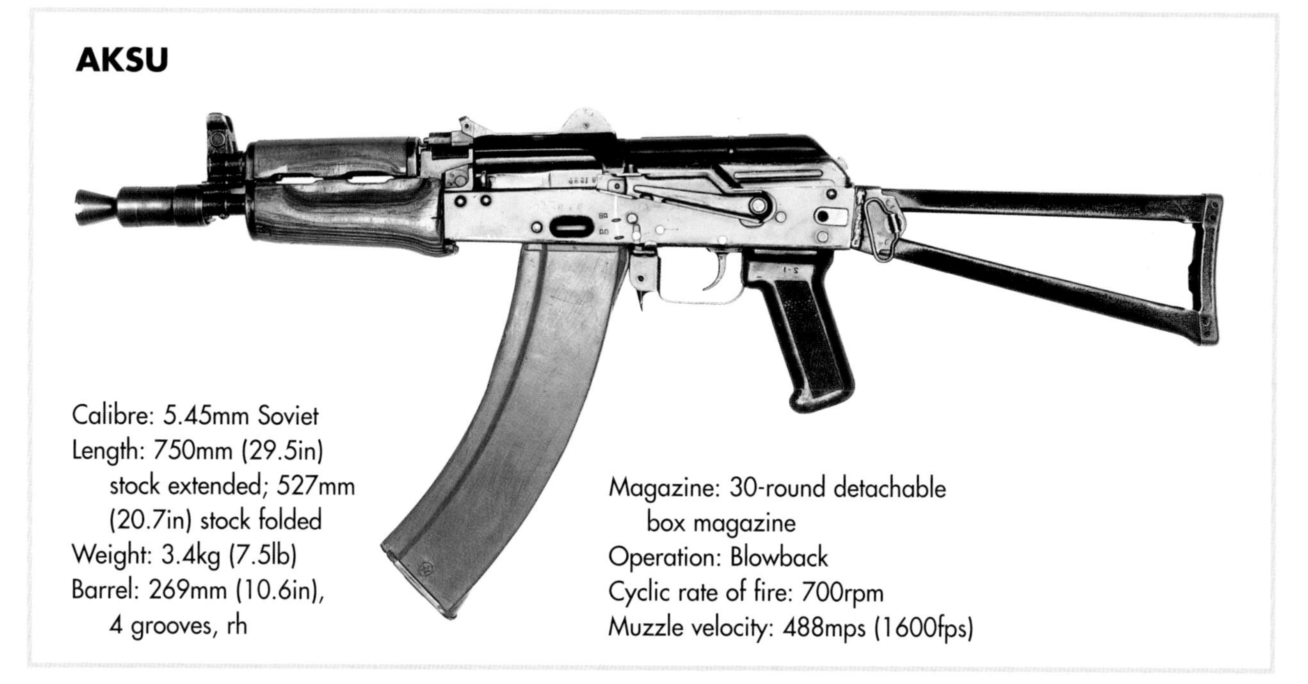

AKSU

Calibre: 5.45mm Soviet
Length: 750mm (29.5in) stock extended; 527mm (20.7in) stock folded
Weight: 3.4kg (7.5lb)
Barrel: 269mm (10.6in), 4 grooves, rh
Magazine: 30-round detachable box magazine
Operation: Blowback
Cyclic rate of fire: 700rpm
Muzzle velocity: 488mps (1600fps)

GUNS FOR VIP PROTECTION: SPECTRE VERSUS

The submachine gun offers a devastating and rapid response to any threat, all in a portable, concealable package. While the early SMGs were essentially battlefield assault weapons, many of the new generation of submachine guns are tailor-made for rescue operations and VIP protection. The Spectre and the Jatimatic are excellent examples of such weapons. Sharing a mission, they have much in common. Both are chambered for 9mm Parabellum, both are centre-fed from a large-capacity magazine, and both have an assault foregrip to facilitate close-range instinct shooting.

Spectre

Calibre: 9mm Parabellum
Length: 580mm (22.83in) stock extended; 350mm (13.78in) stock folded
Weight: 2.9kg (6.63lb)
Barrel: 130mm (5.12in), 6 grooves, rh
Magazine: 30- or 50-round detachable box magazine
Operation: Blowback
Cyclic rate of fire: 850rpm
Muzzle velocity: 400mps (1312fps)

STRENGTHS

- Enormous magazine capacity (50 rounds)
- Double-action first shot for rapid entry to action
- Accurate to 150 metres (164 feet)

WEAKNESSES

- Not very concealable
- Bulky with 50-round magazine loaded
- Heavier than the Jatimatic

JATIMATIC

Unusually for a submachine gun the Spectre fires from a closed bolt, improving accuracy. It also fires its first round double-action, so does not need to be cocked before being brought into action. Like the Jatimatic, it can function with a smaller-capacity 'carry' magazine. The Jatimatic weighs about half as much as the Spectre and has a folding foregrip rather than a fixed one. Its offset barrel helps control muzzle climb. Selection is by trigger pressure, allowing single shots or full-auto fire to be selected without having to adjust controls, although in a stressful situation this can lead to the user simply emptying the weapon.

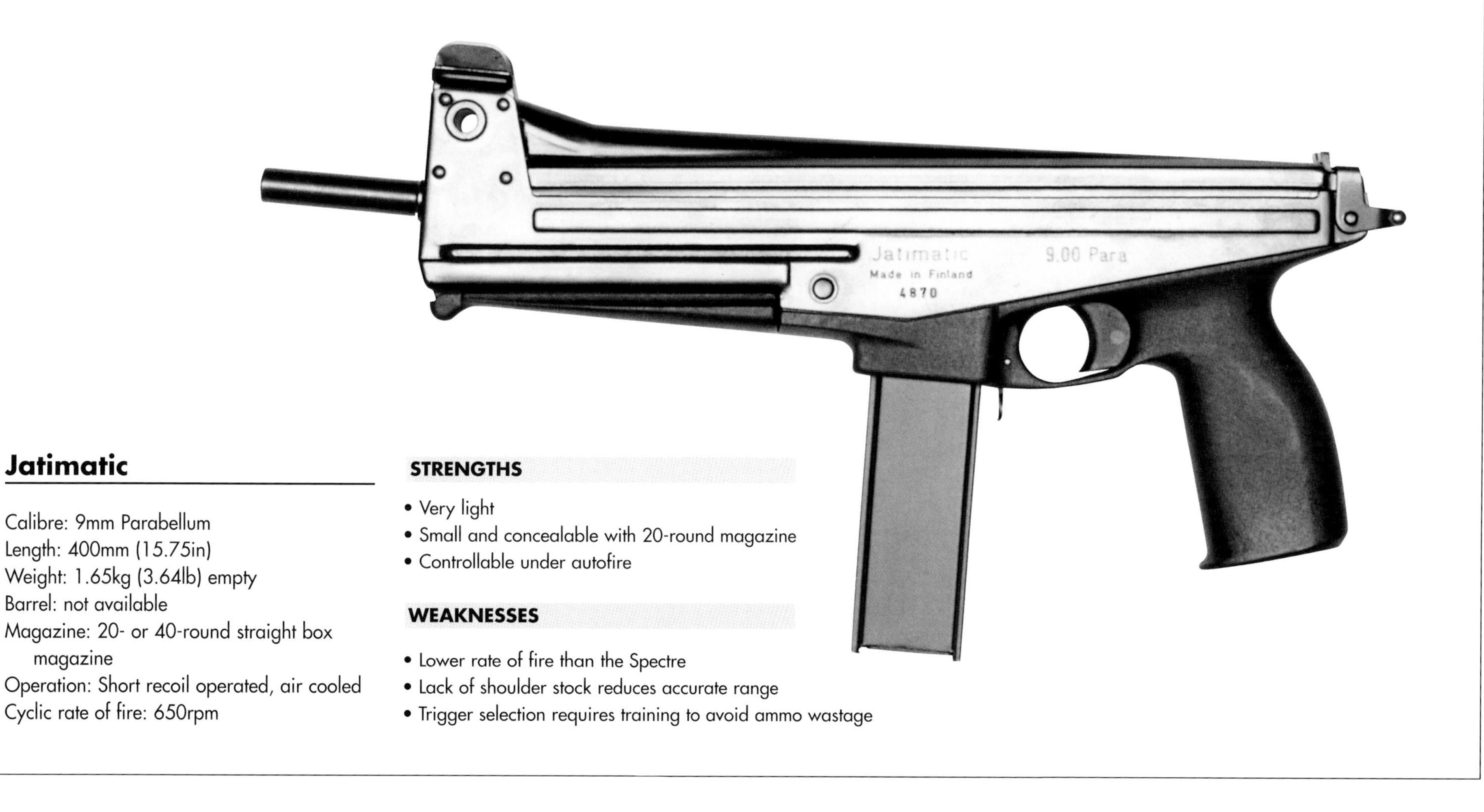

Jatimatic

Calibre: 9mm Parabellum
Length: 400mm (15.75in)
Weight: 1.65kg (3.64lb) empty
Barrel: not available
Magazine: 20- or 40-round straight box magazine
Operation: Short recoil operated, air cooled
Cyclic rate of fire: 650rpm

STRENGTHS

- Very light
- Small and concealable with 20-round magazine
- Controllable under autofire

WEAKNESSES

- Lower rate of fire than the Spectre
- Lack of shoulder stock reduces accurate range
- Trigger selection requires training to avoid ammo wastage

BXP

Calibre: 9 x 19mm Parabellum
Length: 387mm (15.2in) stock folded
Weight: 2.5kg (5.5lb)
Barrel: 208mm (8.2in), 6 grooves, rh
Magazine: 22- or 32-round box magazine
Operation: Blowback
Cyclic rate of fire: 1000rpm
Muzzle velocity: 370mps (1214fps)

Self-defence

One novel idea for a concealed personal defence weapon is the 'briefcase' SMG, allowing a cocked and loaded submachine gun to be carried unobtrusively in public. The case is sometimes also made of bullet-resistant materials to offer a measure of protection even before the gun is deployed.

the weapon loaded then decocked, it cannot accidentally discharge upon striking a hard surface, such as when dropped. Of course, once the first round is fired the weapon then reverts to normal blowback operation until the trigger is released and the weapon decocked.

The weapon is fed centrally by a 30- or 50-round magazine, the latter using quad-stacking to get a lot of ammunition into a small space. This is an impressive amount of firepower, and may be decisive in a short engagement where other weapons will require reloading much sooner. The 850 rounds per minute cyclic rate allows for taking down opponents quickly without being excessively high – the Spectre can burn through its 50-round magazine in just over three seconds, around the same time it takes for an Uzi to dispose of the ammunition in its 32-round magazine.

BXP

The South African BXP, chambered for 9mm Parabellum, represents an interesting compromise between machine pistol and carbine-type SMGs. It is configured like an Uzi, with a wraparound bolt and 208mm (1.18-inch) barrel in a package just 387mm (15.2 inches) long. The weapon, however, comes with an ingenious folding metal stock that doubles as a foregrip when not in use. The BXP is well enough balanced for one-handed firing at need, although at 1000 rounds per minute it can get through its 22- or 32-round magazine very quickly.

As well as being very well made, mostly from stainless steel, the BXP has some interesting features. It can accept a compensator to reduce felt recoil or a suppressor as standard, and can even launch rifle grenades. While this capability will not be needed in most security applications, it does add to the overall versatility of the weapon.

These weapons are designed to fulfil a very definite need. They are not simply a means to fire as many bullets as possible as fast as possible, but are tailored to the needs of the security agent or personal protection officer. Such weapons can of course be used to protect one's own self from threats, but recently a new concept has emerged – the Individual Defence Weapon.

Individual Defence Weapons

There are essentially two types of IDW: carbine types for non-infantry military personnel who might possibly have to defend themselves in the course of their duties, and handgun types for individuals who want more than handgun firepower available in the event of an attack.

It could be argued that any good handgun would make an excellent IDW, and there is a lot of truth in this argument. However, the quest for a 'handgun-plus' has brought weapon makers back to the assault pistol concept yet again. Full-automatic pistols are difficult to control and wasteful of ammunition. Yet the concept is attractive: if small size could be combined with controllable automatic fire then many users would find such a weapon very useful.

Parker-Hale IDW

One attempt to create such a weapon is the Individual Defence Weapon from Parker-Hale. Resembling a blocky handgun with a solid foregrip and capable of mounting a fold-out stock, the IDW falls between an assault pistol and a true SMG.

The IDW's rate of fire is restricted by a patented device to 400 rounds per minute rather than the more usual 800 rounds per minute for an SMG or more than 1000 for most assault pistols. This makes the IDW more controllable and therefore more practical for combat use. According to the manufacturers, the IDW experiences no muzzle climb at all under burst fire. Selecting between single shot and two- or three-round bursts is by trigger pressure and therefore depends greatly upon the firer's levels of competence and stress.

If the concept of the IDW is successful, it may be that a new category of personal weapons will be created somewhere between a pistol and a submachine gun, combining the best features of each.

The future of the submachine gun

It seems likely that the days of the battlefield SMG are numbered. Automatic shotguns may take over the close-assault role, while carbine-type Personal Defence Weapons may replace SMGs as defensive weapons for non-infantry troops. Ever smaller, lighter and shorter assault rifles (and their carbine cousins) threaten to fill all the niches left to light automatics while retaining rifle-calibre advantages of range and accuracy in case they are needed.

In the close-quarters environment of security, hostage rescue and VIP protection work, however, the SMG continues to reign supreme. Long range is rarely necessary and powerful rifle cartridges may pose a hazard to bystanders or protectees if they overpenetrate or ricochet (which rifle rounds tend to do in urban environments, travelling appallingly long distances in unpredictable trajectories). Secondary injuries caused by fragments of, for example, walls detached by a rifle bullet impact are also a factor. The SMG is not so prone to these problems. Its shorter, fatter rounds are more likely to stop in the target than pass through, and lose their lower muzzle energy more quickly.

For the shooter who needs to deal with a sudden threat, rapidly, the SMG can be brought into action as quickly as a handgun, can engage targets more accurately and at longer range, and offers more firepower without being much more awkward to carry or stow. Stopping power is better, since a burst is more likely to result in disablement than a single hit, and in the most desperate situations automatic fire may suppress an enemy long enough to escape or to seek cover.

The role of the submachine gun has changed greatly since its invention. However, the need for light, fast-shooting weapons has never gone away, and probably never will.

Right: The Parker-Hale Individual Defence Weapon (IDW) in carbine mode with stock extended. The receiver is little larger than a handgun, and can take various accessories including the optical sight seen here.

AUTOMATIC SUPPORT WEAPONS

By the start of World War II it was obvious that automatic weapons had many roles in modern warfare. In addition to the mostly static defensive role they had fulfilled in World War I, machine guns were useful in adding supporting firepower to infantry formations. Today, machine guns and other automatic squad support weapons are a vital feature of modern combat.

In 1745 a British battalion encountered a French one at the Battle of Fontenoy and, so the story goes, was chivalrously invited to fire first. Declining the honour, the British commander allowed his French counterpart to let fly a volley. Just as the French troops were about to shoot, a man in the ranks uttered the soldier's ironic prayer: 'For what we are about to receive may the Lord make us truly thankful'. The volley came in and men went down.

As the French began to reload, the British battalion – which had suffered casualties but remained essentially intact – took the opportunity to march up close and deliver a point-blank volley before charging in with bayonets to complete the rout.

Left: The MAG 58 General Purpose Machine Gun (GPMG) has given almost half a century of hard-hitting service in over 80 armed forces worldwide. It can fire 250 rounds of 7.62mm ammunition in less than 25 seconds.

Volley fire versus constant fire

Even though there is reason to doubt the truth of this romantic tale, not least because Fontenoy was a decisive victory for the French, it does seem to indicate a serious tactical lapse by the French commander. Volley fire was generally conducted by sub-units firing in sequence rather than the whole battalion together. For one thing the front rank of the enemy force would absorb the whole of a volley, leaving those behind unscathed, whereas ripple fire would crumble away the front. More importantly, a battalion firing by sub-units (companies or platoons) would always have fire in reserve.

Massed volley fire at the last moment might break a cavalry charge, and the psychological effect of several men going down is significant. The tacticians of the musket era, however, knew that constant fire was generally more effective than a sudden onslaught followed by a respite.

Early support weapons

This dichotomy of constant fire versus massed volley was continued in the early battlefield support weapons. Some early battlefield support guns, like the Gatling or Gardner types, employed a constant stream of fire to cut down enemy troops while others, often termed 'volley guns', utilized several rifle-type barrels firing at once to create concentrated firepower. This was in many ways less of an engineering challenge than creating a repeating weapon, but it is interesting to note that there are no modern equivalents of the volley gun (other than the effects of exploding shells and grenades), while constant-fire weapons remain very much a part of modern warfare. Most of these early support weapons were prone to malfunction, or were simply not effective for tactical reasons. Some designers, however, were sufficiently impressed by the concept to try to create better versions.

Above: This pre-Maxim Gardner gun is essentially several rifles reloaded by a gravity feed and fired in sequence by a man turning a crank – a clever piece of engineering but not really a true machine gun.

Up to this point weapons had been either volley guns or mechanical repeaters such as the Gatling or the Gardner, with ammunition fed into the breech either by turning a crank or rocking a lever backwards and forwards. These were not proper machine guns in that they had to be powered from outside. A true machine gun uses the effect of firing one round to load the next, and the weapon will continue to fire as long as the trigger is pulled and ammunition is available. Hiram Maxim demonstrated such a weapon in 1884, and changed the world of firearms forever.

The machine gun earns its spurs

The Maxim gun employed some very advanced engineering for its time. Maxim had managed to solve problems of reliable ammunition feed and ejection, allowing the user to sweep an area with fire and thereby deny it to enemy forces, or to slaughter close-order infantry who tried to advance across such an area.

At first the armies of the world were sceptical of this new weapon and very unsure of what to do with it. One prominent British officer stated publicly that two machine guns per division would be entirely sufficient and that they should be deployed on the flanks, well 'out of the way'. Others saw a little more clearly the opportunities offered by these weapons, but an effective doctrine for their use still had to evolve.

The general consensus was that machine guns were artillery weapons. They were big and bulky, and fulfilled a similar role to light cannon firing canister rounds. Canister was an anti-personnel round made up of many bullet-sized projectiles contained in a tin that ruptured on firing. In effect, this turned a cannon into a huge shotgun, which could be deadly at close range. Military planners in the late nineteenth century seized on the parallel and deployed their machine guns accordingly. Even though the weapons were already bulky, they were fitted to cannon-style gun carriages and deployed in batteries, standing wheel to wheel in the open and firing at advancing enemy troops.

The Gatling gun

During the American Civil War, Gatling machine guns were considered something of an oddity and few saw use. One of the first combat deployments was in 1862 at the Battle of Antietam – unfortunately the Gatlings failed to distinguish themselves, jamming almost immediately.

This was not a very good idea. As the French had found with their Mitrailleuse guns in the Franco-Prussian War, weapons based on rifles are only effective at rifle range. Deploying them as artillery either results in them being too far back to be of any use or allows enemy riflemen to engage the gunners. However much firepower an individual machine gun battery had, there were always as many riflemen in the opposing forces, all seeking to silence the machine gun.

After some experimentation, it was discovered that machine guns worked best on a lighter tripod mount and in the infantry support rather than artillery role. Variations on this system included a rather charming Belgian practice of mounting machine guns on small wheeled carriages pulled by dogs. These early weapons are often termed 'medium machine guns'. While more mobile than larger artillery pieces, they were still heavy and bulky, and suited only to set-piece battles or defensive operations.

Cooling the barrel

Automatic fire takes its toll on a weapon. Heat builds up very quickly in metal components, sometimes resulting in 'barrel droop', reducing accuracy and eventually making the weapon unusable due to excessive distortion. Heat also increases wear on the barrel, reducing service life. If a weapon becomes hot enough, ammunition can 'cook off' in the chamber and fire without the trigger being pulled. This causes the gun to 'run away'; it can only be stopped by interrupting the ammunition supply.

For this reason, controlling heat build-up in machine guns is very important. Machine gun barrels must be heavier than standard rifle barrels to withstand the greater heat, but they must also be cooled in some way. Air-cooling is possible, essentially allowing the weapon to dissipate heat by transferring it to the air around. This is effective up to a point, although most modern weapons assist cooling by having quick-change barrels. As one barrel becomes excessively hot (or ideally, before it does) it is removed and replaced with a cool one. Alternating barrels in this manner is quite rapid for a well-trained crew serving a properly designed weapon.

Maxim Gun

The Maxim and most of the designs based upon it used a water-filled jacket around the barrel to absorb heat and carry it away from the metal. Water-cooling systems are of course heavy and bulky, but then so was the Maxim Gun itself.

British troops found the Maxim Gun to be extremely effective in the colonial wars of the 1880s and 1890s. Even the prodigious Zulus, who were often willing to accept massive casualties to close with the rifle-armed British troops, were dismayed by the firepower of the machine gun. The Zulus may have lacked sophisticated military technology but they were certainly not idiots. Bitter experience and simple mathematics made it clear that while spear-armed heroes could perhaps get the better of professional riflemen, against an enemy armed with machine guns they were doomed.

The Maxim came in several variants for naval and land service in fixed and mobile mounts. It was chambered in .455, .45 and .303. The latter became standard after 1889. Firing at a cyclic rate

Below: This portrait of Sir Hiram Maxim with his Maxim machine gun shows how the early machine guns with their wheeled carriages had more in common with artillery pieces than todays' infantry support weapons. The Maxim Gun nevertheless had a devastating effect during its early Colonial service. Within years, every army was purchasing Maxim's weapon or creating its own versions.

Maxim Gun .303

Calibre: .303 British
Length: 1180mm (46.5in)
Weight: 18.2kg (40lb)
Barrel: 720mm (28.25in), 4 grooves, rh
Magazine: Belt feed
Operation: Recoil, water-cooled
Cyclic rate of fire: 600rpm
Muzzle velocity: 600mps (1970fps)

of 600 rounds per minute the Maxim was effective against 'area' targets (e.g. formed units of soldiers) out to 2000 metres (6562 feet); the belt feed allowed continuous fire to sweep an area. Even if the firer could never have hit a given target with a single round at that range, the gun's rate of fire mean that there was a real chance of a hit even at extreme range. Closer in, machine gun fire proved murderous.

The action of the Maxim

The Maxim action was based on recoil operation, whereby the force of recoil from the firing (as opposed to gas pressure on the bolt or a piston) forces the barrel and bolt to move backwards. Barrel movement is arrested by lugs, but the bolt is freed by a toggle system to keep moving. This movement extracts the empty (fired) cartridge case and draws in the next round. The movement of the bolt is brought to a stop by a spring, which then causes the bolt to run forward again, chambering the new round. The toggle is locked back into place by the arrival of the bolt and the weapon is ready to fire. If the trigger is still held, the cycle begins again when the new round fires.

The Maxim Gun was the first medium machine gun. In time lighter weapons would emerge that offered more mobility. More advanced weapons have greater range and/or reliability. Heavier weapons with greater range and destructive power would eventually lead to light automatic cannon used in combat vehicles and aircraft. For the time being, however, the Maxim was the king of the battlefield. From an oddity that need only be fielded two per division – if at all – the machine gun was fast becoming something no army could afford to be without. Other designers were quick to follow in Maxim's footsteps.

Left: Mounted on a clumsy and extremely heavy carriage, this Red Army-operated Maxim 1910 fires on Finnish troops near Viborg in 1940. The vast weight of this artillery-style Sokolov mount would have reduced the Maxim's mobility, making it a primarily defensive weapon.

Ships and planes

Volley guns, repeaters and finally early machine guns were deployed in the fighting tops of many warships from 1870 onwards, to sweep the deck of enemy vessels.

The first 'gunbus' – an aircraft armed with a machine gun – took so long to reach combat altitude during a German raid on its airfield, that the British Royal Flying Corps concluded that there was no future for machine-gun-armed aircraft.

Maschinengewehr 08

German forces received a Maxim-type machine gun, the Maxim Maschinengewehr 08, in the years running up to the start of the Great War. Water-cooled, this weapon could sustain 450 rounds per minute almost indefinitely. Initially fielded on a heavy steel mount weighing more than 60 kilograms (132 pounds), the 08 eventually gained a bipod mount, bringing overall weight of the gun and mount down to a rather more manageable 26.44 kilograms (58.29 pounds).

The Maschinengewehr 08 was chambered for a fairly heavy 7.92x57mm round, feeding in 250-round belts. Like the original Maxim it was effective out to around 2000 metres (6560 feet), and it was devastating when sweeping along the wire-festooned approaches to a defensive position.

Maschinengewehr 08

Calibre: 7.92mm Mauser
Length: 1175mm (46.25in)
Weight: 26.44kg (58.29lb)
Barrel: 719mm (28.3in), 4 grooves, rh
Magazine: 250-round belt
Operation: Short recoil, water-cooled
Cyclic rate of fire: 300–450rpm
Muzzle velocity: 892mps (2925fps)

Vickers Machine Gun

Arguably the best of the Maxim derivatives, the Vickers is one of the most famous weapons of all time. Based on the successful Maxim design, the Vickers was a clear improvement. It was lighter and shorter, with a better feed than its predecessor. Chambered for .303, the same ammunition used in service rifles, the Vickers was fed from a 250-round fabric belt that was 8.23 metres (9 yards) long. This is the origin of a phrase: giving someone the 'whole nine yards' from a Vickers amounted to overkill.

To deal with the inevitable heat build-up, the Vickers had a quick-change barrel which was surrounded with a water-filled jacket holding four litres (7 pints). Generally speaking, after about 3000 rounds of continuous fire, the water in the jacket reached boiling point. Roughly a litre would evaporate for every 1000 rounds of subsequent fire. A rubber tube from the jacket could be run into a container of water, which condensed some steam for reuse. Vickers gun teams tended to go through a lot of water in the course of an engagement.

The water-cooled Vickers could maintain 600 rounds per minute for long periods and was reliable under most conditions. Indeed, the weapon could be fitted almost unchanged into a vast array of vehicles, aircraft and defensive installations. Production ceased at the end of World War II, but it was deployed in combat until the 1960s.

Firing the Vickers

The sights on a Vickers are interesting. There is a basic 'iron' sight for close-range shooting, and for longer-range precision firing the weapon has a dial sight allowing range and an offset for wind to be input, while the weapon is aimed using a sighting tube located above this device. Alternatively, a gun could be locked to fire on a single axis for area denial. The trigger is a thumb-push device located between the two rear handles on the receiver. The Vickers was perhaps the finest of the first-generation machine guns, and has passed almost into legend as one of the best weapons of all time. Few other machine guns could match the performance of a 10-gun Vickers detachment during the British attack on High Wood in August 1918, which fired an average of 100,000 rounds per gun over the course of 12 hours.

Runaway guns

There are tales of soldiers setting up a Vickers gun to cover a specific area, such as a crossroads, and restricting its arc of fire with posts jammed into the ground on either side of the barrel. The thumb-push trigger could then be jammed and the machine gun left to bounce between the posts under recoil, filling the target area with deadly, although somewhat random, fire while the crew took cover. The gun would continue to spray fire until the ammunition supply was exhausted.

Vickers Machine Gun

Calibre: .303 British
Length: 1155mm (40.5in)
Weight: 18kg (40lb)
Barrel: 723mm (28.5in), 4 grooves, rh
Magazine: 250-round fabric belt
Operation: Recoil, water-cooled
Cyclic rate of fire: 600rpm
Muzzle velocity: 600mps (1970fps); later 730mps (2400fps)

Right: A British gun team mans a Vickers medium machine gun. The simple tripod mount was far more mobile than many other machine guns, but all the same the Vickers could not easily keep up with advancing infantry.

The second generation

The Maxim-type machine gun was a huge success and served well in both World Wars. By the outbreak of World War I, however, designers were already looking for ways to make machine guns lighter or more mobile. Some excellent weapons emerged in time to serve in the trenches, or above them aboard early combat aircraft. Not all of the second generation designs were particularly successful, however, although many pointed out blind alleys for others to avoid.

Saint-Etienne M1907

While other nations were fielding effective Maxim variants, the French entry was the poor Saint-Etienne Modèle 1907, which was chambered for the same 8mm round as the Lebel rifle. Over-complex and unreliable, the Modèle 1907 suffered terribly in dirty conditions and thus was almost useless on the Western Front, except as an improvised obstacle.

The weapon varied from the Maxim design in several important ways. It was gas- rather than recoil-operated, air-cooled and fed using strips of ammunition containing 24 or 30 rounds. It also had a device attached to the gas cylinder to allow the rate of fire to be adjusted. In attempting to be innovative, the designers created a weapon whose main difference from the Maxim design was that it was almost completely useless.

Saint-Etienne M1907

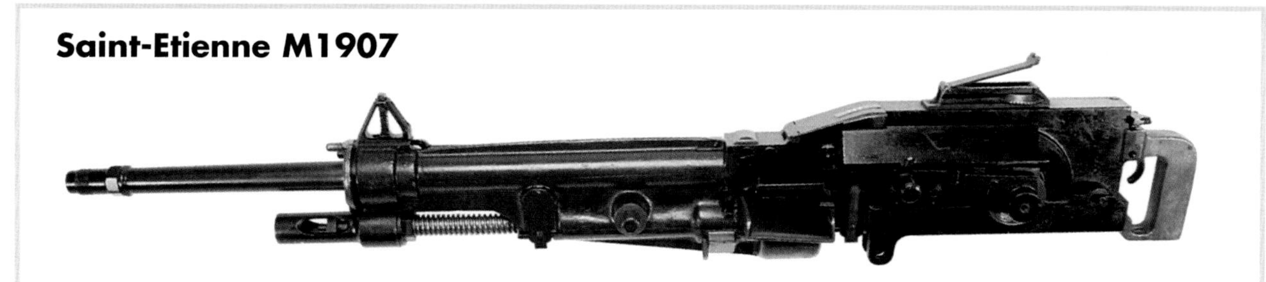

Calibre: 8mm Lebel
Length: 1180mm (46.5in)
Weight: 25.75kg (57lb)
Barrel: 710mm (28in), 4 grooves, rh
Magazine: 24- or 30-round metallic strip
Operation: Gas, air-cooled
Cyclic rate of fire: 500rpm
Muzzle velocity: 700mps (2300fps)

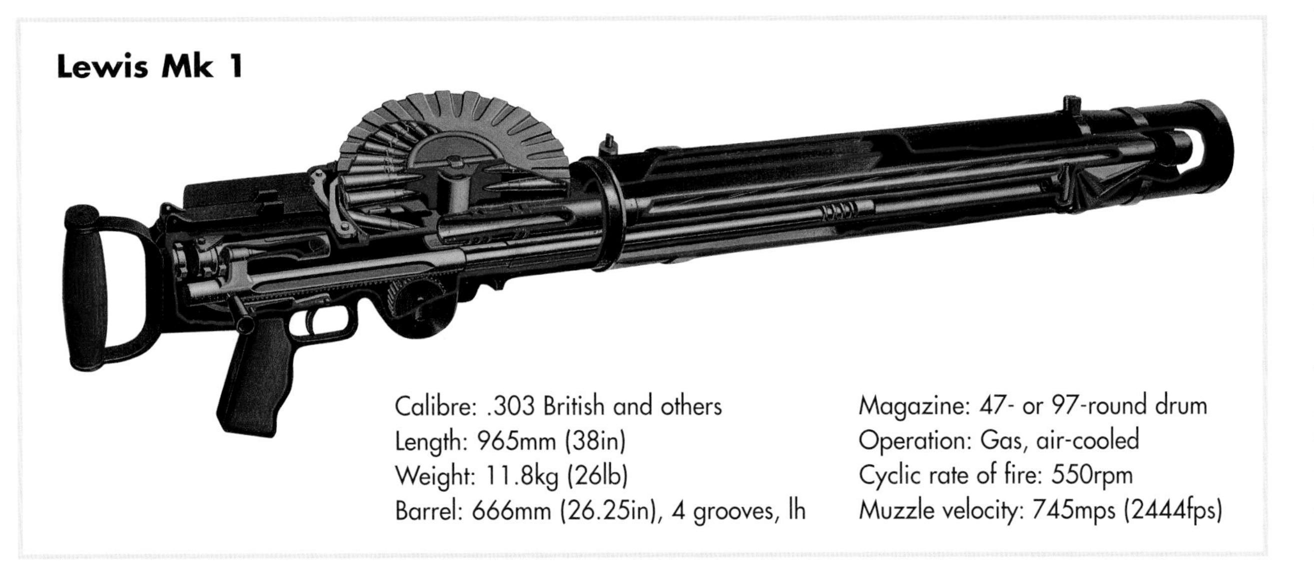

Lewis Mk 1

Calibre: .303 British and others
Length: 965mm (38in)
Weight: 11.8kg (26lb)
Barrel: 666mm (26.25in), 4 grooves, lh
Magazine: 47- or 97-round drum
Operation: Gas, air-cooled
Cyclic rate of fire: 550rpm
Muzzle velocity: 745mps (2444fps)

Below: A Lewis Gun team with additional ammunition drums ready. The air-cooled Lewis was more mobile than most of its contemporaries and was more amenable to being fired from scanty cover such as a trench parapet or a shallow shell hole.

Belt feed

The modern aluminium disintegrating-link belt was first used in the Bergmann MG10 and MG15, fine weapons that never achieved much success due to the dominance of the Maxim '08.

Non-disintegrating link-fed and cloth-fed machine guns do still exist, but have the disadvantage that the belts cannot simply be snapped together to form different lengths.

Lewis Gun

Other designs of World War I era fared rather better. One classic of the times was the Lewis Gun, a distinctive weapon fed from a top-mounted circular drum holding 47 or 97 rounds. The weapon was gas-operated and effective out to 1000 metres (3280 feet) at 550 rounds per minute.

Despite the fact that the Lewis was a very fine weapon, it was rejected by the US Army, to whom it was originally offered. The result was that the gun was adopted first by Belgium, in 1913, and then by the British Army, the following year. The Lewis Gun could be manufactured much more quickly and easily than the Vickers – a factor which soon won the favour of British military planners. It also proved be a popular weapon in the field.

Normally chambered in .303, the Lewis Gun was taken up by other users, sometimes in different calibres, during its service history. In British service it saw action in both World Wars and was respected for its performance by the troops that used it.

Browning M1917/1919

Another legend of the Great War that went on to serve admirably in World War II and long after, the Browning M1917 was developed just before the US joined the conflict. It was adopted in 1917 (hence the designation) to replace the French-designed Fusil Mitrailleur M15, or 'Chauchat', which was then in service. The Chauchat has an unfortunate reputation as possibly the worst-designed light machine gun in history, although many users would argue that this description over-rates the Chauchat's qualities.

Browning M1919

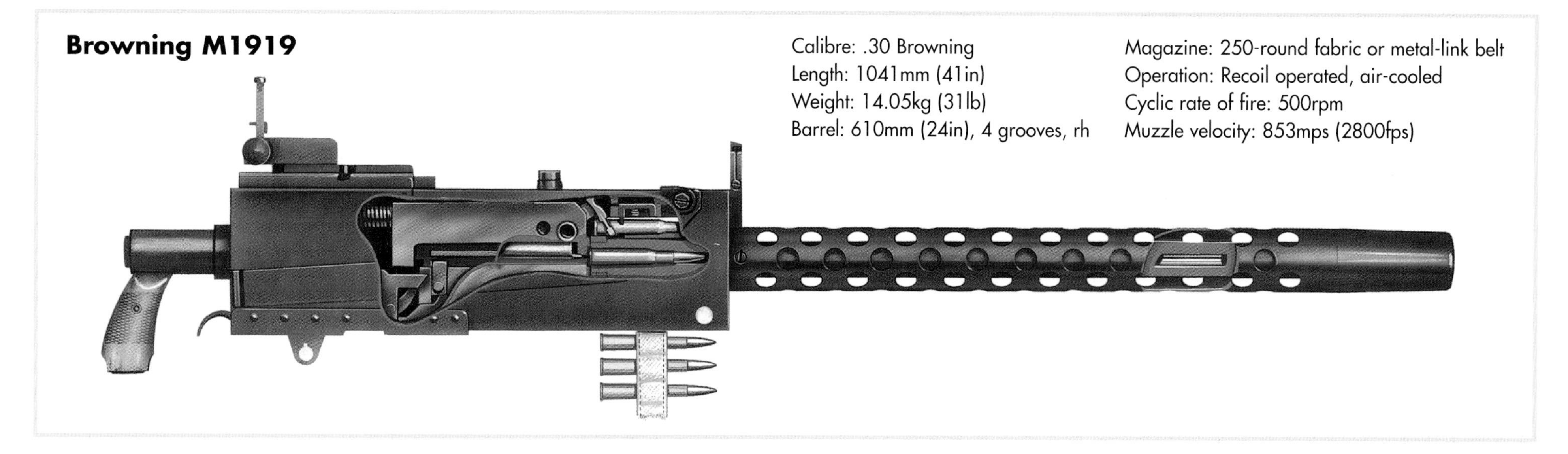

Calibre: .30 Browning
Length: 1041mm (41in)
Weight: 14.05kg (31lb)
Barrel: 610mm (24in), 4 grooves, rh
Magazine: 250-round fabric or metal-link belt
Operation: Recoil operated, air-cooled
Cyclic rate of fire: 500rpm
Muzzle velocity: 853mps (2800fps)

The Browning was something else entirely. Water-cooled and in many ways resembling the British Vickers, the M1917 was lighter and had a slightly simpler mechanism. It coped admirably with the unforgiving trench environment and was adapted for use aboard various vehicles.

Almost 70,000 Brownings were constructed before the war ended, and its service history continued for many years thereafter. Immediately after the war the M1917 was redesignated as the M1919. This weapon was built around the same receiver but had a heavier barrel and an air cooling system. The Browning M1919 went through several models, of which the A4 was the most numerous, with almost 450,000 fielded during World War II. The M1919 was adapted for several roles including anti-aircraft and vehicle-mounted combat. The A6 version, with a stock and bipod for rifle-squad support, was not a success, but overall, though, the Browning .30 machine gun was a fine weapon.

Although it has finally passed out of production, the .30 calibre Browning fought through two World Wars, Korea and afterward, and some examples are still in use worldwide almost a century after its first adoption.

Hotchkiss Modèle 1914

Most automatic weapons at the time of the Great War used fabric belts to feed cartridges into the mechanism, but other systems were available. Early Hotchkiss weapons used a rigid metal strip holding 24 or 36 rounds, which worked well enough, but when the Hotchkiss Mle 1914 was fielded it used what may well have been the first example of the disintegrating metal belt. A string of 3-round metal strips was connected together to create a continuous belt feed, the standard number of rounds on the belt being 249.

Below: A Jeep-mounted Browning .30 calibre machine gun. The British Long-Range Desert Group made extensive use of jeeps heavily armed with an assortment of machine guns; some vehicles carried six or more weapons. This vehicle also carries Vickers-Berthier G.O. machine guns.

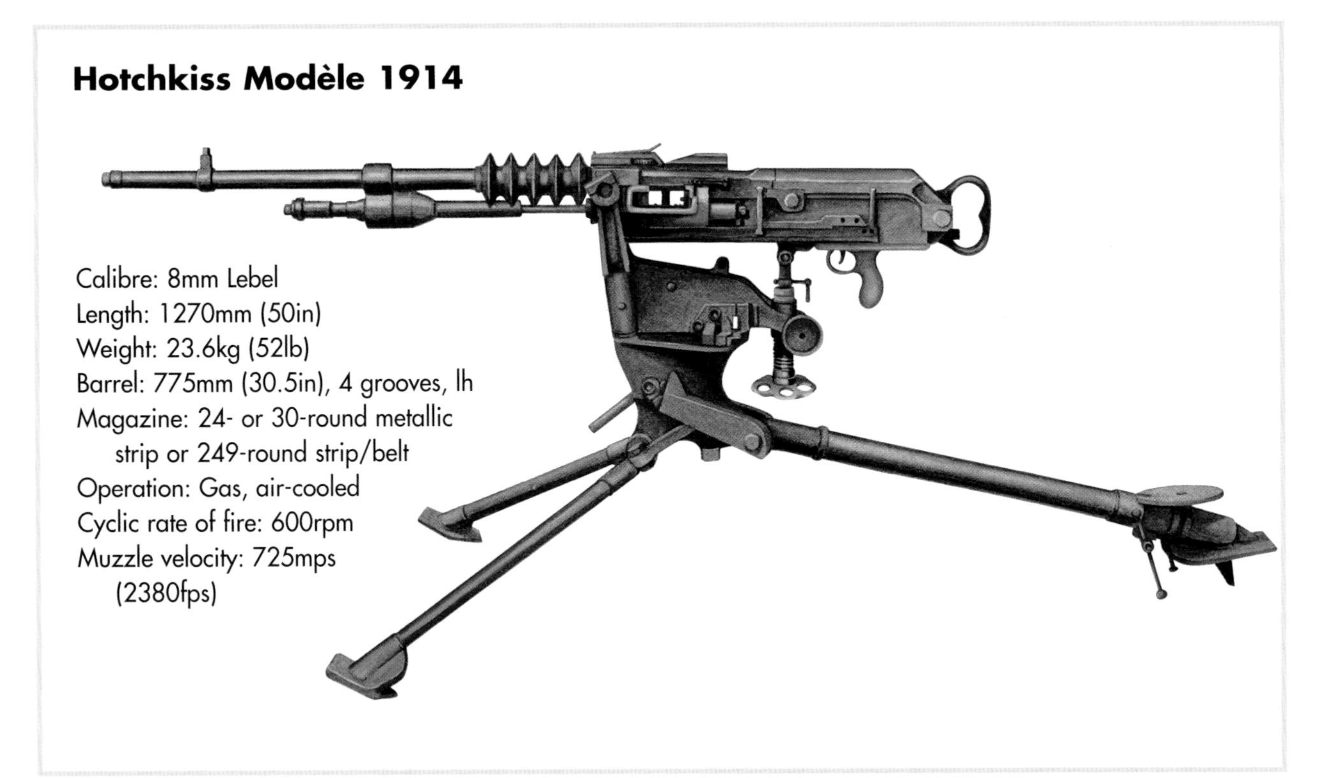

Hotchkiss Modèle 1914

Calibre: 8mm Lebel
Length: 1270mm (50in)
Weight: 23.6kg (52lb)
Barrel: 775mm (30.5in), 4 grooves, lh
Magazine: 24- or 30-round metallic strip or 249-round strip/belt
Operation: Gas, air-cooled
Cyclic rate of fire: 600rpm
Muzzle velocity: 725mps (2380fps)

Most modern machine guns use disintegrating-link belts, wherein individual rounds are held together by metal clips to create a flexible belt of any desired length. The link can be reused and as the pile of detached links builds up around a weapon, new belts can be quickly made from boxed ammunition and simply attached to the last round of the current belt. Although the Hotchkiss Mle 1914 used a different system, it showed the potential of a metal-link belt and was a fine weapon in its own right.

The gun itself was a reliable gas-operated weapon normally chambered for the 8mm Lebel cartridge. It was effective to 2000 metres (6560 feet) or more and, although its weight precluded much mobility, was considered good enough to be taken into service by France, Britain, the US and other nations. After the Great War it gained considerable overseas popularity, being sold in Central and South America as well as in Europe.

Madsen Let Maskingevær

The Danish Madsen light machine gun, first produced in 1897, saw service in the Russo-Japanese War and finally ceased production in 1955. The Madsen was based on the Martini rifle and, weighing less than 10 kilograms (22 pounds), it was a true light machine gun that could be carried by a member of a rifle squad. Variants were chambered in several different calibres, including 6.5mm, and fed by box magazine as well as belts, depending upon the buyer's wishes. The Madsen was taken up by more than 30 countries and, despite an unusual feed system necessitated by the basic Martini design, turned out to be a reliable and very usable weapon.

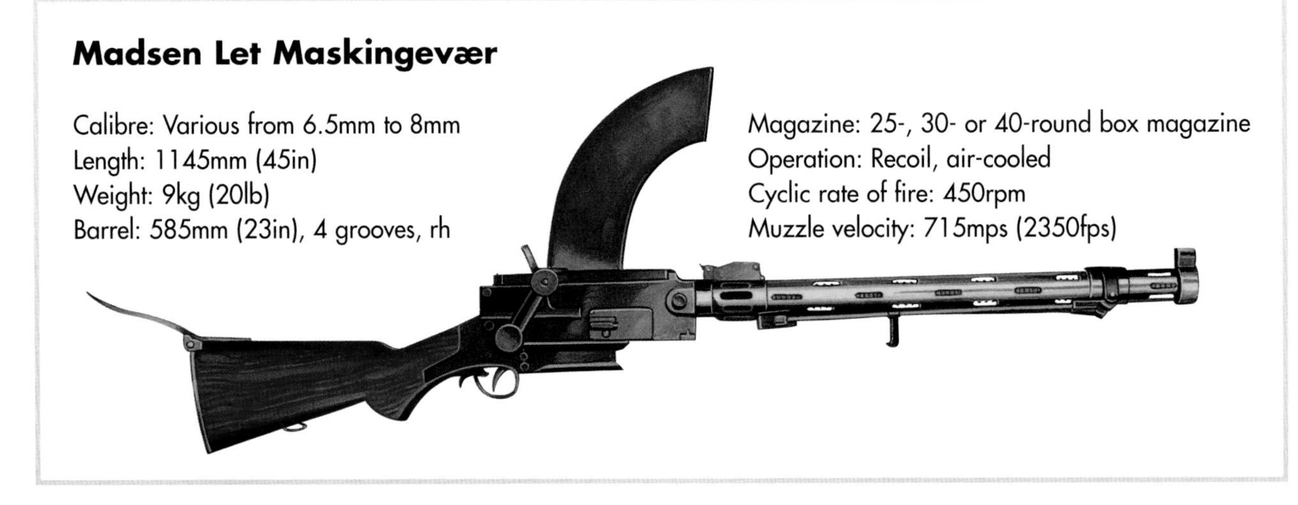

Madsen Let Maskingevær

Calibre: Various from 6.5mm to 8mm
Length: 1145mm (45in)
Weight: 9kg (20lb)
Barrel: 585mm (23in), 4 grooves, rh
Magazine: 25-, 30- or 40-round box magazine
Operation: Recoil, air-cooled
Cyclic rate of fire: 450rpm
Muzzle velocity: 715mps (2350fps)

The Great War did not of course prevent future conflict. It provided the perfect opportunity, however, for the light machine gun to prove itself in combat and thereby guarantee that all future wars would be fought by troops supported by automatic weapons.

World War II and the Cold War

By the outbreak of World War II it was obvious that automatic weapons had many roles in modern war. In addition to the mostly static defensive role they had fulfilled in World War I, machine guns were useful in adding firepower to infantry formations, either in the support role or, if they were light enough, actually accompanying rapidly advancing troops.

This was the beginning of the concept of the Squad Support Weapon. Up to this point infantry formations were essentially rifle units, in which every man held the same armament. Now began the gradual shift towards the squad automatic weapon as the main fighting power of a unit, with riflemen to support and protect its crew. This of course required automatic weapons that were light enough to be carried by rifle units. Some such weapons were based on existing rifle designs; some were adapted from existing machine guns. Others were custom-designed. Not all of these weapons were successful, including a variant of the Browning M1919 with a rifle-type shoulder stock.

Right: A young German MG34 machine gunner and his assistant march through the snow along the Eastern Front during the winter of 1941–2. The German MG34 was the first General Purpose Machine Gun. It served on all fronts during World War II and became the basis for a family of weapons that is still in service today.

MG34 and MG42

Among the very best weapons of the war (and arguably among the very best weapons of all time) was the German MG34 and its descendants. The MG34 was a forerunner of the modern General Purpose Machine Gun, chambered as it was in 7.92mm, a rifle calibre. The same weapon could be mounted on a vehicle, tripod or air-defence mount, or used with its bipod for close support in an infantry formation. Ammunition feed was either a 250-round belt or a 75-round drum, allowing the weapon to be used in the assault mode. Firing at 900 rounds per minute out to 2000 metres (6560 feet) or more, the air-cooled MG34 could sustain rapid fire for some time; changing barrels was a simple matter of twisting the hot one loose and replacing it with another.

The MG34 was an excellent weapon but rather expensive to manufacture. For this reason it was replaced in service by the MG42, which was

cheaper to make in the numbers required. Most of the basic principles of the weapon were retained, but manufacturing methods were changed to suit mass production. Thus the MG42 had more stamped parts and less expensive machining than the MG34. The action was slightly modified and barrel change further improved.

The MG42's distinctive sound – rather like tearing paper – was largely due to its awesome 1200 rounds per minute cyclic rate. The sound, like the weapon itself, was dreaded by Allied troops throughout the war. The MG42 is a truly classic weapon whose excellent design lives on in its later derivative, the MG3 General Purpose Machine Gun.

Bren

British forces also saw the need for a squad-level machine gun. Lewis Guns and other weapons were available, but the classic wartime squad-level automatic weapon was the Bren gun. Designed in Brno, Czechoslovakia, and manufactured in Britain at Enfield (hence its name) the Bren was chambered for .303 in British service, and served in the armouries of other nations too. The distinctive curved magazine was required because the British .303 rifle cartridge had a rim at its base, unlike the rimless 7.92mm German round that had been used in the original Czech design.

Fed from a 30-round top-loading magazine and firing at 500 rounds per minute, the Bren was

Left: The Bren gun was an excellent squad-level support weapon. Shown here in New Guinea, an Australian gunner rests his weapon on a tree stump while his companion advances with his Bren in the assault position.

superbly accurate out to beyond 1000 metres (3280 feet), owing to the very light recoil. Its accuracy was the source of one of the few complaints ever raised about it: a machine gun is supposed to spray an area with bullets, but the Bren was so accurate that it would put a whole burst into the aim point. This was contrary to the idea of area-effect fire, although in the hands of a skilled gunner it could be deadly. Few weapons users have ever wanted a less accurate weapon, and this 'fault' was not a serious failing.

The Bren evolved through several slight alterations, including re-chambering to NATO standard 7.62mm and some alterations to speed up manufacture. All versions were easy to operate and maintain, and this contributed to a very long service life. Brens served with the British Army for more than 50 years. A few examples even saw action in the 1991 Gulf War, demonstrating that quality never goes out of fashion.

Right: The simple DP machine gun was sufficiently rugged to survive in the hands of conscripts and soldiers such as this young Russian partisan along the Eastern Front in 1941–2.

Degtyarev DP

The Degtyarev DP machine gun was another top-loading light machine gun. It was introduced in 1928 and served throughout World War II. The weapon's mechanism was extremely simple and, as is typical with Russian military equipment, not only idiot-proof but very nearly soldier-proof. Even without the assistance of dreadful climatic conditions, conscript soldiers can break virtually anything, so robust construction is a distinct advantage.

The DP was fed by a 47-round drum, which was the weapon's only real weak point as it could easily be damaged, which in turn resulted in feed problems. Firing 7.62x54mm rounds at 500 rounds per minute out to about 2000 metres (6560 feet),

Degtyarev DP

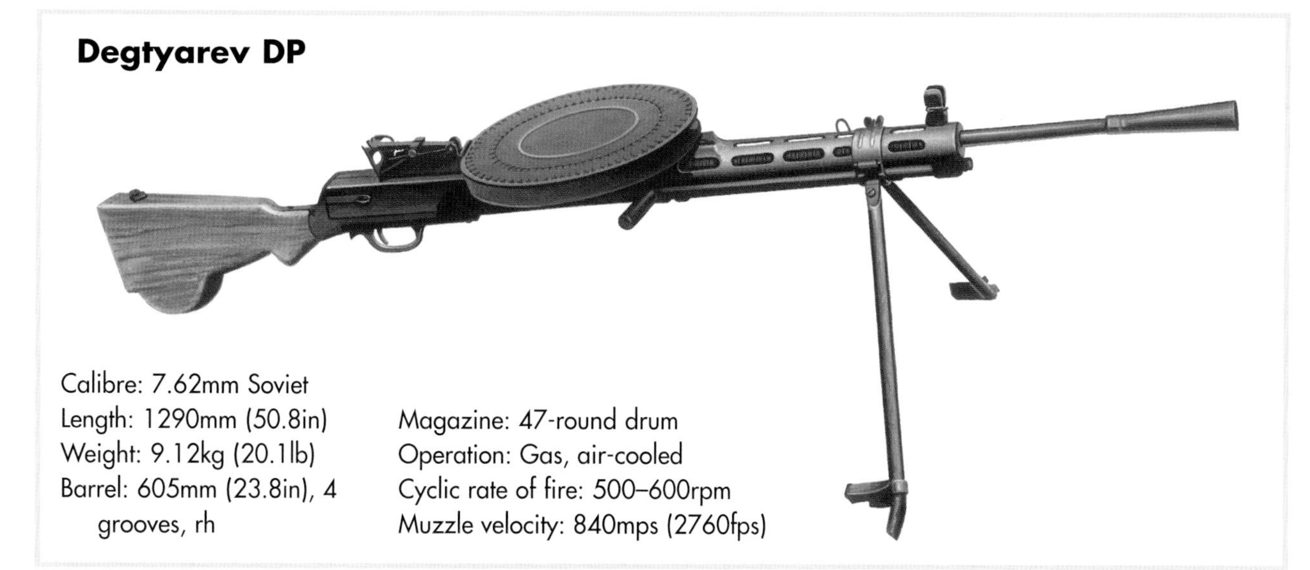

Calibre: 7.62mm Soviet
Length: 1290mm (50.8in)
Weight: 9.12kg (20.1lb)
Barrel: 605mm (23.8in), 4 grooves, rh
Magazine: 47-round drum
Operation: Gas, air-cooled
Cyclic rate of fire: 500–600rpm
Muzzle velocity: 840mps (2760fps)

Courage under fire

Gurkha Lance-Corporal Rambahadur Limbu was awarded the Victoria Cross for his actions in Borneo in 1965. After carrying two squad team-mates to safety under heavy machine gun fire he retrieved his weapon and assaulted the enemy position alone, destroying it with close-range Bren gun fire.

LIGHT MACHINE GUNS: MG42 VERSUS BREN

World War II saw the emergence of some of the world's best weapons, among them the Bren and MG42 light machine guns. Both were of European design: the MG42 German and the Bren Czech. It is a testament to their quality that they both remained in service, in one form or another, for many decades. The MG42, known as the 'Spandau' to the British, was a little too light for the GPMG role and a little too bulky to make an ideal squad support weapon, but it was certainly deadly. Its 1200 rounds per minute fire offset any reduction in accuracy caused by recoil, even if it meant that the barrel had to be changed frequently.

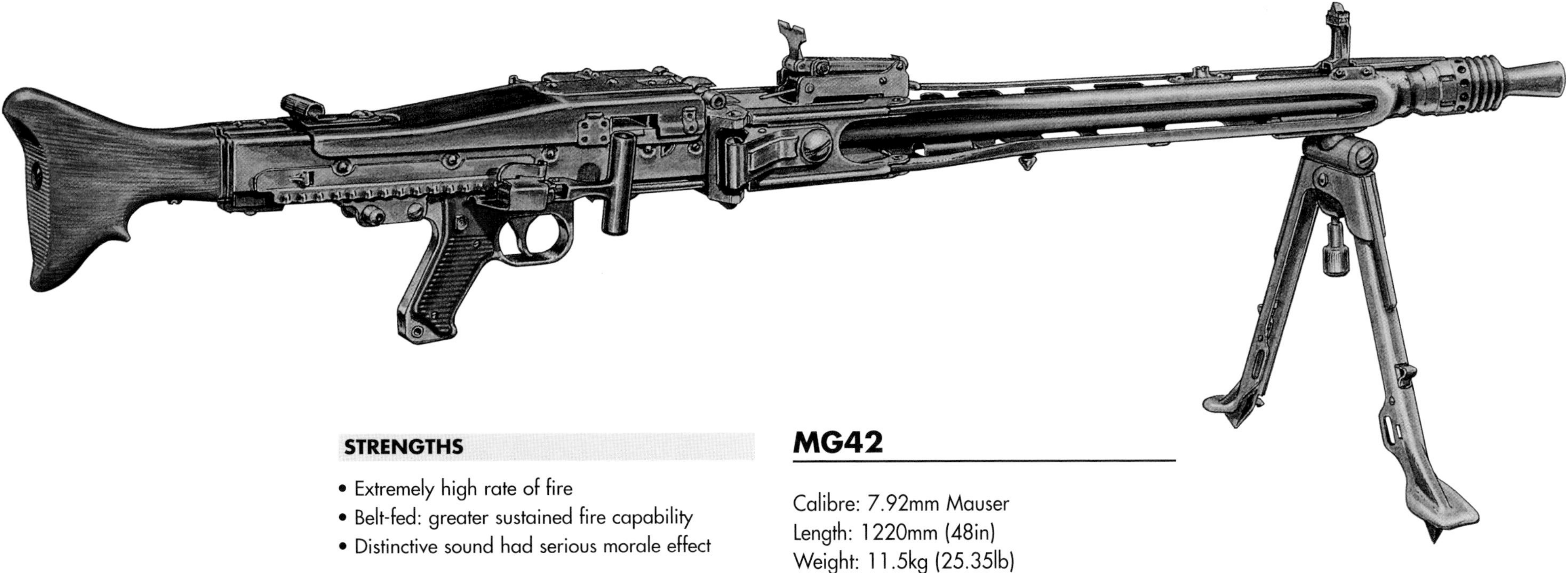

STRENGTHS

- Extremely high rate of fire
- Belt-fed: greater sustained fire capability
- Distinctive sound had serious morale effect

WEAKNESSES

- Rapid fire requires frequent barrel changes
- Bulky and less mobile than the Bren
- Susceptible to dirt and environmental conditions

MG42

Calibre: 7.92mm Mauser
Length: 1220mm (48in)
Weight: 11.5kg (25.35lb)
Barrel: 535mm (21in), 4 grooves, rh
Magazine: 50-round belt
Operation: Short recoil, air-cooled
Cyclic rate of fire: 1200rpm
Muzzle velocity: 800mps (2650fps)

Both weapons served in support, vehicle armament and anti-aircraft roles.The Bren was fed by a top-mounted 30-round magazine, allowing it considerable mobility. It could be used in the support role on a tripod, vehicle mount or its integral bipod, or as an effective squad automatic weapon, almost as a large and heavy rifle. The Bren was also extremely accurate, allowing it to undertake sniping tasks and to harass enemy personnel at long range. The Bren's low rate of fire (500 rounds per minute) was an asset under some circumstances but limited its effectiveness when engaging enemy aircraft or engaging in area fire.

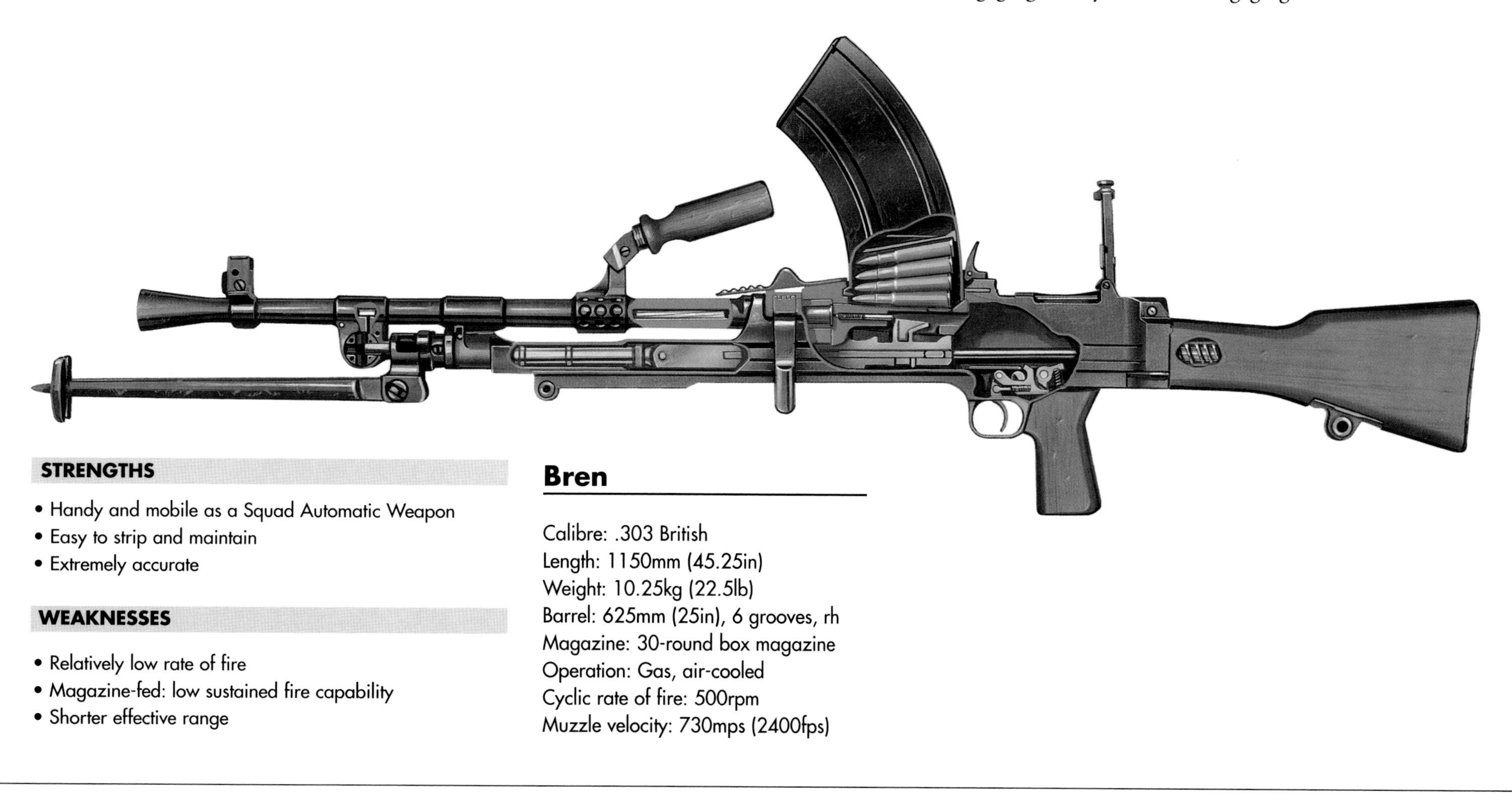

STRENGTHS

- Handy and mobile as a Squad Automatic Weapon
- Easy to strip and maintain
- Extremely accurate

WEAKNESSES

- Relatively low rate of fire
- Magazine-fed: low sustained fire capability
- Shorter effective range

Bren

Calibre: .303 British
Length: 1150mm (45.25in)
Weight: 10.25kg (22.5lb)
Barrel: 625mm (25in), 6 grooves, rh
Magazine: 30-round box magazine
Operation: Gas, air-cooled
Cyclic rate of fire: 500rpm
Muzzle velocity: 730mps (2400fps)

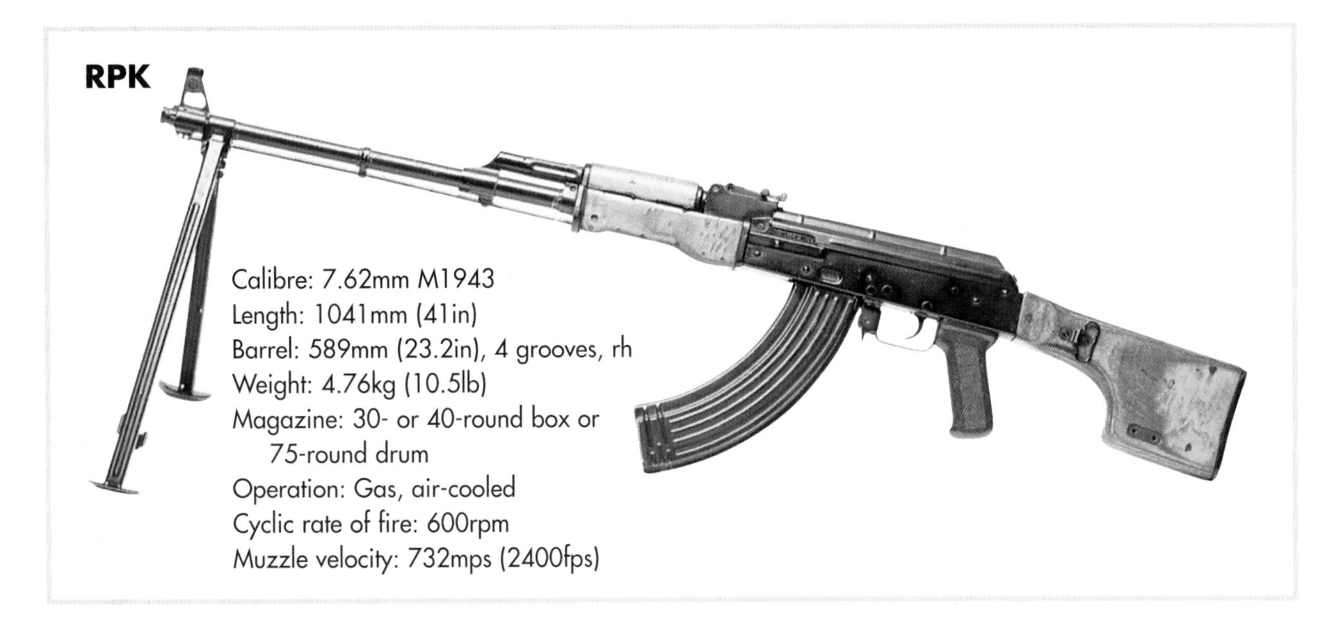

the DP was an effective weapon despite a slight problem with the gas-operation system. Like other weapons in which the gas piston spring was close to the barrel, heat could weaken the spring over time and eventually cause the mechanism to fail.

Like the Bren, the DP had a built-in bipod and could be used effectively on the move since it did not need a trailing belt. Also in common with the Bren, the DP was very light for an effective machine gun.

Modular machine guns

Several support weapon versions of standard rifles now exist, such as those based on the Steyr AUG, SA80 and AK-47. One advantage is that any rifleman can grab the squad support weapon and use it effectively, without requiring special training. Rifles and support weapons may also share parts and ammunition.

RPD

Also designed by Degtyarev, the RPD (Ruchnoy Pulemyot Dagtyareva) machine gun emerged in the early years of the Cold War and by the early 1950s had become a standard light machine gun in the armies of the Soviet Union and its allies.

Firing 7.62x39mm rifle ammunition from a 100-round belt contained within a drum, the RPD was capable of 700 rounds per minute and effective out to about 900 metres (2953 feet). Its main flaws were a tendency for the ammunition drum to become clogged with dirt and the constant likelihood of overheating, since the barrel was not changeable. The need to limit automatic fire to prevent heat build-up is also encountered on other more modern weapons that, like the RPD, are essentially rifles trying to operate in the machine gun mode.

Although it had its problems, the RPD remained in service in the Soviet Union until the 1970s and was constantly improved. Examples of this machine gun are still in use worldwide, especially where other ex-Soviet arms are popular, such as nations that have adopted the Kalashnikov rifle family and its associated ammunition.

RPK

Although the Soviets already possessed a light machine gun in the form of the RPD, it was decided to design a better weapon to replace it. The result was the RPK, which was essentially a Kalashnikov AKM rifle conversion. The original assault rifle can clearly be seen in the RPK, although the machine gun version has a longer, heavier barrel and a bipod.

The RPK can deliver 600 rounds per minute out to about 800 metres (2625 feet), but since it is not possible to change the chrome-lined barrel it quickly overheats at sustained high rates of fire. It will survive for a time, but like all scaled-up assault rifles this weapon is not really capable of true machine gun firepower.

However, with 30- or 40-round magazines or a 75-round drum available in a weapon weighing little more than an assault rifle, the extra firepower offered by the RPK has been attractive enough for many nations to adopt it. Examples recently saw action in Iraqi hands, where they won the respect of the opposing Coalition troops.

Like the AKM rifle, which was later updated to the AK-74 to fire smaller calibre (5.45mm) ammunition, the RPK is also available in 5.45mm, designated the RPK-74.

Right: This Italian Modello 30 has somehow found its way into the hands of Soviet soldiers fighting near Stalingrad in 1942. The poor design of the weapon is outweighed by the fact that it is there; these soldiers are probably glad just to have weapons and ammunition, whatever their origins.

Fucile Migliatore Breda Modello 30

Not all the projects of this period were successes. Some, despite clever features, turned out to be less than practical. The Italian Breda Model 30 was one such. Not only is it a strange-looking object, its design was basically unworkable in the field. The feed system consisted of a detachable box magazine that could be filled from rifle chargers (i.e. devices used to quickly load a rifle that had an internal magazine). This magazine held only 20 rounds and was soon empty even at very modest rates of fire (475 rounds per minute). Ejection was also unusually complex. The Model 30 featured a quick-change barrel, but no changing handle to help remove the hot barrel.

Although it demonstrated some interesting ideas, the Model 30 turned out to be little use in the field and quietly disappeared.

The heavies

Not normally considered small arms, heavy machine guns and light autocannon play an important part in infantry warfare, usually from vehicle or heavy tripod mounts, or in the anti-aircraft role. Far too heavy to be carried by an individual soldier, these weapons deliver massive firepower out to considerable distances.

Fucile Migliatore Breda Modello 30

Calibre: 6.5mm M95 and others
Length: 1230mm (48.5in)
Weight: 10.2kg (22.5lb)
Barrel: 520mm (20.5in), 4 grooves, rh
Magazine: 20-round integral box magazine
Operation: Blowback, air-cooled
Cyclic rate of fire: 475rpm
Muzzle velocity: 610mps (2000fps)

Browning M2HB

Calibre: .50in Browning
Length: 1655mm (65in)
Weight: 38.5kg (84lb)
Barrel: 1143mm (45in), 8 grooves, rh
Magazine: 110-round metallic-link belt
Operation: Recoil, air-cooled
Cyclic rate of fire: 450–550rpm
Muzzle velocity: 898mps (2950fps)

Browning M2HB

The all-time classic heavy machine gun is the Browning M2HB (the HB stands for 'heavy barrel'). This weapon grew out of a US Army request for a weapon capable of engaging aircraft and the armoured vehicles that were becoming increasingly prominent in combat. The M1921, which resulted from this request, was an M1917 re-chambered for the new .50 calibre round then being marketed by Winchester.

After the M1917 was adapted to create the air-cooled M1919, the M1921 eventually adopted air cooling, along with a heavy barrel to help reduce heat problems, and was redesignated the M2HB in the 1930s. This weapon, sometimes referred to as 'Ma Deuce', has been in service ever since.

Heavy hitter

The M2HB is effective out to 3000 metres (9843 feet) or more, and firing at about 500 rounds per minute can chew up or punch holes in light vehicles and other semi-hard targets. It has been adapted for use aboard ships and aircraft as well as vehicles and installations. There is very little on the average urban street that will stop a .50 calibre machine gun round, as has been demonstrated in recent conflicts.

More than three million M2HBs have been produced to date, and it seems likely that this fine weapon will continue to soldier on for many years.

Left: The Browning M2HB heavy machinegun in an infantry support role. Effective against infantry and light vehicles out to 3000 metres (9843 feet), the '.50-cal' can devastate areas of the battlefield and deny them to enemy troops.

This impression is reinforced by the appearance on the market of updated M2HBs, fitted with quick-change barrels. These (very slightly modified) weapons are designated M2HB (QCB) for 'Quick Change Barrel'.

DShK and DShKM

If a military force somewhere in the world perceives a need for a given weapon, it is likely that something similar will appear in other places too. The Soviet answer to the M2HB was the DSh series of machine guns. Chambered for 12.7x108mm, a cartridge of the same diameter as the Western equivalent but 9mm (0.35 inches) longer, the original DSh was introduced in the 1930s. It was modified in 1938 into its wartime form, the DShK, known as 'Dushka' to its users, and received extensive use along the Eastern Front. The DShK then became the DShKM in 1946, when the problematic rotary-fed system was dropped in favour of a far simpler flat-feed.

Although the DShK was almost 3 kilograms (6.61 pounds) lighter than the Browning M2HB, a particular idiosyncrasy of the series was its very heavy carriage, which in many ways resembled an artillery mount. This turned a weapon that started out as an improvement on the M2HB into something a lot heavier, but could at least be quickly converted into an anti-aircraft mount.

'Dushkas' have served with many nations and in various roles, notably as a vehicle-mounted weapon, in which it excelled. The anti-aircraft version was extremely effective in Vietnam. Although the weapon is no longer in service in an infantry role, some are still retained as anti-aircraft weapons.

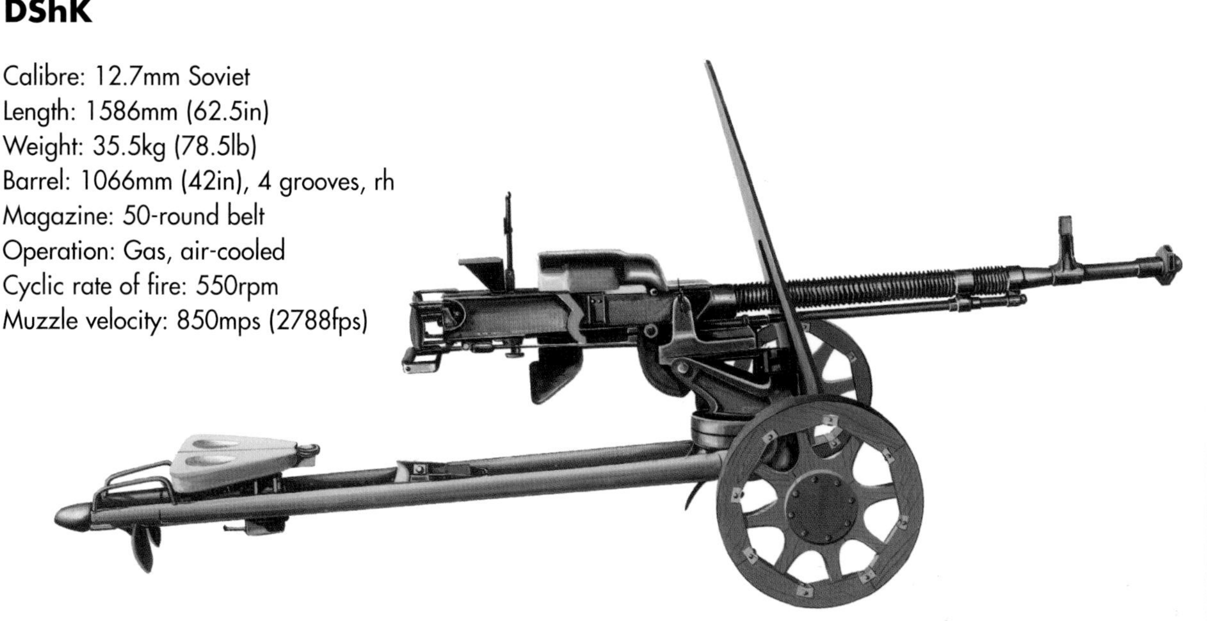

DShK

Calibre: 12.7mm Soviet
Length: 1586mm (62.5in)
Weight: 35.5kg (78.5lb)
Barrel: 1066mm (42in), 4 grooves, rh
Magazine: 50-round belt
Operation: Gas, air-cooled
Cyclic rate of fire: 550rpm
Muzzle velocity: 850mps (2788fps)

Left: Like the M2HB, the DShK heavy machinegun serves in a variety of roles. This example is mounted on the top hatch of a Soviet tank for anti-aircraft and anti-personnel work.

Left: A direct descendent of the MG34, the MG3 is in service with the German army. It is available on a range of mountings for anti-personnel, anti-aircraft and defensive roles.

Maids of all work: GPMGs

The modern General Purpose Machine Gun is exactly what its name suggests. Heavy enough to deliver respectable firepower at a decent range, the GPMG is still light enough to accompany infantry squads. GPMGs are unlike the earlier 'medium' machine guns in that the latter tended to be chambered in rifle calibres but were heavy in construction, limiting their mobility. GPMGs are not that much heavier or bulkier than rifles.

GPMGs, in keeping with their title, do not just support infantry squads. They are mounted on vehicles, set up in emplacements and in general used wherever an automatic weapon is necessary but there is not the budget or the capacity for a heavier weapon. Thus vehicles not expected to come into close contact with enemy infantry (for example, artillery vehicles or combat vehicles armed with anti-tank missiles) may mount one on a pintle near the top hatch, just in case. Light vehicles may be unable to carry anything bigger: a GPMG is better for self-defence than just relying on whatever small arms the crew may have.

MG3

The first GPMGs emerged during World War II, although they were not given their current designation until some years later. One of the first was the MG34. This weapon was replaced by the similar but cheaper MG42, and from this the MG3 was developed. The MG3 retains and even exceeds its predecessor's incredible cyclic rate of 1200 rounds per minute, although this can be adjusted by using a heavier bolt.

Like its predecessors, the MG3 is an excellent weapon. It is chambered for NATO 7.62x51mm and belt fed. Accurate out to 3000 metres (9843 feet), the MG3 is one of the best GPMGs available today, even though the basic design is half a century old.

The MG42/59 is an export version of the MG3 used by the German military with a slightly lower rate of fire. It is used by other European forces, including those of Austria.

M60

The standard GPMG used by the United States armed forces for many years, the M60 had numerous initial problems and went through many development cycles in an attempt to solve them.

Barrel heat

Constant fire places machine guns under great strain and there is an upper limit to how fast a weapon can fire before heat build-up destroys the barrel. The M60 General Purpose Machine Gun can continue to fire longer than most since the barrels are lined with Stellite, a non-ferrous metal that considerably extends the barrel's lifespan. Nonetheless, firing the guns while the barrels are white hot rapidly damages the gun.

Miniguns are one way around this problem with barrel heat build-up – several barrels rotate and fire in turn, allowing a rate of fire up to 10,000 rounds per minute without immediately ruining the weapon.

Chambered in 7.62x51mm and firing at 550 rounds per minute, the original M60 served in Vietnam, where it earned the nickname 'Pig'. Compared with contemporaries such as the FN MAG 58, the M60 suffered from a number of quite serious faults. The hot barrel could not be changed without special gloves and each barrel had its own cylinder and bipod meaning the weapon had to be partially dismantled to make the change. Reliability was also something of a problem at times. Nevertheless, the M60 was effective out to 3000 metres (9843 feet) and provided fire support to generations of US soldiers.

In the E3 version, the M60 finally became what it should have been along. Substantially lighter than the original and fitted with an assault foregrip, the M60E3 has a bipod fitted to the receiver rather than the characteristic 'perforated girders' on the muzzle of the original. The barrel-change problem has been solved and reliability is better too.

M60s have seen service with infantry and fitted to a variety of vehicles. With the advent of Light Support Weapons and 5.56mm light machine guns, it may be that 7.62mm GPMGs are going out of fashion. In that case, it is likely that the M60 will hang around in reserve for many more years rather than being replaced by something new.

FN MAG 58 (L7A2)

Emerging at about the same time as the M60, the Fabrique Nationale MAG 58 machine gun was chambered for the same 7.62mm ammunition and entered service with the British Army (among others), where it was given the designation L7A2 General Purpose Machine Gun.

Like the Bren, an earlier British service weapon, the FN MAG proved to be reliable and accurate. From a tripod mount it is accurate out to 1800 metres (5905 feet); in the hands of a prone infantryman using the integral bipod it is considered effective to 1200 metres (3937 feet). For area suppression an effective range of 3000 metres (9843 feet) is accepted.

The rate of fire can be adjusted between 600 and 1000 rounds per minute by using a regulator fitted to the gas-operation system, and barrel changes are simple. The versatility of this fine weapon, coupled with its robust and reliable nature, led to great popularity and it has served with more than 80 armed forces around the world.

The L7A2 is also a standard vehicle-mounted weapon with British forces. Although theoretically it has been replaced in infantry use by the L86A1 Light Support Weapon, it has seen action wherever British military forces encounter combat.

The MAG 58 is half a century old, yet remains an excellent battlefield weapon and is one of the most widely used weapons of all time.

PKM

Calibre: 7.62mm
Length: 1160mm (45.7in)
Weight: 9kg (19.84lb)
Barrel: 658mm (25.9in)
Magazine: 100-, 200- and 250-round metal-link belts
Operation: Gas
Cyclic rate of fire: 690–720rpm

SIG 710

Calibre: 7.62mm
Length: 1143mm (45in)
Weight: 9.25kg (20.39lb)
Barrel: 559mm (22in)
Magazine: Belt feed
Cyclic rate of fire: 800–950rpm
Muzzle velocity: 790mps (2592fps)

PK series

From the late 1950s GPMGs were acquired by armed forces worldwide in ever greater numbers. The Soviet Union's belt-fed PK, which entered service in 1964 and utilizes the long 7.62x54mm round, earned a reputation for reliability due in part to its adoption of the proven Kalashnikov action and a minimal number of moving parts.

Several variants of this weapon exist for infantry and vehicle use, and different mountings are sometimes given separate designations. The most important variant is the PKM, which has a lighter barrel and slightly different construction methods.

Effective out to about 2000 metres (6560 feet) at 720 rounds per minute, and capable of sustained fire, the PK series is ageing but is reasonably effective. Korean troops fighting in Vietnam found it entirely acceptable and it remains in service in many nations, an old warhorse with a few more active years remaining.

SIG 710

Switzerland is famous for its neutrality in foreign affairs, but neutrality must be guarded. In this the Swiss have two important advantages: very difficult terrain for an invader and a well-armed citizenry with large numbers of military reservists available. Despite, or perhaps because of, the fact that almost every adult can lay hands on a military weapon at a moment's notice, the Swiss have an extremely low rate of armed crime. The weapons that arm the Swiss military and reservists are among the best ever produced, and the SIG 710 is a fine example.

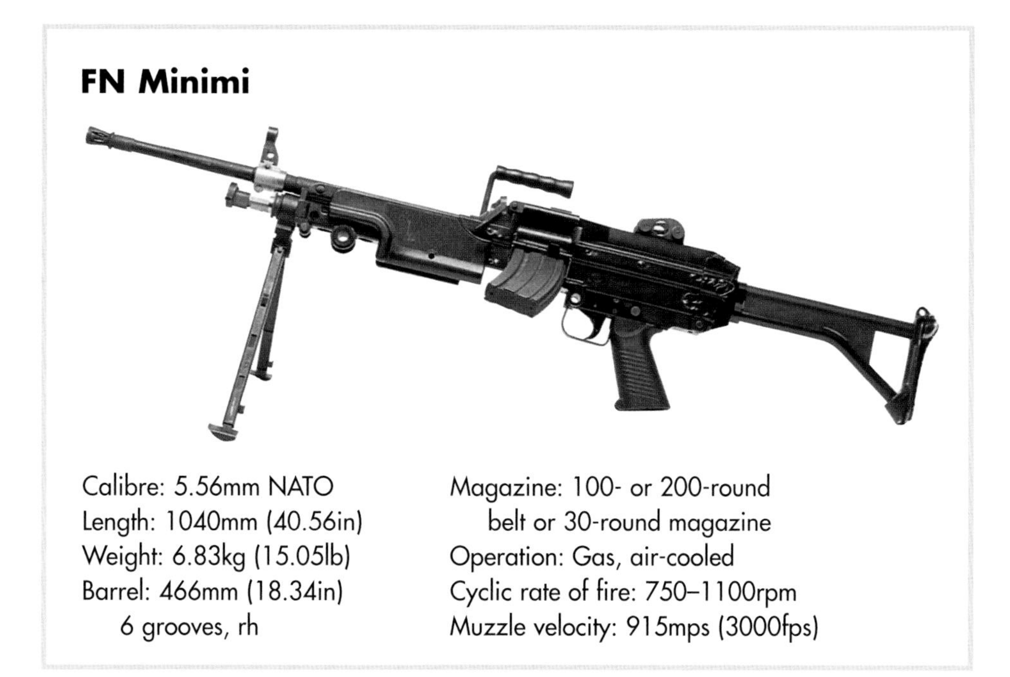

Above: A US support gunner fires his M249 light machine gun from a natural position reinforced with a few sandbags. The M249 uses the same ammunition as infantry rifles in the squad, but its 200-round box affords it huge firepower.

A beautifully made GPMG chambered for NATO 7.62x51mm, the 710 is notable for its overall quality and especially the ease of changing barrels. Like many other Swiss weapons the 710 is too expensive for most users, although it has found some favour in South America.

Smaller calibres

Across the small arms industry in general there is a move towards smaller calibres and lighter weapons. 5.56mm rather than 7.62mm has become the norm for rifle ammunition, and it makes sense that a squad support weapon should be chambered for the same calibre ammunition as the rest of the unit's personal weapons. This eases the logistics burden in general and allows ammunition to be shared at need.

FN Minimi (M249 SAW)

Until recently, however, 5.56mm was considered a light machine gun and rifle calibre rather than one suitable for a true GPMG. This assumption was challenged by the Fabrique Nationale Minimi, which is in service with the US military as the M249 SAW (Squad Automatic Weapon).

Only 40mm (1.57 inches) longer than an M16 rifle, the Minimi is not a great deal heavier than a rifle but offers very impressive firepower. It can take M16 magazines or 200-round belts carried in an ammunition box underneath. The weapon can also be fed by a disintegrating-link belt of whatever length can be constructed if it is to be used in a static position.

The Minimi is effective beyond 2000 metres (6560 feet) in the area-fire role and can deliver a rate of fire between 750 and 1100 rounds per minute. It can be mounted on a tripod or other fixed mount, but is ideally suited for fire support in the close urban environment. A variant is available with a telescoping stock and short barrel, creating an assault weapon with a lot of firepower.

The Minimi has found favour with several armed forces, and it is not hard to see why. It offers reliable sustained firepower in a small, lightweight package – exactly what today's infantryman needs.

MODERN SQUAD SUPPORT WEAPONS: L86A1 LSW

The move from 7.62mm GPMGs to lighter 5.56mm Squad Automatic Weapons makes sense in many ways – a support weapon based on the current service rifle can share components, spares and ammunition, and any rifleman can take up the support weapon and use it effectively. There are many, however, who would rather have a 'real' machinegun than an overgrown rifle. The advantages offered by the L86A1 Light Support Weapon are real enough, but even though the L7A2 GPMG requires a type of different ammunition to squad rifles and weighs more, it does offer more sustained firepower and a harder-hitting cartridge.

STRENGTHS

- Shares ammunition and even magazines with squad rifles
- Can act as a sniper weapon
- Lightweight and mobile

WEAKNESSES

- Poor sustained fire from 30-round magazine
- Light cartridge
- Barrel cannot be quick-changed, further limiting sustained fire

L86A1 Light Support Weapon

Calibre: 5.56mm NATO
Length: 900mm (35.43in)
Weight: 5.4kg (11.9lb)
Barrel: 646mm (25.43in), 6 grooves, rh
Magazine: 30-round detachable box magazine
Operation: Gas, air-cooled
Cyclic rate of fire: 700rpm
Muzzle velocity: 970mps (3182fps)

VERSUS FN MAG 58 (L7A2)

It is interesting to note how many British GPMGs re-emerged from wherever they had been stored in time for the first Gulf War. Officially they had been replaced by LSWs in British service, but whatever officialdom thought, the people who were going to be doing the fighting felt the need to bring the best weapons they could lay hands on – and in their opinion the best they had was not the LSW. However, all military procurement is an exercise in trade-offs. It may be that once the initial suspicion of anything new has worn off, the LSW concept may be found to be rather better than was originally thought.

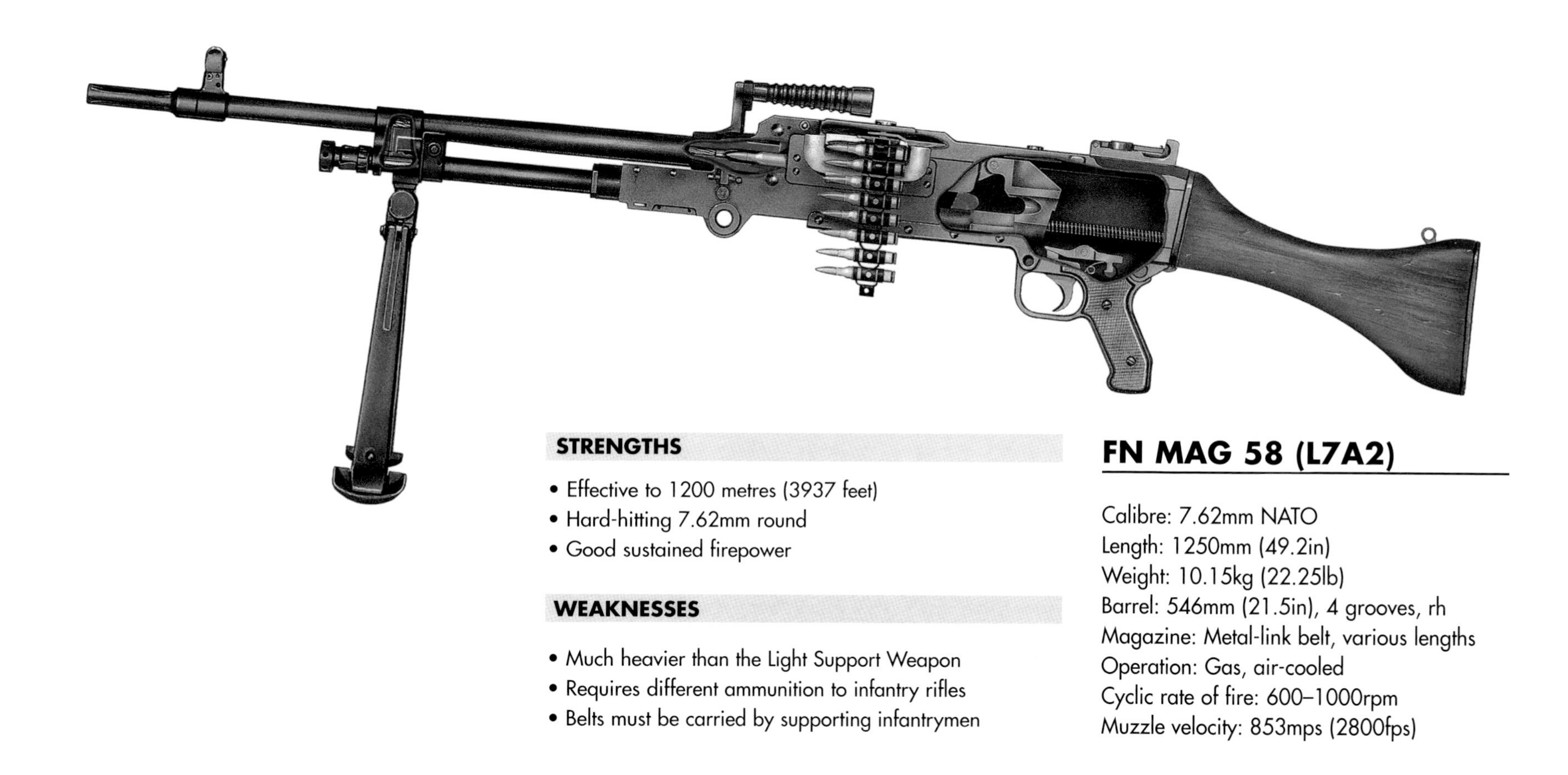

STRENGTHS

- Effective to 1200 metres (3937 feet)
- Hard-hitting 7.62mm round
- Good sustained firepower

WEAKNESSES

- Much heavier than the Light Support Weapon
- Requires different ammunition to infantry rifles
- Belts must be carried by supporting infantrymen

FN MAG 58 (L7A2)

Calibre: 7.62mm NATO
Length: 1250mm (49.2in)
Weight: 10.15kg (22.25lb)
Barrel: 546mm (21.5in), 4 grooves, rh
Magazine: Metal-link belt, various lengths
Operation: Gas, air-cooled
Cyclic rate of fire: 600–1000rpm
Muzzle velocity: 853mps (2800fps)

CETME Ameli

Calibre: 5.56mm NATO
Length: 970mm (38.19in)
Weight: 6.35kg (14lb) standard; 5.2kg (11.46lb) lightweight
Barrel: 400mm (15.75in), 6 grooves, rh
Magazine: 100- or 200-round boxed belt
Operation: Gas, air-cooled
Cyclic rate of fire: 850 or 1200rpm
Muzzle velocity: 875mps (2870fps)

Heckler & Koch HK13E

Calibre: 5.56mm NATO
Length: 1030mm (40.55in)
Weight: 8kg (17.64lb)
Barrel: 450mm (17.72in), 6 grooves, rh
Magazine: 20- or 30- round detachable box or belt feed
Operation: Roller locked delayed blowback, air-cooled
Cyclic rate of fire: 750rpm
Muzzle velocity: 925mps (3035fps)

CETME Ameli

Another very good 5.56mm-calibre GPMG is the CETME Ameli. It looks like a German MG3 but is in fact only related in that CETME engineers have in the past used German ideas such as the roller-locking blowback system developed by Heckler & Koch. This system is indeed used in the Ameli and has proven reliable even at 850 or even 1250 rounds per minute. The Ameli is chambered for NATO standard 5.56x45mm ammunition, carried either in plastic boxes or on disposable belts.

To date the Ameli has been sold to the Mexican and Spanish armed forces. Two versions are available: the basic model and a lightweight version weighing only 5.2 kilograms (11.5 pounds).

Squad Support Weapons

The General-Purpose Machine Gun is a useful addition to the infantry armoury, but there are other ways to provide fire support. One possibility is to equip some troops with a beefed-up assault rifle rather than a true machine gun. Such weapons are given various designations, among them Squad Support Weapons or Squad Automatic Weapons.

The nature of modern warfare requires ever lighter weapons, suited to close urban terrain and mechanized warfare. However, even if every member of a rifle unit has an automatic weapon available, there may still be a need for more firepower. The unit should also have a weapon with a better range and suited to more sustained fire than the usual assault rifle. Such weapons are known as Squad Support Weapons. They fall somewhere between a rifle and a light or general purpose machine gun.

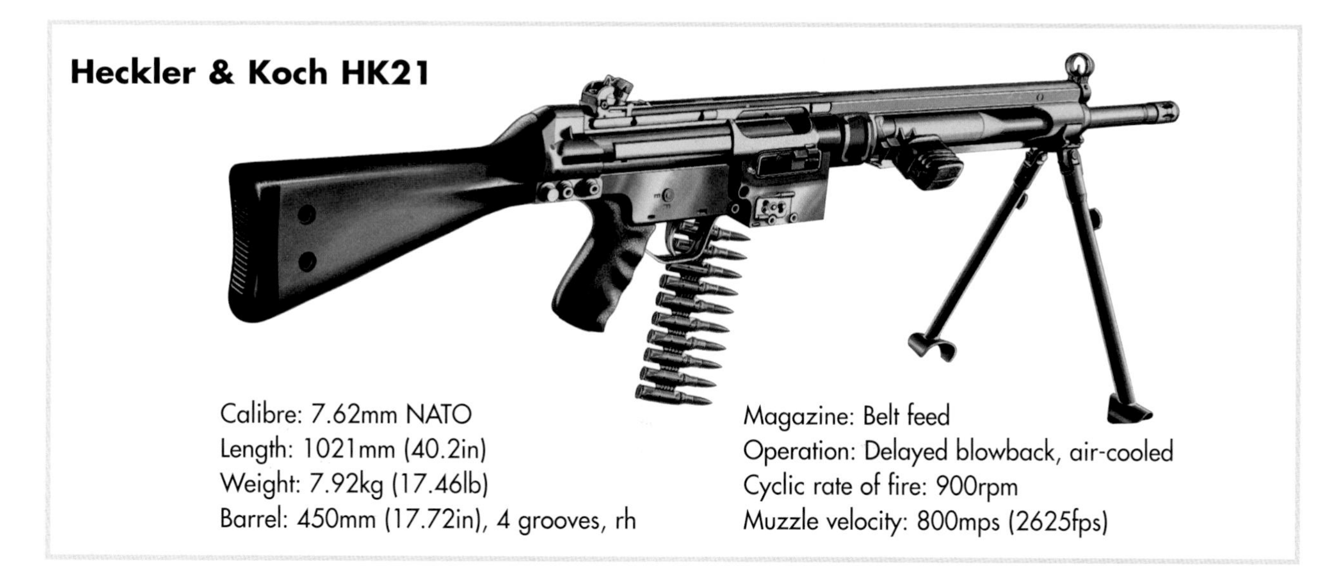

Heckler & Koch HK13E

Many squad support weapons are simply heavy barrelled versions of existing assault rifles, usually but not always adapted to use large magazines or a belt feed. One example of such a weapon is the HK13E. This weapon was based on the HK33 assault rifle and is essentially the same weapon, apart from the barrel. After trials it was found that a few modifications were necessary to convert the rifle into a good machine gun. Thus the HK13E differs from the assault rifle version in that it has a slightly longer receiver, adapted for full-automatic or three-round burst fire, and is designed for quick conversion from magazine to belt feed.

Like most such weapons, the HK13E is still little more than an overgrown rifle. With belt feed it is a useable light machine gun, but most users will have to make do with 20- or 30-round magazines, which simply do not contain enough ammunition for effective fire support.

Heckler & Koch HK21

A more recent 'rifle-turned-support weapon' from Heckler & Koch is the HK21. Derived from the G3 assault rifle, the HK21 is closer to a true light machine gun than the HK13E. Normally chambered for 7.62x51mm and belt fed, the HK21 has a bipod and, in the developed HK21E variant, a

Right: The L86A1 is the current standard British squad automatic weapon. Half rifle and half machinegun, features include a rear grip for firing from a defensive position.

foregrip for 'assault' firing. All versions of the HK21 retain the parent rifle's general level of excellence. Like the HK13 before it, the HK21 gained a longer receiver during its lifetime and is capable of burst fire as well as full automatic. Effective ranges of 2000 metres (6560 feet) and more have been claimed.

L86A1 LSW

Perhaps the epitome of the Squad Support Weapon concept is the British L86A1 Light Support Weapon. This weapon is derived from the SA80 assault rifle, with which it shares many components. The Light Support Weapon (LSW) has a longer, heavier barrel with a bipod, a rear grip and a different bolt arrangement. Accuracy is good, using the same SUSAT optical sight as the SA80. It is even possible to use the L86A1 as a sniper weapon. Nonetheless, the L86A1 is not a very good machine gun. Its 30-round magazine can be emptied very quickly at 700 rounds per minute and there is no quick barrel-change facility, so firing must be carefully controlled to avoid overheating. Calibre is 5.56mm rather than the more powerful 7.62mm round that every self-respecting machine gunner wants to fire.

This weapon is not a machine gun, however, and was never meant to be one. It is a 'Light Support Weapon' with a little more range and firepower than an assault rifle, yet retaining many of that weapon's advantages, such as lightness. The LSW concept has the backing of British Army planners, who feel it is adequate for the sort of conflicts a modern force will face. Time will tell whether this assumption is correct, although it is interesting to note how many 7.62mm L7A2 GPMGs emerged from dark corners when British forces were deployed to fight in the Gulf.

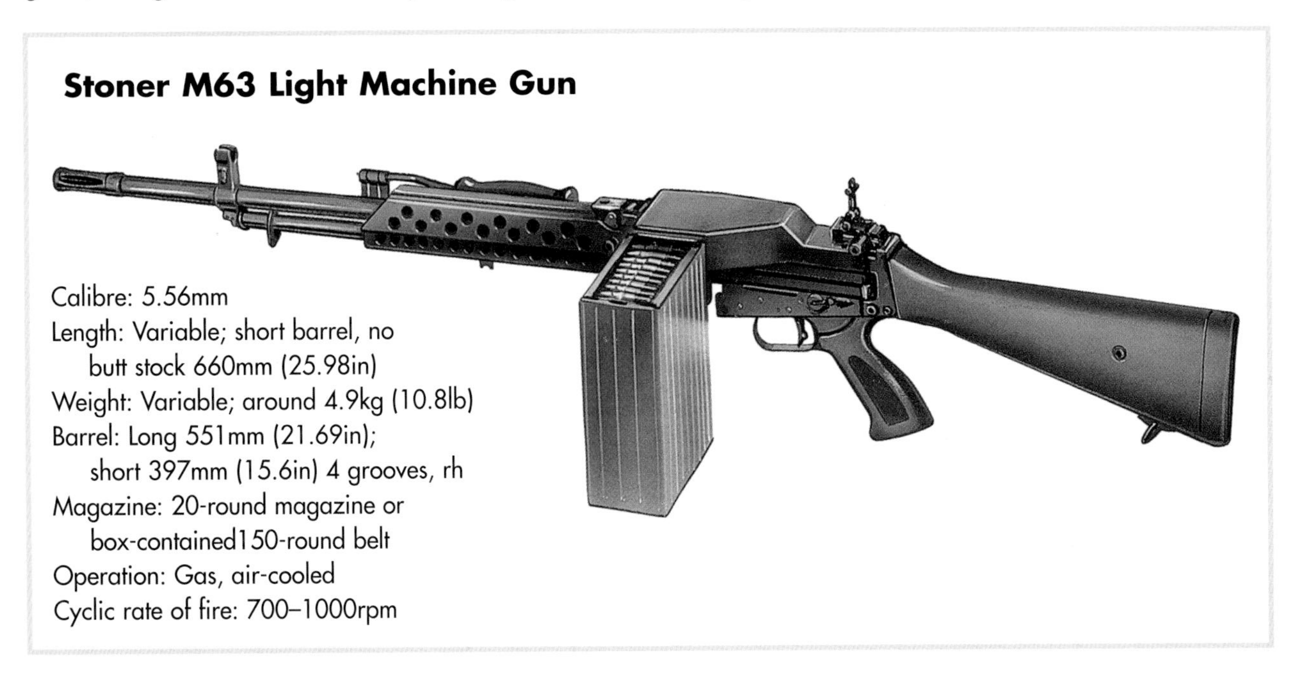

Stoner M63 Light Machine Gun

Calibre: 5.56mm
Length: Variable; short barrel, no butt stock 660mm (25.98in)
Weight: Variable; around 4.9kg (10.8lb)
Barrel: Long 551mm (21.69in); short 397mm (15.6in) 4 grooves, rh
Magazine: 20-round magazine or box-contained150-round belt
Operation: Gas, air-cooled
Cyclic rate of fire: 700–1000rpm

The future of the machine gun

Automatic support weapons are a vital feature of modern armed combat. Even though modern assault rifles afford the infantryman an impressive capability, there will always be a need for more sustained firepower. Concepts like Light Support Weapons are interesting and offer some new possibilities, but these weapons simply do not do the job of a good machine gun.

At the squad level, weapons such as the Minimi are likely to dominate in the near future. Using lighter calibres than the traditional GPMG, they allow the squad to carry more ammunition, which may be important in a protracted firefight. Such weapons need a reasonable range but must also be compatible with the trend towards light, handy personal weapons. Thus they cannot be too big.

It is possible that eventually some kind of combination machine gun/grenade launcher weapon will become available for squad-level support: the OCIW project hopes to create a combination rifle/support weapon, so a heavier 'support' version is entirely possible. Such a weapon, however, is more likely to take the form of a single-barrelled weapon in 15–20mm calibre, capable of firing small grenades or higher velocity discarding-sabot rounds, perhaps with several loaded into a single shell.

Such ideas are somewhat speculative, based on earlier experiments with rifles. In the meantime, soldiers will continue to rely on advanced light or general purpose machine guns to deliver the fire support they need.

Survival of the heavy machine gun

Heavier machine guns will also likely remain a feature of the battlefield. While the mid-calibre (e.g. 7.62mm) weapons may disappear in favour of 5.56mm and similar light rounds, heavy machine guns need a heavy round if they are to engage vehicles, aircraft and installations as well as infantry. For this reason, the bigger calibres are likely to remain in service for many years to come. Observers have forecast the demise of the .50 calibre at the hands of 20–30mm autocannon, but this is unlikely – the .50 is simply too good a compromise between anti-personnel and 'heavy' weaponry.

It is possible that a replacement for the .50 calibre machine gun may emerge using smaller calibre advanced ammunition, for example in a long 9mm or 10mm, but again this is not too likely. At long ranges bullets are heavily affected by wind: the heavier a round, the less it will deviate. High-velocity 10mm machine guns might hit as hard as or harder than a .50, but at the sort of ranges at which they will be used in preference to 5.56mm weapons their performance may be wayward due to atmospheric conditions. Besides, the vast stocks of ammunition available worldwide for the existing calibres means that a replacement would have to offer very significant advantages before it would be taken up by any military force with a budget to meet.

It seems likely that future machine guns will be chambered in the same calibres as existing ones and will be based on the same tested principles. New manufacturing processes and materials, however, will allow the creation of some interesting variations on the theme. Modular weapons based on the same receiver but using different parts to build a machine gun, rifle or carbine have already been tried with some success. Such systems are likely to be attractive to users seeking to replace a rifle and a support weapon at the same time, or any buyers wishing to reduce their maintenance costs into the future.

Left: The Stoner modular weapon system was a clever idea that never really caught on. It did see some service in the hands of elite units such as the US Navy SEALs during the Vietnam War. Perhaps the modular concept is one that will see further development in the future.

Stoner M63

An example of such a system was developed in the 1960s by the legendary Eugene Stoner. Using a basic receiver it was possible to fit different barrels, stocks and magazines to create a rifle, carbine, light machine gun or GPMG. This weapon, designated M63, did not achieve widespread success despite promising results in Vietnam. Although few other designers have shown an interest in modular weapons, the Stoner system has been picked up by various manufacturers, however, and has seen limited production intermittently over the past four decades.

Chambered for 5.56x45mm, the Stoner machine gun can be configured as a GPMG with or without a bipod or as a tripod-mounted version. Feed devices can be 20-round magazines, belt feed or a boxed belt. All versions of the Stoner machine gun are capable of between 700 and 1000 rounds per minute and are effective out to 1000 metres (3280 feet). It is a very useful weapon in any configuration. It may be that a modernized version of the Stoner concept will achieve market success and pave the way for a new generation of modularized weapon systems.

SHOTGUNS

Smoothbore weapons such as shotguns may lack range, but they have more than proved their worth as security, close-assault and anti-ambush combat weapons. The ability of smoothbore firearms to fire a range of ammunition types, from buckshot to tear gas canisters, makes them a popular choice for many different applications.

Early firearms, such as muskets, had a smooth bore. That is to say, no rifling grooves were cut into the inside of the barrel. Rifling makes a bullet spin, which stabilizes it in flight and improves accuracy. It is only useful in weapons where the projectile is large enough to 'grip' the rifling, so where multiple small projectiles are fired rifling is of no consequence. Indeed, it can play strange tricks with shot dispersal.

During the US Civil War, rifled cannon were available, which had a long range and impressive accuracy compared to the smoothbore 'Napoleons'. However, when firing canister (a multiple-projectile round rather like a giant shotgun shell) at short range, the Napoleons were considered superior since rifled cannon threw shot in strange spiral patterns rather than a predictable cone.

Left: Security forces armed with pump-action shotguns patrol Caracas during election disturbances in 2002. Shotguns are more likely to wound than kill at moderate to long range, making them preferable in riot-control situations.

Thus if multiple projectiles are to be fired, a smooth bore is in fact desirable. Large projectiles can still be used. Solid ball or solid slug shotgun ammunition does impressive damage, and at close range accuracy is not really a factor. Early muskets could easily double as shotguns; indeed, buck-and-ball ammunition, consisting of a large projectile and a few smaller ones, proved effective in close-range engagements during the US Civil War. Any black-powder smoothbore weapon could be loaded with nails, scrap metal or regular lead shot, for use in this role.

Shot dispersal

Modern shotguns use prepackaged all-in-one cartridges, of course, and cannot simply be loaded with whatever comes to hand. The projectile in the cartridge, however, can be almost anything: a single lead slug or ball, several large balls ('buckshot'), many small balls ('birdshot'), or something else entirely, such as rock salt or special projectiles like miniature tear gas grenades.

Other than when firing special-purpose ammunition, shotguns are intended to fire a conical spread of small projectiles. This increases the chance of a hit and offers some other advantages. Small projectiles come to rest quickly when they hit something. If this is a human or animal, large amounts of kinetic energy are dumped into the target causing knockdown and shock – vital when stopping an onrushing attacker. If the shot hits a wall it is not likely to penetrate and will lose much of its energy as it ricochets, reducing the risk to bystanders.

Deterrence and impact

Shotguns are popular for home security for this reason. The homeowner, perhaps confronting an intruder in the dark, has in his hand a forceful deterrent that, if fired, will quickly disable the attacker, yet pose no threat to a young child sleeping in the next room. In addition, interviews with criminals have shown that the noise of a pump-action shotgun slide is one of the most

Left: Shotguns are well-suited to a maritime role. On-board security personnel need to be able to fire quickly and with devastating effect, ideally without damaging the ship.

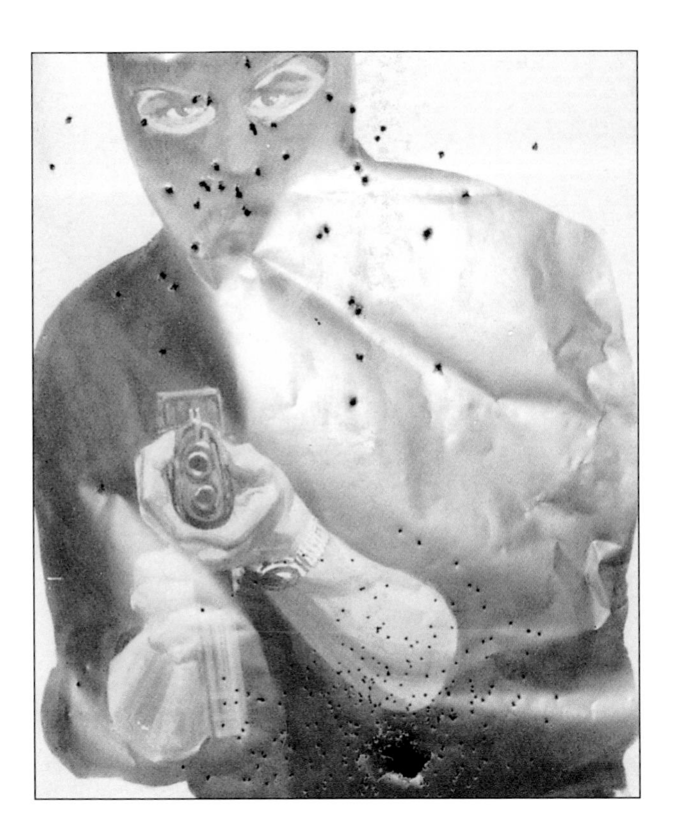

Right: The spread of shot from a shotgun is not only more likely to hit a target at close range, but actually has greater stopping power than a bullet due to the multiple impact of the pellets. The upper part of this target shows a typical pellet spread from a range of around 45 metres (150 feet). The lower part of the target shows the effect of a single heavy shotgun slug.

intimidating sounds in the world – most attackers would rather flee than face a 12-gauge in the hands of a determined individual. In addition, shotguns are generally robust devices that can be used to good effect at close quarters.

Shotguns have never been popular for 'battlefield' use since they lack range. Even at very moderate ranges the effectiveness of a shotgun drops off quickly as pellets disperse and are slowed by air resistance. Military shotguns, however, are becoming a possibility for the close-combat role.

Overall, though, the shotgun is a short-range security weapon. Police officers and military security forces make extensive use of smoothbore weapons, often in quite novel ways. For example, aboard a naval ship a shotgun-armed security rating or marine can fire his weapon into the deck, causing pellets to ricochet into the legs of a suspect individual. This is likely to be temporarily disabling with little risk of lethal injury – an important consideration in some circumstances.

Shotguns are especially useful aboard ships as they are not likely to puncture bulkheads or damage important features such as wiring conduits. Similar comments apply to homeowners and anyone needing a weapon for use in cities. They can also be useful to hunters and those needing to dispose of small vermin.

Gauges and loading

Most shotguns are rated in 'gauges' or 'bores'. This is a rather archaic practice derived from the rating system of smoothbore cannon. Cannon were rated in pounds. For example, if an iron ball the same diameter as the bore of a cannon would weigh 12 pounds (5.4kg), that weapon was designated a 12-pounder. Shotguns use a similar system based on fractions of a pound. If a ball the size of the bore of a given shotgun would weigh one-twelfth of a pound (37.8 grams), that shotgun is rated as a 12-bore, or 12-gauge. Common shotgun gauges are 10, 12, 16, 18 and 20, with the 12-gauge being standard for security work.

Shot spread

Spread of shot is important with a shotgun. If the shot is too concentrated, the area-effect benefit of the weapon is lost and it becomes an inferior rifle. On the other hand, if shot spreads out too widely the weapon's effective range is greatly reduced – one pellet will cause a wound but most shotguns rely on the impact from multiple pellets to deal with the target. In order to disperse projectiles in the desired manner, shotguns have a restriction known as the 'choke' at the mouth of the barrel. Some weapons have a variable choke to allow shot spread to be optimized to certain ranges.

Many civilian weapons have an ovoid rather than circular bore, which also affects shot spread. This has the incidental effect of preventing the weapon from using military ammunition, which is circular rather than ovoid. Many sporting guns (and the sawn-off versions created from them) have either a single barrel or twin barrels arranged either side by side or one atop the other, each with its own firing mechanism. Reloading is accomplished by 'breaking' open the gun (normally the barrels tip downward on a hinge), manually extracting the spent cartridges and inserting new ones before closing the weapon. This is a slow process, which is not a problem when shooting vermin or fowl but rather more serious when in combat.

For the shotgun to become a serious combat weapon, a repeating version was necessary. The advent of cartridge firearms made this possible.

Coach guns to 'Trench Brooms'

As already noted, smoothbore flintlock shotguns were common from the invention of black-powder weapons. Some had a deliberately flared muzzle. This was not to spread shot but to make loading easier; loose shot or whatever else was to hand could be quickly loaded into such a weapon, known as a blunderbuss. Blunderbusses were popular with coachmen. Kept near the driver's seat, they made an excellent deterrent to highwaymen, not all of whom lived by the romantic 'money or your life' ideal. Another weapon popular with coachmen was the 'coach gun' or 'coach pistol'. This was essentially a flintlock double-barrelled shotgun

Right: Camouflaged by a cloud of dense green smoke, a US Navy SEAL takes part in special operations with the Small Boat Unit (SBU) in Panama, 1994. His Remington pump-action shotgun provides excellent close-range suppressive fire in case of ambush.

with very short barrels – equivalent to the sawn-off shotgun of today. Coach pistols lacked range but were deadly. While they were not as portable as true pistols, they could be highly effective in close combat. Similar weapons are still in use today.

Repeating shotguns

Cartridge-fed shotguns emerged at the same time as other weapons, and by the 1880s pump-action repeating shotguns were available. Such weapons had major advantages over single- or double-barrelled weapons. With only one or two rounds available and combat going on at very short range, the shotgun-armed combatant was at a severe disadvantage compared with someone armed with, for example, a revolver.

Early pump- (or slide-) action shotguns were not very different from those in use today. A tubular magazine under the barrel held several rounds (often six), which were chambered by sliding the foregrip to work the action. Lever-action shotguns, which used movement of the trigger guard in much the same manner as the Sharps carbine to chamber rounds, were also developed but never achieved the popularity of the pump.

Pump-action shotguns were found to be very useful in the trenches of World War I, where knockdown power was vital in a close-range action. The mechanical pump-action was tolerant of dirty conditions and in the case of a misfire a new round could be chambered by working the action again. With six rounds available, the shotgun-armed combatant outgunned an opponent with a revolver.

Sawn-off shotguns

Sawing most of the barrel off a shotgun reduces its effective range to just a few metres. Such weapons are not suited to combat except at the closest of quarters but make an excellent deterrent or threat. Sawn-off shotguns are illegal in most regions.

A British man was recently convicted of possessing an illegal weapon after stuffing a sawn-off shotgun down his trousers, intending to use it to intimidate a friend. Instead he accidentally discharged the weapon, inflicting serious and rather personal injury.

Winchester Model 12

A typical example of the sort of weapons used in these desperate muddy scrambles is the Winchester Model 1917 'Trench Gun'. With its seven-round magazine and reliable pump action, the Winchester was popular with troops who were required to bet their lives on their weapon's ability to hit and disable enemy soldiers. The Trench Gun was somewhat heavy and within a few years of the end of the war was replaced in service by a developed version, the Winchester Model 12. Like its predecessor, the Model 12 had a bayonet lug, although this was rarely used. The Model 12 was in service throughout World War II and was retained in US Marine Corps use until the 1960s.

Some shotguns (and other weapons too, such as early SMGs) used in the Great War became known as 'Trench Brooms', since they would 'sweep the trenches clear of the enemy'. To assist in this task, 'slam-fire' capability was built into some pump-action weapons. Essentially, the weapon would fire as soon as a round was chambered if the trigger was

Left: US troops in Vietnam. The soldier in the foreground is armed with a Remington M870 shotgun, allowing him to put down heavy short-range firepower into the jungle if necessary.

Right: When dealing with an urban hostage situation such as this siege in Tennessee, the safety of innocent bystanders – and sometimes even small dogs – is paramount. Shotguns will down the target instantly but will not send a bullet through a wall to endanger people on the other side.

held. Rapidly working the pump allowed the user to blast a great deal of buckshot into the target area in a short period. However, slam-fire capability weakens the mechanism and can cause malfunctions. This capability gradually went out of favour.

Remington M870

Modern versions of these early pump-action shotguns are not very different from their predecessors. One modern classic is the Remington M870. A 12-gauge pump-action weapon fed from a seven-round tubular magazine under the barrel, the Remington has gained popularity as a sporting and hunting weapon and as a 'riot gun' used by law enforcers. It is also in use with the US Navy and Marine Corps, who adopted it as a replacement for the venerable Model 12 'Trench Gun', as a shipboard security and boarding-party weapon.

Available with a folding metal stock (as the 'P' variant) and in various length and magazine configurations, the Remington is clearly a 'combat' shotgun. Its pistol grip makes it easy to use at close range and the impact of heavy buckshot at that distance is enough to stop the most determined attacker. The price has been pushed up by the weapon's popularity as a civilian security weapon, but it remains one of the most popular shotguns ever manufactured. More than four million of the weapons have been sold.

One very unusual variant of the Remington is a cut-down version designed to attach to the underside of an assault rifle, creating a combination weapon with two triggers. It can be used like a small grenade launcher to fire gas and other special rounds, while retaining the rifle's firepower for when necessary. Alternatively, such a weapon affords the user a lethal/non-lethal option, carrying birdshot, baton rounds or beanbags in the shotgun, and thus offering the rifleman a flexible response to a range of threats.

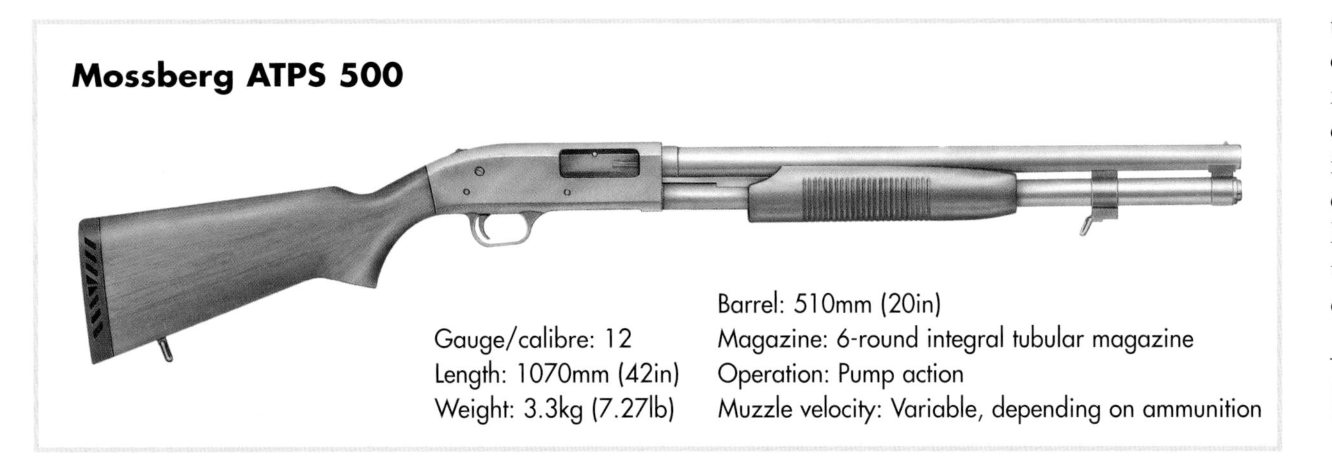

Gauge/calibre: 12
Length: 1070mm (42in)
Weight: 3.3kg (7.27lb)
Barrel: 510mm (20in)
Magazine: 6-round integral tubular magazine
Operation: Pump action
Muzzle velocity: Variable, depending on ammunition

Mossberg ATPS 500

Another conventional shotgun, Mossberg's ATPS 500, is also available in civilian, security and military variants, all of which are basically the same well-made weapon with different features. With six 12-gauge rounds available in the tubular magazine, the 500 has convincing firepower.

Unlike most shotguns, the ATPS 500 was designed with military use in mind. It has a bayonet mounting and can carry a telescopic sight for use when firing solid ammunition, although being a smoothbore weapon its accuracy is still limited.

Ithaca Model 37 M and P

Ithaca is famous for its shotguns, mainly but not exclusively in a military context. Most weapons are specifically designed for law enforcement and military markets, where they have been very popular since the 1940s. The Ithaca Model 37 M and P (which stands for Military and Police) is available with a 470mm (18.5-inch) barrel and a five-round internal magazine or a 508mm (20-inch) barrel with an eight-round capacity.

An excellent close-range weapon, the 37 M and P was the basis for the Model LAPD, a gun developed to meet the needs of law enforcement agencies and capable of firing heavy solid ammunition.

Other Ithaca models include the Deerslayer, Roadblocker and the Stakeout. All are variants on the standard combat shotgun with various configurations of barrel, stock (or no stock) and magazine. The Stakeout is interesting in that it is designed for concealability. With a short barrel and four-round magazine, and no stock, the Stakeout is deadly at close range, though its recoil is very heavy. Many Ithaca weapons have a circular bore rather than an ovoid one to allow the use of military cartridges that are not available for civilian weapons.

Beretta RS 202P

Beretta manufactures the RS 202P shotgun, a pump-action weapon fed from a six-round internal magazine. This weapon certainly looks the part, with a folding stock and perforated barrel shroud, but does not actually differ much from civilian models. It can, however, deliver a range of ammunition types and features a variable choke as well as a shot expander, allowing the fire pattern to be optimized to the user's needs.

These weapons are all conventional pump-action shotguns and do their job well. For combat

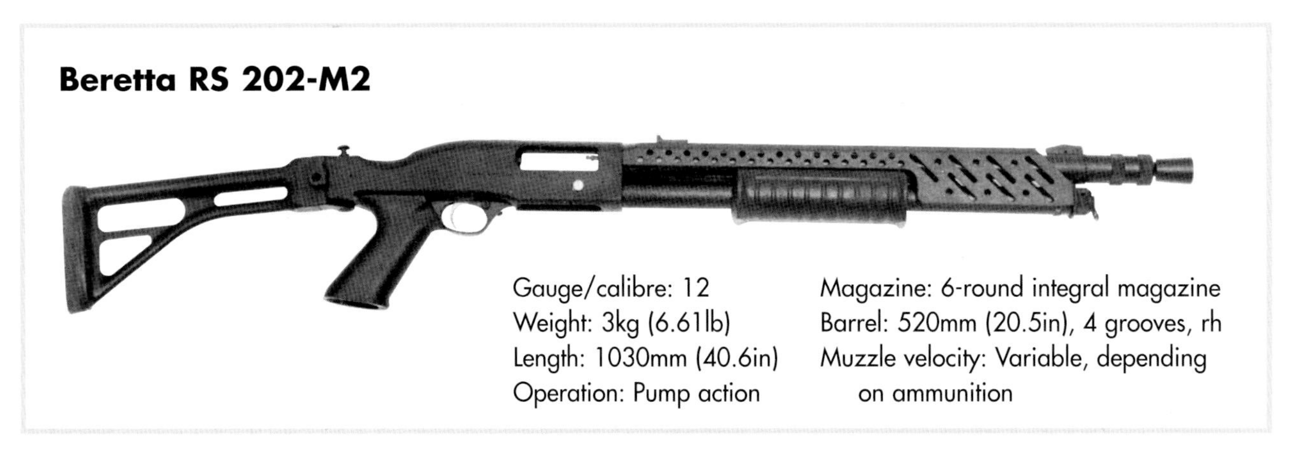

Gauge/calibre: 12
Weight: 3kg (6.61lb)
Length: 1030mm (40.6in)
Operation: Pump action
Magazine: 6-round integral magazine
Barrel: 520mm (20.5in), 4 grooves, rh
Muzzle velocity: Variable, depending on ammunition

applications, however, a number of specialist weapons are available that, while not purely military weapons, are beyond the typical civilian's needs.

Advanced combat shotguns

The pump-action shotgun is a mechanical repeater, requiring the user to work the action in order to chamber a new round. This causes a significant delay between shots, so effective self-loading shotguns would offer the user a significant advantage. One problem with developing such weapons is that the mechanism needs to be very strong to resist the forces generated by powerful cartridges and to move heavy cartridges into the breech. Semi-automatic shotguns have for long been regarded with suspicion, since early models proved unreliable. Technological improvements, however, have resulted in ranges of reliable, effective self-loading shotguns that are now available to those expecting to engage in close combat.

Ithaca Model 37

Gauge/calibre: 12
Length: 1016mm (40in) for 508mm (20in) barrel
Weight: 2.94kg (6.48lb) or 3.06kg (6.75lb)
Barrel: 470mm (18.5in) or 508mm (20in)
Magazine: 5- or 8-round integral tubular magazine
Operation: Pump action
Muzzle velocity: Variable, depending on ammunition

Innovations

The Ithaca Model 37 shotgun incorporates an unusual feature – it loads and ejects cartridges through a port on the underside of the gun. This protects the mechanism from fouling by dirt and other environmental factors and makes the weapon easier for left-handers to use.

Franchi SPAS 12

Perhaps the best-known of the advanced combat shotguns, and one of the most fearsome-looking weapons ever made, the Franchi SPAS 12 shotgun has been around since 1979. It can operate in semi-automatic or pump-action mode, and has a cut-off for the seven-round internal magazine, allowing a single round of special ammunition to be loaded into the breech manually instead of feeding from the magazine.

The Franchi has a shot spread of around 900mm (35.4 inches) at a 40-metre (131-feet) range, reducing the need for precise aiming. For indoor use there is also an optional attachment which provides a much greater close-range spread. A special grenade launcher attachment for the muzzle allows firing of grenades to 150 metres (492 feet). The folding stock has an elbow hook to enable one-handed firing. This, however, requires a strong user: the Franchi SPAS 12 is not the lightest of weapons and no 12-gauge shotgun is known for the mildness of its recoil.

High Standard M10A

Despite the general rule, some combat shotguns are obviously very different to their civilian counterparts. One such weapon is the High Standard M10A, which employs the Bullpup configuration. Among its interesting features is a flashlight built into the body of the weapon, above the barrel, and behind which is a carrying handle. The shoulder stock can be turned sideways to allow for one-handed shooting, and the overall short length of the weapon makes it very handy, even though magazine capacity is only five rounds. The M10A has never achieved widespread fame despite its interesting qualities.

Mossberg Model 500 Bullpup 12

Another Bullpup-configured shotgun, the Mossberg Model 500 Bullpup 12 is essentially a Model 500 shotgun reorganized into a package of impressive appearance, with a carrying handle on top and an assault foregrip. Like its more conventional sibling, the Bullpup 12 has a bayonet fitting and either a six- or eight-round magazine. It has been taken up by police and military forces in the US and overseas.

SECURITY SHOTGUNS: REMINGTON M870 VERSUS

Shotguns are excellent security weapons and have been used by civilian and military personnel in this role for many years. The combination of stopping power and low penetration is attractive to those who might have to shoot in proximity to hard surfaces that could pose a serious threat of ricochets, or might put at risk people on the other side of nearby walls. For many years the standard security shotgun was a tough, reliable pump-action weapon little different to those of 50 years before. It did the job adequately but it was not ideal for combat applications, where the delay in chambering a new round could be fatal.

STRENGTHS

- Ultra-reliable pump action
- 40 years of successful service
- Lighter than the SPAS 12

WEAKNESSES

- Slow to reload
- No magazine cut-off
- Little room for future improvement

Remington M870

Gauge/calibre: 12
Length: 1060mm (41.73in)
Weight: 3.6kg (7.94lb)
Barrel: 533mm (21in)
Magazine: 7-round integral tubular magazine
Operation: Pump action
Muzzle velocity: Variable, depending on ammunition

FRANCHI SPAS 12

Weapons like the SPAS 12 represent a new generation of semi-automatic shotguns designed for close-combat applications. There is still some doubt as to the reliability of self-loading shotguns, although weapons like the SPAS 12 are serving to dispel such qualms. The SPAS 12 is capable of rapid fire, although it has the same seven rounds available as the Remington. On the other hand, those who might have to shoot or die still place great faith in the simple, tried-and-tested, almost indestructible pump-action. The Remington M870 is a classic example of this type with many years of police and military service behind it.

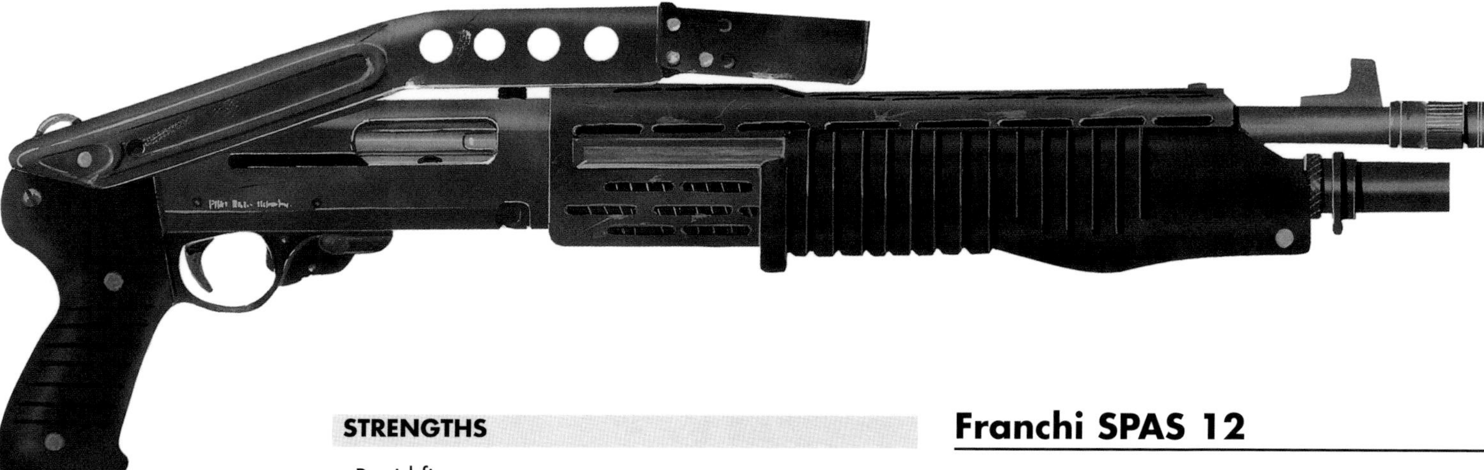

STRENGTHS

- Rapid fire
- Magazine cut-off allows special ammunition to be used
- Special stock allows one-handed use

WEAKNESSES

- Semi-automatic shotguns can be unreliable
- Complex mechanism
- More expensive than conventional shotguns

Franchi SPAS 12

Gauge/calibre: 12
Length: 930mm (36.6in) stock extended;
710mm (27.95in) stock folded
Weight: 4.2kg (9.26lb)
Barrel: 460mm (18.11in)
Magazine: 7-round integral tubular magazine
Operation: Pump action and gas
Muzzle velocity: Variable, depending on ammunition

Gauge/calibre: 12
Length: 780mm (30.7in) stock extended; 500mm (19.68in) stock folded
Weight: 4.2kg (9.26lb)
Barrel: 304mm (12in) or 457mm (18in)
Magazine: 12-round rotary magazine
Operation: Double action trigger pull

Left: This South African Striker looks clumsy and can be slow to load, but it offers massive firepower when it counts. The revolving-drum shotgun is in use with law enforcement agencies worldwide, allowing a versatile and decisive response to a serious situation.

Striker

The Striker, first developed in South Africa, is of unique appearance. It consists of a carbine-type receiver with a folding stock and two pistol-type grips, fed by a 12-round drum magazine situated just in front of the trigger assembly.

The Striker is bulky but not especially heavy, and its balance and layout are good, making for a very usable weapon. It is robust, simple and, unusually for a self-loader, fires using a double-action trigger pull. Several law enforcement agencies worldwide have adopted it for special response situations.

H&K/Benelli M1014

Less revolutionary in design, the Heckler & Koch/Benelli M1014 shotgun was developed in response to a US military requirement for a weapon to replace the various shotguns in service with the Marine Corps. The Marines have always liked shotguns for shipboard security, jungle warfare and close-quarters battle, and decided that their next weapon would be a semi-automatic.

The weapon selected by the XM1014 project was the Benelli Super 90, which had already won approval from law enforcement and hostage rescue forces. Put into production by Heckler & Koch as the M1014, the first batch was delivered in 2001.

Unusually for the product of a selection committee, perhaps, the M1014 is remarkably free of bells and whistles. It has a seven-round tubular magazine, is chambered in 70mm 12-gauge and shoots a single round when the trigger is pulled before auto-loading the next. The only unusual features are the sliding stock, which makes it easier to use the weapon in tight spaces, and the capability to mount a range of sights.

The M1014's gas-operated, semi-automatic system is extremely reliable and reputedly immune to fouling. It is driven by two rods, positioned either side of the bolt carrier, which push it back as they themselves are driven back by gas pressure drawn from ports in the barrel. This is an improvement on the standard Super 90 recoil-operated system, which sometimes fails to feed when a heavy accessory, such as a night vision

Right: Although virtually useless on the open battlefield, the shotgun can be highly effective in close-quarters urban or jungle firefights. Many British patrols in Malaya and US patrols in Vietnam included a man or two armed with a shotgun rather than a regular assault rifle.

device, is fitted to the weapon. The M1014 represents everything a combat shotgun should be – efficient, reliable and easy to use, yet able to respond decisively to any threat.

Military applications

One military use for semi-automatic shotguns is for responding to an ambush in close terrain such as jungle. A soldier armed with a self-loading shotgun can sweep an area very quickly and may hit partially exposed or concealed ambushers without even seeing them. The noise and disturbance of buckshot crashing through branches or striking a wall behind which an ambusher might be hiding can have a useful suppressive effect, while even a single pellet can cause a 'flinch' reaction that will gain time for the ambushed patrol to respond more effectively.

Assault shotguns

Generally speaking, although combat shotguns have some military applications they are more suited to law enforcement and security work than battlefield conditions. True military or 'assault' shotguns, however, are now emerging.

Assault shotguns are naturally more limited in range than assault rifles, but can hit their targets further out than the usual 100 metres (328 feet) maximum assumed for conventional shotguns. For the close assault role, a weapon firing heavy charges of flechette or buckshot, perhaps on full-automatic, is without doubt a fearsome weapon. Overcoming the engineering challenges posed by such weapons has resulted in some innovative designs appearing in the last few years. Some of these innovations were derived from the RHINO (Repeating Hand-held Improved Non-rifled Ordnance) project implemented in the United States in 1979. Others have appeared as by-products of other projects or natural progression from existing concepts.

Shotgun customization

Different configurations of stock and magazine capacity are available as standard on many modern shotguns. Some users like to customize their weapons further with various add-ons. A 10-round magazine extension is available, for example, that will fit many combat shotguns, offering extra firepower at the cost of increased weight and bulk.

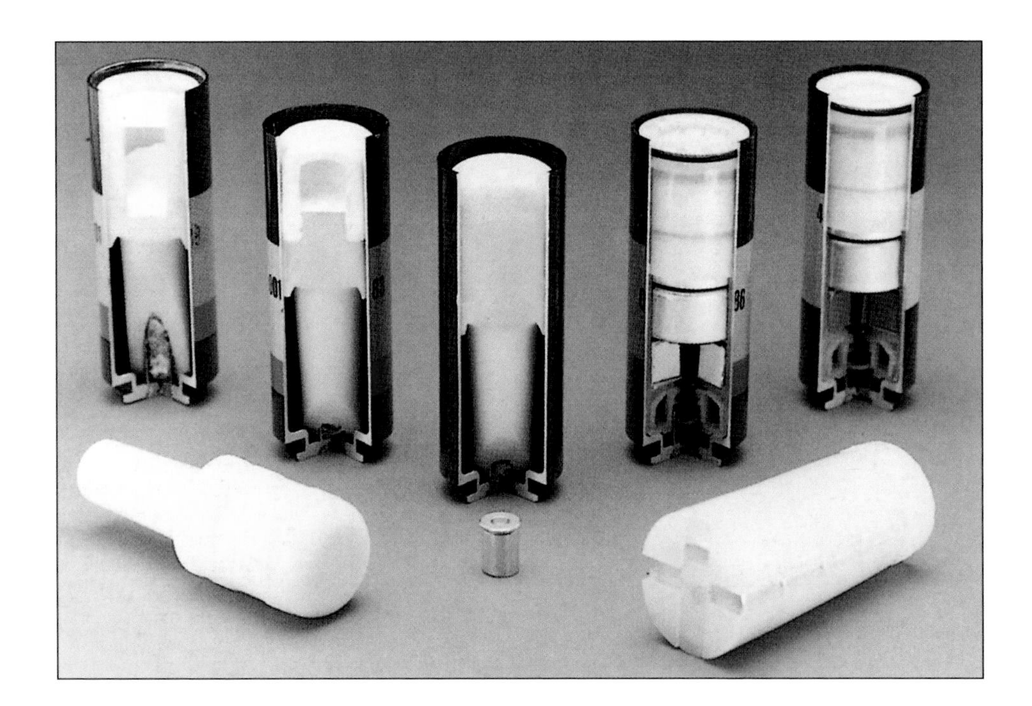

Left: The range of 'non-lethal' riot-control shotgun ammunition includes these plastic baton rounds, which are designed to hurt and stun targets rather than wound or kill. They can be lethal on occasion, but by accident rather than by design.

Right: Three different types of shotgun ammunition. The cartridges contain, from left to right, birdshot, flechette round and a Brenneke rifled slug.

Ammunition for special applications

One big advantage of shotguns is their ability to fire different ammunition for various circumstances. Weapons like rifles and handguns are essentially limited to firing a single bullet and while some specialist ammunition is available, such as 'wadcutters' for target shooting, hollow-point rounds or low-velocity ammunition for aircraft security, the choices are fairly limited. Shotguns, however, can fire a range of ammunition types. These come packaged into a cartridge of common dimensions, which can be used in any appropriate weapon.

The standard modern shotgun round, or 'shotshell', is a plastic casing that contains the propellant and whatever projectile or projectiles are to be used. Behind this is a brass base that contains the primer. The base is rimmed to create a gas seal in the breech. The projectile load is normally either a few (9–12) lead spheres (buckshot) or a larger number of small spheres (birdshot).

In a 12-gauge shotgun (the standard for combat applications), buckshot tends to be about 7.5mm (0.29in) in diameter. Larger weapons can use more shot or heavier shot, smaller ones use lighter projectiles. Buckshot is the standard combat loading and causes several powerful impacts at the same time, greatly enhancing knockdown power for hunting large animals or stopping human attackers.

Solid projectiles lack the range and accuracy of rifle rounds but are effective to 50 metres (164 feet) or more. A 12-gauge solid slug can punch through a wooden railway sleeper; even if the target wears body armour and the ball does not penetrate (the penetrative characteristics of an 18mm sphere are not impressive), the impact alone is enough to knock down and disable most people. Some slugs are rifled to impart a stabilizing spin, increasing effective range out to about 200 metres (656 feet).

Solid ball or solid slug ammunition is powerful enough, but it is also possible to launch explosive rounds, tungsten penetrator slugs and specialist rounds designed to blow doors off their hinges. Many such rounds need a pump-action weapon, since they do not generate enough gas pressure or recoil to operate a semi-automatic shotgun.

Non-lethal ammunition

Shotguns can also be used in a non-lethal manner. One method is the 'beanbag' round, which resembles a golf ball filled with lead shot. Beanbags hit hard but distribute their force over a wider area

Right: Police use shotguns to fire CS gas and rubber bullets to quell violent clashes between militant supporters of the Venezuelan President Hugo Chavez and opposition protestors in Caracas in 2002.

than normal, resulting in the target being stunned, winded and bruised rather than killed. Beanbag rounds can kill by accident, of course, but they are considered as non-lethal weapons since fatalities are rare and unintentional.

Non-lethal projectiles also include lightweight birdshot, salt and plastic 'batons' with similar characteristics to the beanbag round. All such loads can cause serious injury or even death, but are much less likely to kill than a load of 00 Buckshot delivered at close range.

CS-gas grenades

Another non-lethal but effective shotgun round is the CS-gas grenade. CS is better known as tear gas, and can be delivered through a door or other light obstacle by a shotgun round. Shotgun-fired grenades are by definition rather small and not very useful in battlefield conditions, but for rescuing hostages in confined spaces they are excellent.

Other shotgun-fired grenades include incendiary rounds for setting fire to a target and illuminating or signalling flares. These have no civilian applications but are sometimes used by military forces. A shotgun-launched air-bursting noisemaker round is also under development. The idea behind this round is to create a shock effect that will startle and alarm the target without any danger of lethality. Having gained the target's full attention – since the next shot may well be a lethal load – there should be no difficulty in securing an arrest or dispersing a crowd. In today's increasingly litigious society, non-lethal responses and the ability to show clearly that 'fair warning' was given may be important to security personnel and those who employ them.

New types of shotgun ammunition have recently been developed. Experiments have been conducted with plastic flechette, in the place of lead balls, and new cartridges have been created that will not fit in standard civilian and law-enforcement weapons. The standard 12-gauge shotshell is 70mm (2.75in) long. Some military shotgun rounds are 76mm (3mm) long and consequently much more powerful. These new military smoothbore weapons are just beginning to carve out a market niche for themselves.

Military shotguns

Military thinkers were impressed with the ability of the semi-automatic shotgun to sweep an area with fire. As far back as the 1950s, a report commissioned by the British army in Malaya had concluded that shotguns provided a more effective patrol weapon than the light machine gun. But until the 1970s there were no true military shotguns, only security weapons with military applications.

If an effective semi-automatic shotgun could be fielded, then a full-automatic version was surely also possible. This intriguing idea was pursued by a number of designers, resulting in some devastating close assault weapons.

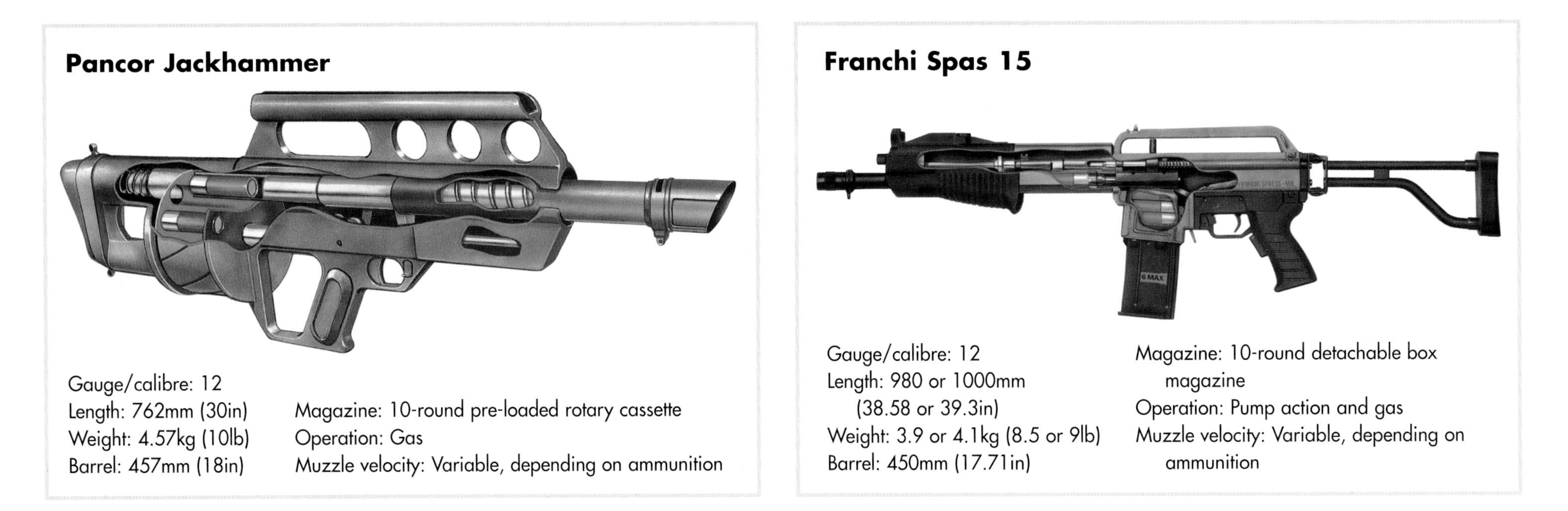

Atchisson Assault Shotgun (USAS)

Emerging in 1972 as a prototype built in a home workshop, the Atchisson Assault Shotgun (also known as the USAS) was a wholly new weapon – a fully automatic shotgun. Designed on a straight-through configuration similar to an assault rifle (and indeed, vaguely reminiscent of the M16 rifle as a result of its use of some M16 components), the Atchisson can feed from a 7-, 10- or 12-round box or a 20-round drum magazine.

One problem with automatic shotguns is that shotshells are bulky and automatic fire gets rid of a lot of them very quickly. The Atchisson uses standard 70mm shotgun ammunition and can fire heavy buckshot, solid ball or lighter ammunition. It is somewhat heavier than an assault rifle and the drum magazines are bulky, but at close range the Atchisson is devastating.

A production version emerged in 1974, with a custom-built receiver rather than the original collection of M16, BAR and Thompson SMG components. This was constructed mainly of Zytel, the same plastic used in M16s, and an improved model went into production in 1984.

The post-1984 version, manufactured in the US and in Korea by the Daewoo group, has a bayonet mounting (curiously, this is above the barrel) and can launch NATO standard rifle grenades.

The Atchisson was a groundbreaking weapon in its time, and served to prove that the assault shotgun was viable. It has never achieved massive popularity or success, but the concept it pioneered is today gathering a great deal of interest.

Franchi SPAS 15

Another rifle-style 'assault' shotgun, the Franchi SPAS 15 is not capable of fully automatic fire, since the manufacturers considered recoil to be too much of a problem under autofire, but it is still clearly a military assault weapon. Configured like an assault rifle, with a folding stock and 10-round magazine in front of the trigger assembly, the SPAS 15 is in some ways fairly conventional and in others a highly innovative weapon.

Essentially a magazine-fed version of the SPAS 12 (depending on the user's specification, the 15 can use pump or gas operation), the SPAS 15 has significant advantages over other combat shotguns. Not only does the detachable box magazine hold more ammunition (10 rounds) than is common with tube-magazine combat shotguns, it can be quickly replaced with a full one whereas a conventional shotgun requires the shells to be reloaded individually.

Franchi also experimented with a Bullpup arrangement and it is possible that such a weapon may emerge in the future. At present the SPAS 15 is a stepping stone between the conventional shotgun and a purely military weapon.

Pancor Jackhammer

Very definitely a leap into the future, the Pancor Jackhammer is a Bullpup-configuration assault shotgun capable of full-automatic fire. It is fed by a 10-round ammunition cassette, which is removed and replaced like a rifle magazine. The cassette cannot be reloaded manually while in the weapon, since it retains the spent cartridge cases rather than ejecting them. The ammunition cassette can also be used as an anti-personnel mine. A detonator clips to the cassette allowing the ammunition within to be triggered in the manner of a miniature claymore mine.

The Jackhammer uses standard 70mm 12-gauge ammunition. Its mechanism is similar to that of the Webley-Fosbery revolver a century ago; the cylinder is grooved and pushed round by a recoil-driven stud.

The future of the shotgun

It is almost certain that conventional shotguns will remain in service as civilian and law-enforcement security weapons for many years to come. Their advantages of low penetration but massive stopping power and area effect suit them perfectly to their current roles. It is hard to imagine anything better for the job coming along.

For the military role, the self-loading or fully automatic shotgun is just becoming a useful weapon, and current developments will build on this. The 1979 RHINO project resulted in great strides forward for the combat shotgun, and a glimpse of the future.

Heckler & Koch CAWS

Olin Industries developed a new enhanced-performance shotgun round: a belted brass round, 76.2mm long (that is to say 3-inches long, as opposed to the standard 2.75inches), that could use flechettes, pellets or solid ball as its payload. Heckler & Koch designed their Close Assault Weapon System (CAWS) around this cartridge, creating an assault shotgun with massive hitting power out to 150 metres (492 feet).

The CAWS is a Bullpup weapon, the construction of which draws on experience gained from the G11 rifle project. Fed by a 10-round magazine, standard rounds for CAWS contain either 20 flechettes or eight tungsten alloy pellets. It has an optical sight as standard and is accurate under aimed fire. Felt recoil is surprisingly light considering the power of the cartridge.

Thus far, the Close Assault Weapon System concept has not been taken up by military buyers and remains a demonstrator project. It shows very clearly, however, what can be done with the automatic shotgun. The ability of smoothbore weapons to fire different types of ammunition may provide a way forward for such weapons. At the change of a magazine, the future combat shotgun can launch miniature grenades, hard-hitting penetrator rounds or non-lethal beanbags, as well as standard anti-personnel ammunition. It may be that this capability will prove to be very attractive to the military of the future.

Three-block war

US military planners are now considering what equipment is effective for fighting what they call 'three-block war'. That is, soldiers may be involved in safe-area security, engineering projects, police operations, counter-terrorism and all-out battle, all at the same time and all within a three-block radius. A weapon that allows a versatile response would do away with the need to carry several different pieces of equipment and select between them under stress in a highly confused situation.

A weapon like the CAWS, equipped with a range of ammunition types, seems well suited to three-block warfare scenarios and this may indeed be the future of the combat smoothbore.

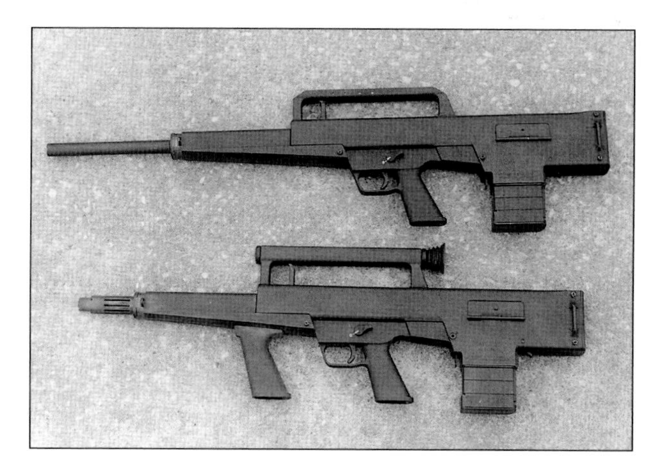

Above: The H&K/Winchester Close Assault Weapon System (CAWS) is available in long and short barrelled versions. This futuristic weapon looks little like the familiar combat shotgun, but fulfils a similar function.

GRENADES AND LAUNCHERS

Grenade weapons have been around for a long time. The ancient Greeks are said to have hurled pots of quicklime at their enemies to blind them, while the invention of gunpowder allowed the creation of small hand-thrown explosive projectiles to cause a blast that, together with the fragmentation of the casing, could pose a serious threat to enemy troops.

Early grenades were somewhat random in effect and not very useful on the open battlefield. A grenadier would have to take out a grenade and light the fuse. He might then wait a moment to ensure it caught light properly, allowing the fuse to burn down a little so that the projectile would go off soon after arriving. Only then would he hurl the device at the enemy.

Assuming the fuse did not go out, or that some enterprising enemy soldier did not throw it back, the grenade would explode, endangering anyone nearby. But at the sort of ranges to which a man can deliver a grenade, there was ample time to shoot the grenadier, leaving a burning grenade rolling around, and grenades of this sort quickly passed out of battlefield use. The term 'grenadier' came to refer to élite infantrymen, but the only grenades they possessed were symbols on their insignia.

Left: An Israeli soldier from the Golani Brigade prepares to fire his rifle-mounted M203 grenade launcher during manouevres in Febuary 1998.

The grenade remained very useful for sieges, especially in defence. A popular trick among fortress defenders was to line up several on the top of the wall, light the fuses and knock them off into the ditch below while it was filled with men trying to storm a breach or escalade the wall with ladders. In such confined and crowded quarters any grenade that detonated would cause fearful carnage.

Grenade launchers

Early grenade launchers were constructed using a short musket with a cup launcher to hold the grenade. These were not exceptionally effective, but they were sometimes used at about the time when explosive shells and early fragmentation rounds (spherical case shot, as invented by Dr Shrapnel) were being introduced to the artillery. One advantage of these cup-type grenade launchers was that the muzzle blast could be used to ignite the grenade fuse as well as propel it. The main disadvantage of this system was that often it failed to do so.

Modern grenades

It was not until the development of modern fusing systems that grenades really came into their own. Grenades of various types can now be hand thrown, launched from rifles or specialist launchers, and even delivered using fully automatic weapons.

Common grenade payloads include traditional explosive/fragmentation types plus incendiary, illuminating, smoke, gas and flares. Some launchers

Left: A German stormtrooper practices throwing stick grenades over a belt of barbed wire in 1917. Standing up to hurl a grenade can be dangerous, but hand grenades have a limited range at the best of times and it is difficult to throw one from any other position.

Early hand grenades

In the days when grenades had external fuses, it was sometime possible simply to pinch out the fuse or pull it out of the bomb before detonation.

Even when a bomb did explode, the effects were not always fatal. Before internal etching made grenade bursts more predictable – and consequently much more deadly – there are numerous reports of soldiers picking up a black powder shell or grenade with the fuse still burning and emerging from the subsequent explosion blackened but unhurt.

can deliver a direct-fire 'multiple projectile' round that resembles a gigantic shotgun shell. The effect at close range can be awesome.

Hand grenades

Hand grenades are extremely useful if used properly. They can be set up as booby traps or thrown in an indirect arc over cover or into a room, allowing hostiles who cannot be seen to be eliminated without exposing friendly personnel to the dangers of storming the position.

The typical hand grenade contains a fusing device preset to a delay of between one and five seconds. This timing device is triggered by the release of a spring-loaded lever, which is normally held in place by a pin. 'Pulling the pin' on a grenade does not actually arm it or start the timer. What it does is release the lever (or 'spoon'). If the grenade, however, is held in the hand against spring pressure and the lever is not permitted to fly off, the fuse will not start to burn and the weapon remains safe. The pin can be pushed back in if the user changes his mind.

Grenades of World War I

The first truly modern hand grenades saw extensive use in World War I. Troops frequently engaged in 'bombing' operations, hurling large numbers of grenades into a nearby enemy positions.

Another effective but hazardous practice involved 'bombing up the terraces'. Trenches were laid out in a zigzag pattern to prevent enemy fire raking along them if they were flanked. An enterprising soldier engaged in trench clearance operations could lob his grenade over the intervening ground and into another section of the same trench. Troops would then charge around the bend and into the next section just after the grenade went off, securing another section of trench in the chaos that followed. Timing and accuracy were vital if this practice were to succeed, but at least the ability of the 'bomber' to engage enemies out of direct line of sight meant that the assault party did not have to charge into the teeth of prepared resistance.

M36 Mills Bomb

A classic grenade of this period was the British M36 'Mills Bomb'. The Mills was a fragmentation type grenade that caused harm by sending metal fragments (pieces of casing) out in a lethal burst. The explosive charge was sufficient to do this but did not comprise the main offensive capability of the grenade.

The Mills Bomb's casing was engraved in a pattern that earned the weapon its 'Pineapple' nickname, but in truth it did not work as it was supposed to. The engraving was supposed to make the casing shatter into a large number of pieces, each big enough to cause serious injury, but instead an M36 tended to produce a few large casing pieces and a lot of virtually harmless tiny fragments. This in turn produced a rather random effect: one grenade might cause grievous slaughter, while an identical one landing nearby had little effect.

Fragmentation

Later fragmentation grenades incorporated refinements to ensure a more predictable, and more lethal, effect. Engraving the inside, rather than the outside, of the casing produces a much better fragmentation pattern, but this makes manufacture slower and more expensive. Most fragmentation grenades now use notched steel wire within an outer casing, or sometimes 'prefragmented' payloads of metal cubes or spheres. Any pattern on the casing of a modern grenade is there to help the user's grip rather than for fragmentation purposes.

Hand grenades are generally more useful in defence than attack. Many spread their fragments further than an average soldier can throw the grenade, posing a hazard unless the thrower can drop the grenade into an enemy position or can himself take cover. A grenade that bursts against a hard surface such as a wall can send fragments out to several times its supposed lethal range. This is fine for troops using grenades to fend off an assault on their position but causes problems on the attack.

Offensive and defensive grenades

One solution is to create a distinction between offensive and defensive grenades. A 'defensive' grenade is the high-fragmentation type, described above. Such weapons are ideal for defending a position or throwing into a confined area, such as a room or enemy vehicle. For offensive purposes other types of grenade are used that have less fragmentation effect but are more explosive. These 'offensive' grenades not only disable nearby enemy personnel with blast effect, but can have a stunning concussive effect at some distance.

DM51

Some grenades are available in a basic 'offensive' configuration and can be enhanced into 'defensive' types by wrapping a fragmentation casing around the main body of the grenade. An example is the German DM51 dual-purpose grenade. The grenade's regular plastic coating has a relatively low fragmentation effect, but this can be boosted with the optional addition of a wrap-around casing consisting of steel balls embedded in plastic.

DM51

Weight: 435g (1lb)
Height: 107mm (4.25in)
Lethal radius: 35m (38yd)

Left: Six stick grenades have had their heads removed and fastened around a seventh. This customized grenade was found in a German foxhole by a infantryman of the 9th Armored Division after US forces took Fritzlar, Germany.

Sticks and pineapples

Hand grenades usually come in the standard 'pineapple' shape. Examples of modern versions that clearly show their origins include the American M61 and M26 grenades (the latter has an electrical impact fusing device) and the British L2.

Some nations, however, have experimented with different configurations for their grenades. German troops in World War II were issued with distinctive 'potato-masher' grenades, which were essentially a cylindrical device containing explosive and fusing, mounted on a wooden handle for throwing. These weapons were favoured by German troops fighting in arctic conditions, since their rifles suffered from mechanical problems induced by the cold of Russia and Scandinavia, and grenades do not jam.

Anti-tank grenades

In addition to being anti-personnel weapons, stick grenades can have some limited success as anti-tank weapons. A streamer or 'drogue' attached to the handle ensures that the weapon flies warhead-first, and an impact fuse detonates the charge when something solid – ideally the hull of a tank – is struck.

RKG3M grenade

An example of the hand-thrown anti-tank grenade is the Russian RKG3M grenade. The warhead's construction is such that a focused jet of plasma (super-hot gas) is created by the detonation, and this can slice through a reasonable thickness of metal armour. The concept of the anti-tank hand grenade is now more or less obsolete, at least as far as the world's major powers are concerned. Such weapons are possibly useful against reconnaissance vehicles and armoured personnel carriers, but modern tanks are too well armoured to be disabled in this way except by a very lucky hit on a vulnerable point. Against the older or lighter military equipment in use in many corners of the world, however, such a weapon may have a chance.

Smoke and incendiary grenades

As well as explosive grenades, there are several burning-type grenades, which produce their effect by an incendiary process. The classic example is the White Phosphorus grenade, the payload of which has the strangely friendly nickname of 'Willie-Pete'. Phosphorus burns on contact with air, and produces a large cloud of white smoke and an impressive incendiary effect, setting things on fire as well as flinging about fragments of blazing phosphorus.

M34 WP grenade

The M34 smoke grenade consists of a compressed fibre or plastic shell filled with 425 grams (15 ounces) of White Phosphorus. Any person caught within the grenade's 30-metre (98.4-feet) burst radius risks being covered in lethal particles of phosphorus burning at around 2700°C (4892°F).

Despite this deadly effect, White Phosphorus grenades are technically only to be used to create smoke or to signal with, since the Geneva and Hague Conventions consider such weapons to be barbaric. To the soldier in combat, the fact that

M26

Weight: 454g (1lb)
Height: 99mm (3.75in)
Lethal radius: 15m (16yd)

grenades such as the M34 produce toxic smoke that acts like tear gas in some ways, and can kill enemy personnel, may be a bonus.

In cooler climates, the intense heat produced by the phosphorus reaction may cause the smoke to dissipate more quickly than intended.

AN-M14 TH3 Thermite grenade

Another incendiary grenade, the AN-M14 Thermite grenade, was a heavy can-like affair, the contents of which burned at an incredible 2200°C (3986°F). The Thermite reaction is used to weld railway tracks and similar large metal constructions. In grenade form it is an extremely deadly weapon that will burn underwater, although the weight of the grenade and the greater general usefulness of White Phosphorus resulted in its withdrawal from service. It is no longer in production.

AN-M8 HC grenade

Not all burning-type grenades are lethal. The AN-M8 HC smoke grenade produces a dense cloud of white smoke lasting around 100–150 seconds. The hydrochloric fumes may irritate eyes and lungs if used in enclosed spaces, but is useful for concealing troop movements from the enemy or to cover a withdrawal. On the attack, a smokescreen can greatly reduce casualties by preventing the enemy from seeing what they are shooting at until the assault force is almost on top of them. Smoke can also be used for reconnaissance.

Right: The explosion produced by a White Phosphorus grenade can be spectacular. Technically White Phosphorus should be used only to create smoke or to signal with, since it is illegal to use this type of grenade against personnel, but this edict is not always enforceable.

Grenade hazards

A security patrol in South Africa had a lucky escape when one of their number threw a White Phosphorus grenade at a terrorist, only to see the grenade rebound from a tree and land among the thrower's squad-mates. There were no casualties, but the target escaped in the resulting scramble.

Left: Stun grenades such as the Haley and Weller E182 grenade carried by this SAS trooper create confusion and disorientation among opponents. They are an essential item of equipment for hostage-rescue and other assault troops.

A tactical trick used by Soviet forces was to put down smoke in front of a suspected enemy position as if to cover an assault, but to remain in cover. Troops fearing an overwhelming assault might begin firing blindly into the smoke, revealing their presence, approximate numbers and possibly the location of support weapons, such as machine guns.

Smoke can also be used for signalling. A coloured smoke grenade will provide an aim point for air support, whether it be helicopters flying in to rescue wounded or a fast jet approaching at speed with bombs and rockets. Smoke grenades will generally burn for a couple of minutes; the smoke cloud will last somewhat longer, depending upon conditions.

Gas grenades

Other burning grenades produce various gases; most common is CS, or tear gas. This can be lethal if enough is inhaled or the victim is trapped in a room with a grenade, but in the vast majority of cases all it does is cause temporary irritation of the eyes and nose, and sometimes vomiting. Tear gas can be used to degrade the effectiveness of enemy personnel but strangely, while it is accepted as a non-lethal security measure for use by law enforcers and troops dealing with civil disturbances, its use is considered unacceptable on the battlefield since it is defined as a 'chemical weapon' and outlawed by treaty.

Other types of gas grenades include CN-DM, which is similar in effect to CS but more likely to induce vomiting, and BZ, which is a psychogenic agent causing hallucinations and disorientation.

Stun grenades

Other non-lethal grenades are in use, mainly by security and hostage-rescue units. The classic 'flash-bang' is used to simulate grenades in military training and, when thrown into a room, can cause disorientation and surprise among the occupants, allowing time for an assault party to enter the room and eliminate the opposition.

Many modern stun grenades, such as the British Haley & Weller E182 and the G60/90, contain several separate charges, each creating further disorientation. The flash from these devices is impressive; the noise is unbelievable. In a confined space they are extremely effective, although they have no real combat value unless followed up with immediate assault.

Launching grenades

Hand grenades are useful tools for the modern weapons user, especially in close urban terrain, where much combat now takes place. Their limited range, however, makes hand grenades of marginal effectiveness on the battlefield. If grenades could be delivered out to a slightly longer range, perhaps with a greater payload, then infantry would gain a measure of self-support, reducing the need to call on artillery, mortars or air support to deal with an enemy position. The answer is to give the infantryman the ability to launch self-propelled grenades. Two answers to that problem have been devised: specialist launchers and grenades that can be launched by any rifleman.

Rifle grenades

There are two ways to launch a grenade from a rifle. One is to fit a variety of cup-type launchers, place the grenade in it and fire it using a special propellant round loaded into the rifle. This idea has been around since the Napoleonic era, when some muskets were adapted into grenade launchers. It works, but there are numerous difficulties. Not least of these is the difficulty of aiming: the massive recoil of the propellant charge is also most unpleasant.

As an alternative, rifle grenades containing their own propelling charge can be fitted directly onto the muzzle of a rifle. They are initiated by firing the rifle into the base of the grenade as it rests on the rifle (hence the name 'bullet-trap' type grenades) or through a central channel in the grenade (the 'bullet-through' type). Such weapons do not need the rifleman to carry and load special propellant rounds; although the recoil of firing some kinds of grenade can be unpleasant, it is not excessive.

Right: Rifle grenades such as this FN Bullet-Through grenade offer advantages over hand-thrown types in terms of range and – with suitable training – accuracy, but are not favoured by all armed forces.

Rifle grenades

Rifle grenades have a greater range than hand-thrown equivalents and can deliver a greater payload into the bargain. Typical payloads include anti-personnel (fragmentation) rounds, anti-armour rounds with a shaped-charge, HEDP (High Explosive Dual-Purpose), which combine anti-personnel and light anti-armour effects, smoke, White Phosphorus and illuminating (flare) grenades.

One of the most advanced rifle grenade types is the FN Bullet-Through series, which includes a telescopic fragmentation grenade with stabilizing fins which is fitted onto the rifle muzzle and launched by firing a normal round into the base.

Bunker busting

In theory a rifle grenade or two carried by every man in a unit should provide a measure of anti-armour capability. In practice, while rifle grenades are a useful addition to infantry firepower, they are not always as effective as their users would like.

Infantry forces are often confronted with fortified positions, bunkers and light armoured vehicles that rifles and machine guns lack the firepower to deal with. If a weapon allows troops to take a position without suffering casualties then it is well worth the cost. Rifle grenades may be useful in these circumstances, but other weapons have sometimes been used. British troops in the Falklands conflict, for example, used MILAN anti-tank missiles to engage fortified Argentine bunkers. This act was criticized in some quarters as a misuse of weaponry but, even leaving aside the human cost of an advance against machine guns, the numbers speak for themselves. At the time a MILAN missile cost about £16,000 ($28,500): the cost of training even one soldier is many times that amount.

Brunswick RAW

Rather than improvised uses of weapons meant for other things, however, or using marginally effective rifle grenades, troops now have a weapon custom-made for destroying infantry bunkers. The Brunswick Rifleman's Assault Weapon (RAW) is a variation on the rifle grenade idea. Shaped like a bowling ball, it is propelled by a rocket motor and spins to stabilize its flight path.

Although it is strange in appearance, the RAW has a large HESH (High Explosive Squash-Head) warhead similar to that used in some anti-tank rounds. This can disable lightly armoured combat vehicles and blast a hole in reinforced concrete. The explosive concussion and secondary fragmentation (that is, the fragments picked up and thrown about by the blast) of this weapon are often deadly to nearby enemy personnel.

The RAW is a nuisance to carry around; its bowling-ball shape and weight of nearly 4 kilograms (8.8 pounds) adds considerably to the infantryman's battle load. However, it is effective in a range of roles and it certainly has merit as an alternative to rushing an enemy position.

Rocket-propelled grenades

Rifle grenades and similar devices are useful but they have their limitations, not least the preparation time involved in placing the grenade on the rifle ready for a shot. A dedicated launcher allows a grenade to be held ready to fire indefinitely. Very similar in concept to a rifle grenade, the rocket-propelled grenade (RPG) is essentially a self-propelled explosive charge (or other warhead) fired from a reusable launcher.

The Soviet Army was always fond of mortars, and deployed vast numbers of them, but the most important system in their eyes was the anti-tank weapon. It was a matter of military doctrine that every combat unit should be able to engage tanks in some way. Since it was impractical to place anti-tank guns and missile launchers in all formations, and the hand-thrown anti-tank grenade was at best marginally useful, the answer was to develop a shoulder-fired unguided weapon with a heavy warhead that could damage or even destroy a tank, and could incidentally be used against other targets.

Below: A US Army sergeant displays a Russian-made RPG-7 projectile, recovered from an arms cache in Najaf, Iraq, 2004. Although not large, this type of weapon does pose a serious threat to personnel and vehicles.

Left: An RPG-7 launcher in the hands of a Soviet infantryman in the 1980s. Thousands of these cheap weapons were constructed in order to give any unit a chance to engage tanks with at least some chance of success.

RPG-7

The most famous weapon of this type is the RPG-7, developed in the Soviet Union in the years after World War II. It consists of a 70mm warhead with its own rocket motor and a shaped-charge warhead capable of slicing through 40cm (15 inches) of steel, screwed together and forming a single unit. The grenade is fired from a reusable shoulder mount, containing the trigger and a simple optical sight. The grenade has a long 'tail', which is slipped into the fore end of the launcher. Once fired, vanes fold out to stabilize the warhead in flight.

The RPG-7 is not very effective against modern main battle tanks, but can destroy lighter vehicles and cause great devastation against 'soft' targets, such as infantry. Vast numbers of RPG-7s, and smaller numbers of similar weapons with better warheads, have been produced. These weapons turn up wherever there is conflict and will continue to do so for many years to come.

This type of launcher, where the projectile essentially sits on the end until it is fired, is sometimes referred to as a 'spigot mortar'. The RPG-7 provides a cheap means by which infantry can cause area damage and engage armoured vehicles. It is a favourite of terrorists, insurgents and low-budget armed forces worldwide and has earned undying notoriety through news images of a hundred conflicts. It will be found in service for a long time to come.

Grenade launchers

A whole family of grenades is available for use with dedicated launchers. Most duplicate the functions of hand and rifle grenades, but there are significant differences. A launcher grenade is a self-contained cartridge, similar to a round of rifle ammunition. The standard calibre in most Western countries is 40mm, with the former Warsaw Pact favouring 30mm calibres. Other launcher calibres are possible, for example some 12-gauge shotguns can launch gas rounds that are essentially small grenades.

The typical cartridge grenade weighs about 250 grams (0.5 pounds) and can be delivered out to about 300 metres (984 feet) from most launchers. In addition to explosive, fragmentation, armour-piecing, HEDP, smoke and gas rounds, some specialist ammunition is available.

Parachute flares and signal rounds

Parachute flare rounds can be launched high into the air to illuminate an area several hundred metres in diameter. A variant on the same concept, signalling rounds burst 200 metres (656 feet) or so above the ground and scatter brightly burning fragments in various colours. 'Starshell' rounds have been used for signalling for many years and are bright enough to be visible by day.

Multiple projectile rounds

For close combat multiple projectile rounds have an effective range of no more than 50 metres (164 feet), equivalent to that of a large shotgun, but deliver massive firepower in a single shot. A non-lethal variant loaded with rubber 'stingballs', instead of buckshot, can be used for riot suppression and security applications.

Another non-lethal 40mm round is called 'Stunbag'. Similar to more recent 'beanbag' shotgun rounds, Stunbag is a cloth bag filled with very fine lead shot. The impact of such a weight, even spread over an area as large as 15cm (5.9 inches) – the size of the fully spread bag – is powerful enough to incapacitate most people. Fatalities can occur, especially when the target is struck in the head, but generally speaking Stunbag will disable without causing lasting harm, making it a useful addition to the non-lethal arsenal.

Baton guns and 'rubber bullets'

'Baton' rounds, made of rubber or soft plastic, can be fired from some grenade launchers or custom designed 'baton guns'. Similar in effect to Stunbag rounds, baton rounds are used to disable criminals without killing them or to break up riots. They can be lethal at close range, but offer riot police and troops a legally justifiable alternative to shooting at rock-throwing rioters.

Baton rounds are sometimes referred to as 'rubber bullets', which can cause some confusion among laymen – surely a rubber rifle bullet would be almost as lethal as a lead one? Another term, 'baton charge', suggests a hand-to-hand assault with nightsticks, which is precisely the contact that baton guns are designed to avoid. Some observers maintain that tear gas and baton rounds are excessive when used against civil disturbances. Given that the alternatives are to allow rioters to run free, to shoot them with live ammunition or to pick up and use the same rocks and petrol bombs as the rioters, such non-lethal weapons are clearly the best alternative in a bad situation.

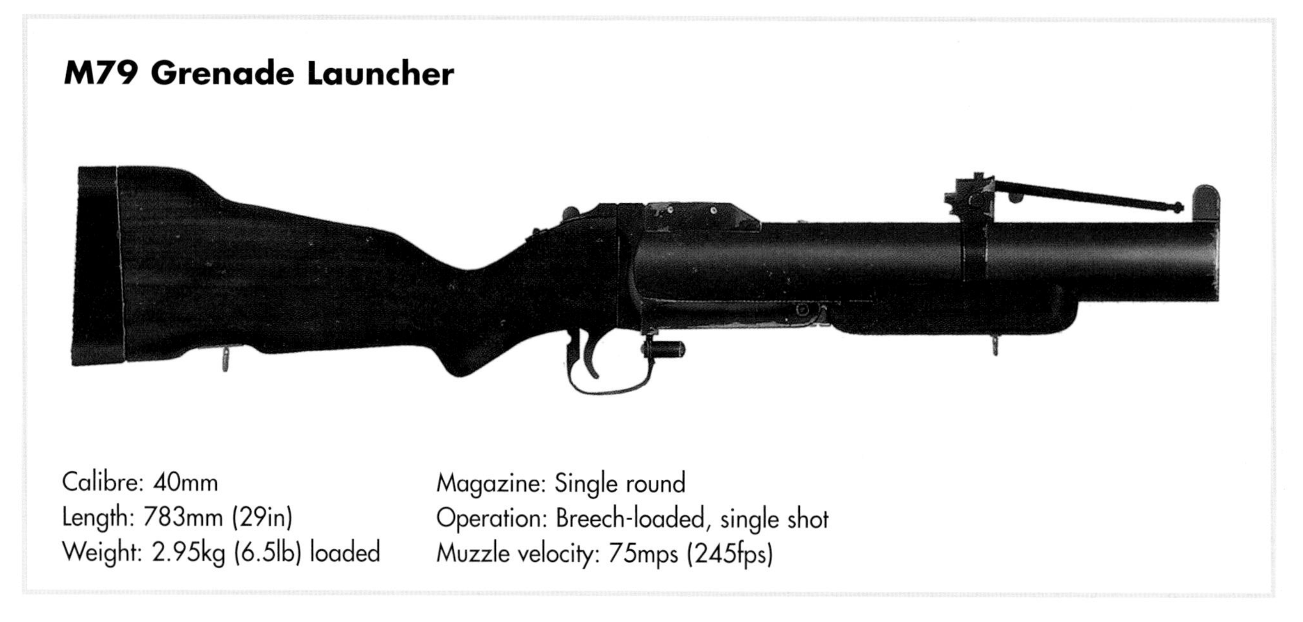

M79 Grenade Launcher

Probably the most famous of all grenade launchers, the M79 'Thump Gun', or 'Blooper', is a single-shot 40mm launcher with a rifle-type stock and flip-up sights. It can deliver a grenade out to about 400 metres (1312 feet) but is really only accurate at less than half that distance. The bore is rifled, imparting a stabilizing spin to projectiles that also serves as a safety device. Grenades are designed so that they do not arm themselves until they have been spinning for a set period, typically enough for them to travel about 30 metres (98 feet). If a round hits an obstruction before travelling that distance it will not detonate, which is most desirable if a 40mm high explosive grenade hits a tree and comes back at the firer, or if the launcher is accidentally fired indoors.

The M79 is reloaded much in the manner of a sporting shotgun: the weapon is 'broken' open and the spent round extracted before a new one is inserted. Although hardly capable of rapid fire, the M79 is reliable and useful in many situations. When loaded it weighs no more than a rifle, although a useful number of grenades adds up to a fair load and must be distributed among several squad mates.

From the early 1970s the M79 was replaced in US front-line service by the M203, but it remains in service with other forces worldwide, offering infantry a measure of self-fire support.

M203

Calibre: 40mm
Length: 380mm (15in)
Weight: 1.63kg (3.5lb) loaded
Magazine: Single round, breech-loaded
Operation: Breech-loaded, single shot, pump action
Muzzle velocity: 75mps (245fps)

Left: The American M203 grenade launcher is attached under the foregrip of the M16 assault rifle. To fire the launcher, the rifle magazine is used as a handgrip and the weapon triggered using its own integral mechanism.

M203

The M203 was originally intended for use only in conjunction with the M16 rifle. Fitting under the barrel, it allowed an infantryman to take a support role yet retain the close-combat advantages of an assault rifle, although obviously at the expense of increasing the weight. The M203 includes a barrel shroud that fits around the fore end of the M16 rifle and incorporates a flip-up sight.

The launcher is a pump-action breech-loading device with its own trigger separate from the rifle mechanism. This self-contained system allowed the development of a stand-alone version of the

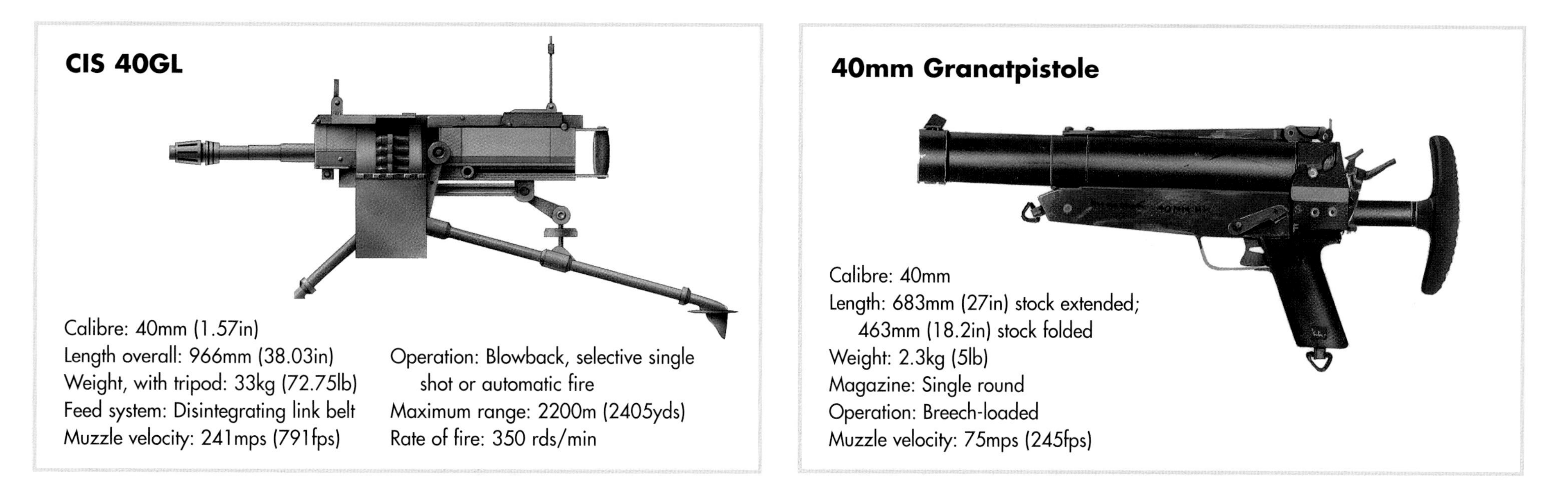

CIS 40GL

Calibre: 40mm (1.57in)
Length overall: 966mm (38.03in)
Weight, with tripod: 33kg (72.75lb)
Feed system: Disintegrating link belt
Muzzle velocity: 241mps (791fps)
Operation: Blowback, selective single shot or automatic fire
Maximum range: 2200m (2405yds)
Rate of fire: 350 rds/min

40mm Granatpistole

Calibre: 40mm
Length: 683mm (27in) stock extended; 463mm (18.2in) stock folded
Weight: 2.3kg (5lb)
Magazine: Single round
Operation: Breech-loaded
Muzzle velocity: 75mps (245fps)

weapon, with its own grips and shoulder stock, and a version with an interbar, which allows it to be used with a range of rifles. The M203's range is similar to that of the M79 but it is more accurate across the whole of that distance, increasing its effective range significantly. The stand-alone version weighs about half as much as the M79.

CIS 40GL

Many other grenade launchers are short, stand-alone designs. Chartered Industries of Singapore (CIS) markets a 40mm grenade launcher very similar to the M203 in configuration, which can stand alone or be fitted via an adapter to a range of rifles. The CIS 40mm is a breech-loader reloaded by breaking open the hinged barrel, which swings to the side. Range and accuracy are comparable to the M203.

40mm Granatpistole

A somewhat older design, but very similar, is the 40mm Granatpistole from Heckler & Koch. With its stock fully closed this weapon is only a little over 460mm (18.1 inches) long, and can be carried in a hip holster. Flip-up sights are fitted; with them in the down position the weapon is accurate out to about 100 metres (328 feet), and with them it can achieve reasonable accuracy (as good as any grenade launcher) out to 350 metres (1148 feet).

The single-shot grenade launcher offers impressive capabilities in a weapon that can be easily carried by an infantryman. Combination rifle/launchers are excellent weapons for small units such as special forces raiders, who need to be able to cause maximum mayhem and deal with any opposition, even though they are few in number.

Repeating grenade launchers

While the single-shot launcher has its uses, troops can always take advantage of all the fire support they can get. Repeating or fully automatic grenade launchers are excellent area-effect fire support weapons. Most are vehicle or tripod-mounted heavy weapons, but handheld repeaters are becoming available.

Milcor MGL

One example is the MGL, manufactured by Milcor of South Africa. Somewhat similar to the Striker shotgun (another South African invention), the Milcor consists of a receiver with pistol and foregrips, a folding stock and a central revolving drum that holds six 40mm grenades. Operation is semi-automatic, using gas pressure from the last

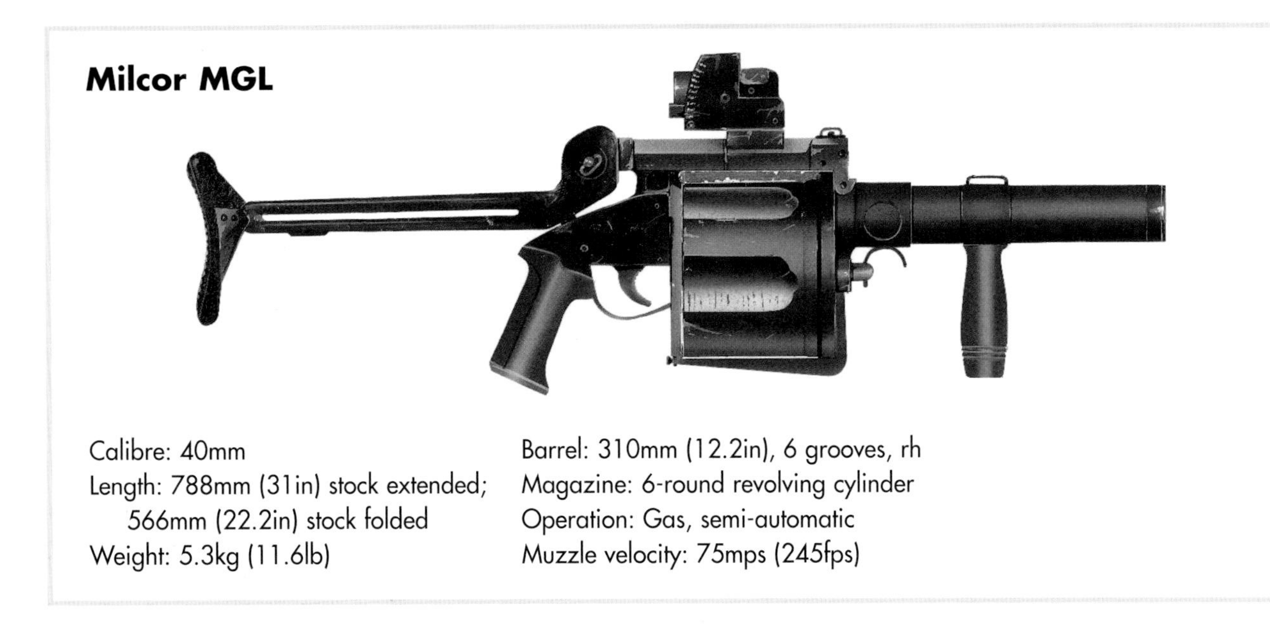

Milcor MGL

Calibre: 40mm
Length: 788mm (31in) stock extended; 566mm (22.2in) stock folded
Weight: 5.3kg (11.6lb)
Barrel: 310mm (12.2in), 6 grooves, rh
Magazine: 6-round revolving cylinder
Operation: Gas, semi-automatic
Muzzle velocity: 75mps (245fps)

fired round to fire two shots per second. Like many other handheld grenade launchers, the MGL is accurate out to about 400 metres (1312 feet). The weapon has no minimum range when firing baton or plastic shot rounds, although explosive rounds have the usual 30 metres (98 feet) arming distance. In addition to the handheld version, a tripod or vehicle-mounted twin variant is available for the support role.

Vehicle-mounted launchers

Support grenade launchers using a belt feed and automatic fire are sometimes referred to as 'grenade machine guns'. There are arguments each way as to whether a GPMG or an automatic grenade launcher is a better system for vehicle-mounted support. Grenade launchers can fire a range of ammunition types, and each round has its own area effect, but then so do rounds from light automatic cannon. One advantage of grenade launchers over autocannon is that they offer comparable firepower at moderate ranges but have little recoil, making them more suitable for use aboard small vehicles and light boats.

The FAV (Fast Attack Vehicle) is an excellent setting for auto-grenade launchers to show their capabilities. Similar in concept to the machine gun-festooned Jeeps and, later, Land-Rovers used for raids by the SAS and Long Range Desert Group in World War II and afterward, the FAV is a light, fast, unarmoured vehicle that is not equipped to carry high-recoil weapons. Designed for reconnaissance, it can make sudden, devastating raids where mobility and enormous firepower are everything. While FAVs can be equipped with anti-tank missile launchers, weapons such as GPMGs and grenade launchers are ideal, allowing the force to arrive suddenly by surprise and vanish again before serious opposition can be mounted. The combination of rapid fire and area effect makes the automatic grenade launcher an ideal weapon for such raiding vehicles.

Mk19

During the Vietnam War the US military discovered a need for riverine patrol craft capable of high firepower. High-recoil weapons were not feasible aboard light vessels such as those chosen, so a mix of mortars, machine guns and grenade launchers was shipped, along with the occasional recoilless rifle or light autocannon. The firepower of these boats was certainly impressive, and much of it came from the Mk19 40mm grenade launcher.

The Mk19 was a large-calibre, low-velocity, blowback-operated machine gun firing whatever 40mm grenades were linked into its belt feed system. Effective, if not especially accurate, out to an impressive 1600 metres (5250 feet), the Mk19 was updated in 1970 to make it more reliable, and was adopted by overseas forces as well.

Fragmentation effect

In Hollywood movies, grenades typically cause a massive explosion that makes people fly about in a spectacular fashion. Real fragmentation grenades are not quite so dramatic, although they are much more lethal: a person nearby can be shredded by the fragments.

A grenade that bursts against a hard surface, such as a road or a bunker wall, can send fragments out to several times its supposed lethal range. Hand-thrown grenades should never be used without care!

AGS-17 Plamya

The equivalent of the Mk19 in Soviet service was the 30mm AGS-17, or Plamya, grenade launcher. Effective out to 1200 metres (3937 feet), the Plamya is fairly similar to the Mk19 and was introduced at about the same time. It saw action in Afghanistan, where some examples were captured and turned on their former owners.

The AGS-17 is deployed as a tripod-mounted infantry support weapon but also arms light attack helicopters and some armoured vehicles. A single-shot version, designated BG-15, has been created for use under the barrel of an AK-74 rifle, rather like the M203/M16 combination. Unlike many other such weapons, however, the BG-15 is muzzle-loaded.

Heckler & Koch GMG

The automatic grenade launcher concept is still under development. Heckler & Koch is working on a GMG (Grenade Machine Gun), which appears similar to the Mk19 in many ways but incorporates modern technology and materials to create an ultra-reliable weapon suitable for the twenty-first-century battlefield.

With all automatic grenade launchers, one of the primary drawbacks is the amount of ammunition required for sustained firing. Unlike the AGS-17 or the Mk19, however, the Heckler & Koch GMG fires from a closed-bolt, improving accuracy and, hopefully, reducing the amount of ammunition required for effective use. Chambered for 40x53mm, this weapon is likely to take its place in the armouries of many nations during the next few years, reaffirming the role of the grenade launcher as a vital battlefield weapon.

The future of grenade launchers

There has been some speculation that future infantry weapons may indeed be mini-grenade launchers rather than conventional rifles. This would allow greater flexibility in 'three-block war' scenarios, allowing personnel to use different ammunition types according to need. Thus a rifleman could use low-penetration flechettes, tear gas, beanbags, discarding sabot armour-piercing, multiple projectile anti-personnel or explosive rounds according to need, mixing lethal, non-lethal

Below: US Marines fire a Mk 19 belt-fed grenade launcher. Rapid-fire launchers of this type are excellent area-suppression weapons that can be fitted to vehicles or, as here, deployed on tripod mounts for infantry support.

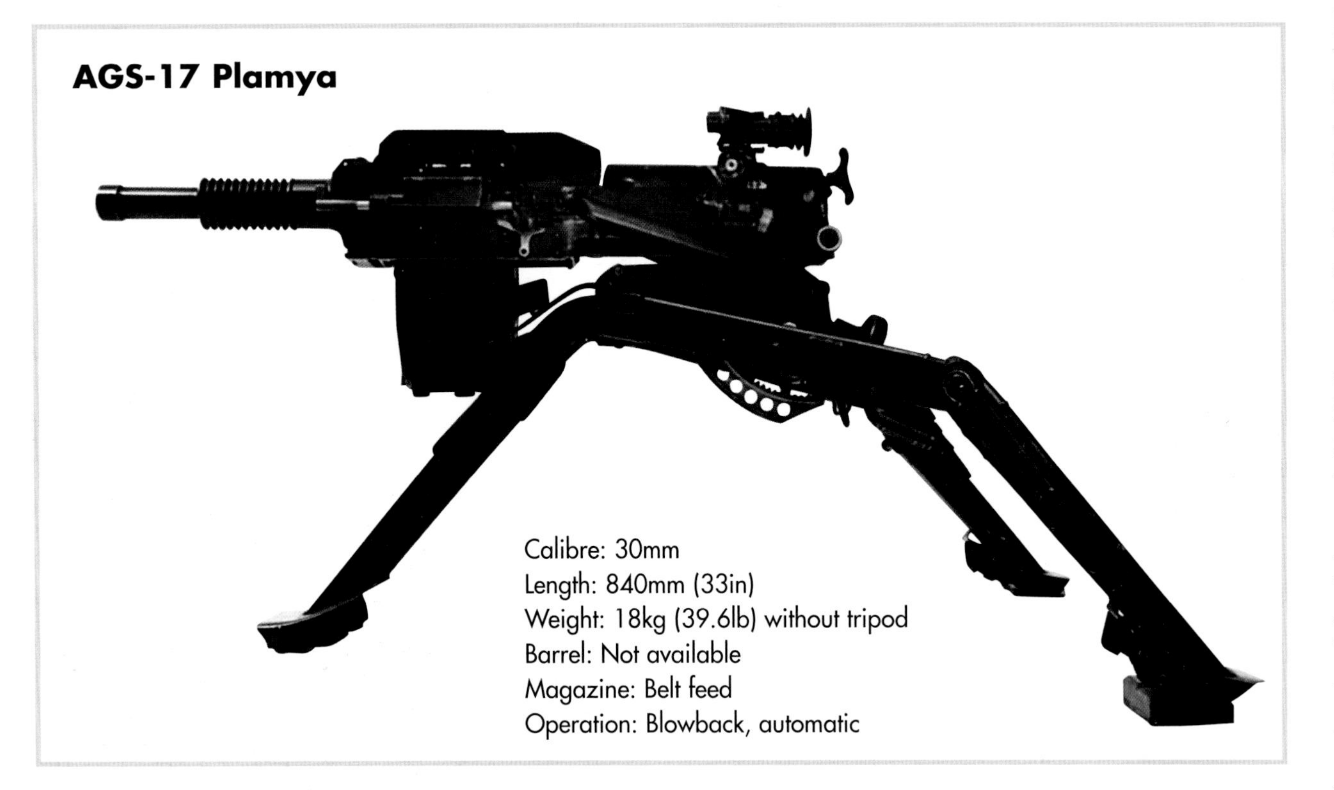

and support munitions as necessary. There is some merit in this idea, but it does not survive contact with reality. In theory it would be convenient to equip each soldier for any situation, but in practice this kind of overcomplication can actually place them in greater danger.

The present system, under which infantrymen carry lethal projectile weapons, works well enough. The choice of lethal or non-lethal response is made by the enemy – if they engage soldiers armed with rifles, they will receive a lethal response. If they do not, they will not be shot at. In a crisis the soldier has only to take tactical decisions – where to seek cover, whether to call for support fire, and which enemy to fire on – rather than fumbling about looking for just the right ammunition for the circumstances. In an even worse scenario he may find he has been placed at a disadvantage by a political decision to arm him only with short-range non-lethal ammunition, when he really needs something more effective.

The grenade launcher will remain what it is today: a support and riot-control weapon that, effective as it may be, is secondary to the main infantry weapons of rifle and machine gun. Grenade launchers have a role to play in the future, but they will always be part of the supporting cast rather than taking centre stage.

Light anti-tank weapons

When the tank made its appearance on the battlefields of World War I, mechanical breakdown was its main enemy. Obstacles that would bring infantry or cavalry to a halt were crossed with ease; machine guns that would mow down an assault force were all but impotent. Only mechanical unreliability and a short effective range prevented the fledgling tank corps from sweeping the field.

It was not long before countermeasures began to appear. Well-spotted artillery could destroy a tank if a shell dropped close by or scored a direct hit, and in the direct-fire role field guns could knock out a tank if they were not destroyed first.

The specialist anti-tank gun was not long in making an appearance. Firing solid shot at high velocity, anti-tank guns could penetrate the thin armour of early tanks with ease. As tanks became better protected, advances in anti-tank guns and their projectiles struggled to keep pace, creating the now familiar seesaw of measure and countermeasure.

Anti-tank guns, being artillery pieces, are not very mobile whereas tanks, by their very nature, are able to change position quickly. There were never enough guns to cover all possible avenues of attack, so alternatives had to be found.

Mobility

Anti-tank rifles, such as the famous Boyes .55 calibre rifle, firing armour-piercing bullets, could penetrate a tank and kill or injure crew members, often by causing secondary fragmentation from the inside of the metal hull. Anti-tank grenades and satchel charges offered infantry a slim chance of destroying a tank. As armour improved, however, and it became customary to accompany tanks with infantry in close support, these measures became even less useful.

Left: The British PIAT was bulky, heavy and really not very good at its job. However, it could destroy or disable a tank with a lucky shot, which made it better than nothing.

Right: The disposable German Panzerfaust launcher was far more effective and easier to carry. It gave any infantryman a fighting chance against a tank, and accounted for many Allied armoured vehicles during World War II.

What was needed was a device that could be carried by an infantryman, enabling him to take on a tank and kill it from a reasonable stand-off range. Among the various expedients were weapons like the German Panzerfaust, the American Bazooka and the British PIAT (Projector, Infantry, Anti-tank). These weapons are all broadly similar in operation, comprising a tube launcher and a large rocket-propelled shaped-charge warhead.

Developed versions of the infantry launcher followed with larger warheads and longer range. With the advent of guidance systems, infantry guided missile systems became possible, which in turn led to an increase in the size of the weapon. While deadly weapons in their own right, anti-tank missiles gradually became too bulky to be carried by infantry other than by specialist tank-killer teams.

Today, guided missiles have more or less replaced the anti-tank gun as the primary anti-armour weapon in most armies, but guided missile systems are large and bulky, often requiring a vehicle to carry them. There is still a need for a weapon that can engage a tank or other hard target yet remain portable enough to be carried by infantry personnel. These weapons can be split roughly into two categories: disposable and non-disposable weapons.

Although crewed by infantry, some weapons are too big to be carried by a single infantryman or a two-man team, so are not considered here. Others consist of a launcher and a throwaway container/tube for the rocket or missile. These weapons are considered to be non-disposable.

Warheads and effectiveness

To a great extent, the effectiveness of an anti-tank weapon depends upon the size and nature of its warhead. A simple high-explosive charge has little chance of damaging a tank, although it will be effective against lighter vehicles and bunkers. Shaped charges, designed to focus a cone of super-heated gas on the target, concentrate the effect of an explosive warhead at the critical point and are much

The Northover Projector

After the evacuation from Dunkirk in 1940, the British army was left with few anti-tank weapons to use in case of invasion. The Northover Projector – a steel pipe using a black powder charge to fire regular grenades – was introduced as a hastily improvised expedient.

The projector could fire grenades around 275 metres (900 feet), although it is unlikely they would have been very effective against tanks. White Phosphorus bottle grenade were later introduced. It is probably fortunate that the anticipated invasion never occured.

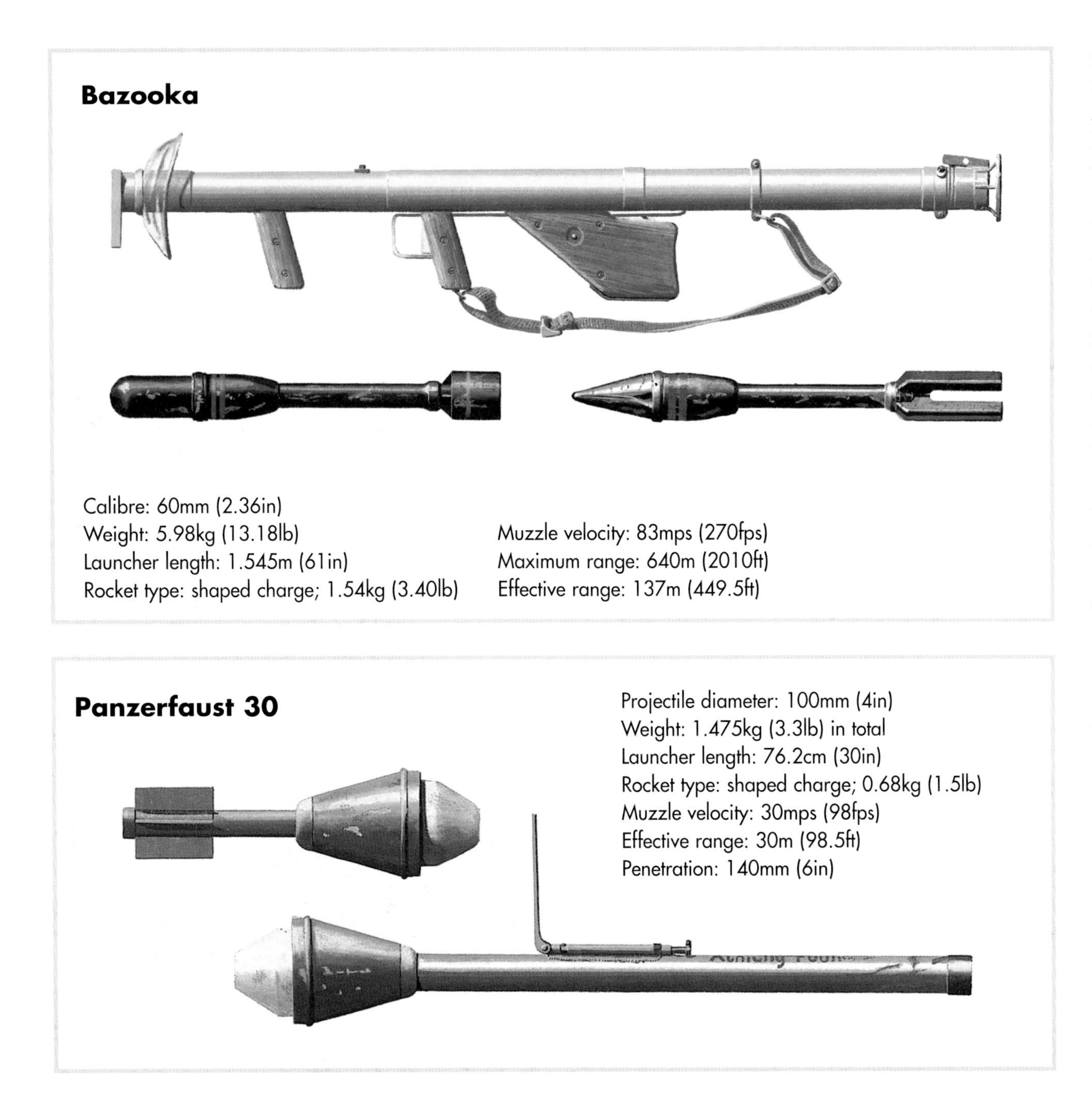

more effective than a simple HE round. More recent advances include HEAT (High Explosive Anti-Tank) and HESH (High Explosive Squash-Head) warheads that incorporate design innovations to make the most of their explosive effect.

Even the most advanced warheads will have a tough time penetrating the frontal armour of a main battle tank. A shot to the side, the rear or, best of all, downward onto the engine deck has the best chance of getting through. Of course, tanks tend to face towards the enemy, so obtaining such a shot can be tricky. In close terrain or during fighting in an urban setting tank-hunter teams can manoeuvre into a favourable position, or infantry may find themselves bypassed and with an excellent chance to take out a tank – if only a suitable weapon were available. The issue of disposable launchers to a proportion of infantry personnel offers a chance that such a weapon will be there when it is needed.

PIAT

Early non-disposable infantry anti-tank weapons were not especially effective, although they were a lot better than nothing. The British PIAT (Projector, Infantry, Anti-Tank) of World War II was known disparagingly as the 'drainpipe' (which it resembled). The launcher was powered by a heavy coiled spring, which drove a spigot to strike the grenade's propelling charge.

The PIAT could be produced at relatively low cost, but it was never a popular weapon: the spring was very difficult to cock in combat situations and it was largely ineffective except at very close range. For all its problems, however, the PIAT was the best weapon available at the time. A close-range shot at the side of an enemy tank might result in a kill or disablement. With the only alternatives being to run away or hide, troops were forced to try their best with this inadequate weapon. It could also fire HE and smoke grenades and was sometimes mounted on light armoured vehicles.

2.36in Bazooka

The US version, a full-tube rocket launcher that became known as the 'Bazooka' from its resemblance to an instrument played by the American comedian Bob Burns, was only a little better than the PIAT. Firing a 60mm rocket with a shaped charge warhead, the Bazooka was a good idea but simply not very effective in battle. Its warhead tended not to penetrate at ranges beyond 50 metres (164 feet), and the large backblast from firing ensured that the users would rapidly become a target for return fire. On the plus side, the bazooka was lightweight and the steel tube design was very simple to produce and use. It had a longer service history that the PIAT, with several new, improved models introduced over time, and inspired the German Raketenpanzerbüchse.

Shaped charges

Because the armour-piercing properties of the shaped charge rely upon the energy contained within the charge rather than the velocity of the projectile, it is not always necessary to fire the bomb for it to be an effective anti-armour weapon. One World War II German anti-tank weapon could be fixed to the side of a target tank before detonation using magnetic plates.

Panzerfaust

The German Panzerfaust was probably the best of the wartime anti-tank rocket launchers. It was sufficiently more effective than the Bazooka for American troops to prefer using captured Panzerfausts to their own weapons. Its design inspired the Soviet RPG-7 launcher, which remains in service today.

The first launcher was designated the Panzerfaust 30, because it had a maximum effective range of 30 metres (98ft). Subsequent versions increased this range to 60 and 100 metres (197 and 328ft) and were designated as the Panzerfaust 60 and 100.

Below: Two versions of the US Bazooka; the original M1 and the developed M9, which could be taken apart for carrying. The Bazooka was replaced by a larger-calibre version not long after the end of World War II.

EARLY ANTI-TANK WEAPONS: PIAT VERSUS

As armoured vehicles became more common, weapons to counter them were also developed. Anti-tank guns, mines and artillery could stop tanks, but the infantry needed something that could be carried by an individual soldier. The usual solution to the tank problem was to find a way to fling a large explosive charge at it and hope for the best. The result was a range of short-ranged low-velocity weapons based on the rocket-propelled grenade principle. Various means of launching these weapons were implemented including the German Panzerfaust and the British PIAT(Projector, Infantry, Anti-Tank).

STRENGTHS

- Reusable
- Rifle-style aiming
- Reasonable muzzle velocity

WEAKNESSES

- Not very effective against armour
- Much heavier than Panzerfaust
- Poor reputation affected morale

PIAT

Launcher length: 1m (39in)
Effective range: 100m (328ft)
Weight: 14.52kg (32lb)
Rocket type: shaped charge; 1.36kg (3lb)
Muzzle velocity: 106mps (350fps)
Armour penetration: 75mm (2.92in)

PANZERFAUST

The PIAT was a reusable weapon which launched a shaped-charge explosive device in a similar manner to a mortar. Instead of dropping the bomb down the barrel, a spring-loaded firing pin initiated the propellant charge in the base of the bomb. Effective range was about 100 metres (328 feet), though 'effective' is not a word normally associated with this weapon! The Panzerfaust was a disposable hollow tube which was tucked under the firer's arm. Raising the sights cocked the weapon. When fired, the backblast cancelled out recoil. Panzerfausts were much preferred by Allied troops to the Bazookas and PIATs available to them.

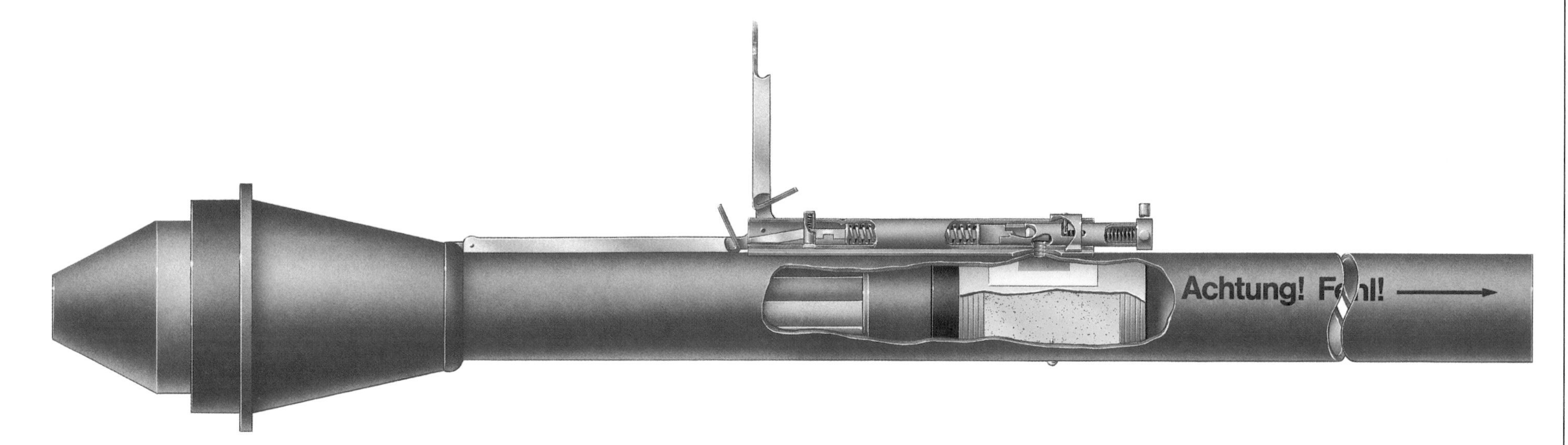

STRENGTHS

- Effective against armour
- Lightweight
- Easy to use

WEAKNESSES

- One shot only
- Awkward to aim
- Low muzzle velocity

Panzerfaust 60

Launcher length: 76.2cm (30in)
Effective range: 60m (197ft)
Weight: 6.8kg (15lb) total
Rocket type: shaped charge: 3kg (6.6lb)
Muzzle velocity: 45mps (148fps)
Armour penetration: 200mm (7.87in)

Second-generation launchers

Wartime experience showed that something more portable and more effective was needed, prompting the creation of a second generation of launchers. It was at this point that the two design philosophies – disposable versus reusable – parted company.

M20 'Super Bazooka'

The United States fielded the M20 'Super Bazooka' just after World War II. This more powerful weapon launches a 3.5in (89mm) rocket with a much larger warhead than its predecessor. Like all such weapons, the Super Bazooka has a minimum range within which its warhead will not arm; at 20 metres (65.6 feet) this is fairly standard. Maximum range is only 100 metres (328 feet), although in truth it is difficult to hit a moving vehicle at much greater ranges with an unguided weapon.

The Super Bazooka will penetrate an unimpressive 250mm (9.84 inches) of armour. It is no longer in service in any NATO nation, although some are still in use with other armed forces. Production continued under licence in Spain and Austria until the 1980s.

B-300

Resembling in many ways the US Bazooka, the B-300 Light Support Weapon is an Israeli development incorporating features from the classic RPG-7. It consists of a reusable launcher/sight assembly and a disposable container/breech for the projectile, which is inserted into the rear of the weapon before firing.

The B-300 weights 8 kilograms (17.64 pounds) with its round aboard, a little less than the Super Bazooka. It is effective to 400 metres (1312 feet) and can penetrate 400mm (15.75 inches) of armour. Users include the US Marine Corps.

M2 'Carl Gustav'

The standard British unguided anti-tank weapon for many years was the M2 recoilless rifle, better known as the Carl Gustav after the Swedish facility where it was first manufactured (and not to be confused with other weapons with that name). An 84mm shoulder-fired weapon, the Carl Gustav is effective out to 450 metres (1476 feet) and can penetrate 400mm (15.75 inches) of armour. It saw use for many years with armed forces worldwide, although it is now no longer in service with most militaries.

The Carl Gustav is a fine weapon whose advantages include a higher rate of fire and better range than many rivals. It is also very versatile and can fire anti-personnel, smoke rounds and flares. However, it is heavy – almost two-and-a-half times the weight of the M20 Super Bazooka – and usually requires a two-man team to load and fire the gun.

RPG-29 Vampir

Similar to the Carl Gustav, the Russian-made RPG-29 (also called 'Vampir') is a light recoilless rifle firing a 105mm shell. The weapon comes with optical and night sights and uses an advanced tandem warhead concept. There is also a single-shot version available, designated RPG-27, which weighs around 3.5 kilograms (7.7 pounds) less.

Tandem warheads are designed to defeat reactive and composite armour by firing a double shaped charge at the same point. Even if the first gas jet is defeated by reactive armour, the second will get through to the steel underneath. The first jet will

B-300

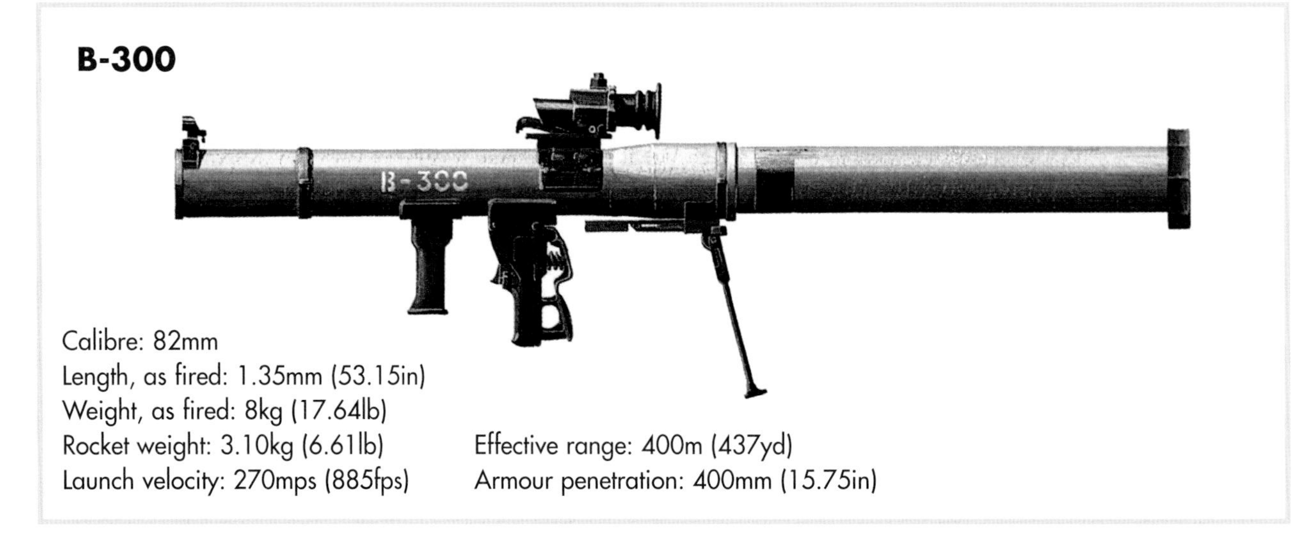

Calibre: 82mm
Length, as fired: 1.35mm (53.15in)
Weight, as fired: 8kg (17.64lb)
Rocket weight: 3.10kg (6.61lb)
Launch velocity: 270mps (885fps)
Effective range: 400m (437yd)
Armour penetration: 400mm (15.75in)

punch through the top layers of a composite defence before being defeated; the second then focuses at the damage point and completes penetration. Tandem warheads are used in some guided weapon systems but are rare in unguided infantry systems.

Panzerfaust 3

Another advanced reusable launcher, the Panzerfaust 3, has been in service with the German army since the mid-1980s. Like the original Panzerfaust, it consists of a reusable launcher and an 'overcalibre' projectile, that is, one that is bigger than the diameter of the launcher.

The Panzerfaust 3 can fire a hollow-charge anti-tank round able to penetrate 700mm (27.5 inches) of armour, a bunker-busting round that can go through 1.6 metres (63 inches) of concrete and a tandem hollow-charge round designed to defeat reactive armour. With built-in telescopic sights the weapon is effective to 500 metres (1640 feet) against bunkers and to about 300 metres (984 feet) against a moving target, such as a tank.

SEP DARD 120

Taking the concept of the man-portable launcher to an extreme, the French produced the DARD 120, a 120mm semi-disposable launcher. Effective out to 600 metres (1969 feet), the 120mm fin-stabilized projectile can punch through more than 500mm (19.69 inches) of armour and offers a realistic chance of taking out a main battle tank from the frontal arc.

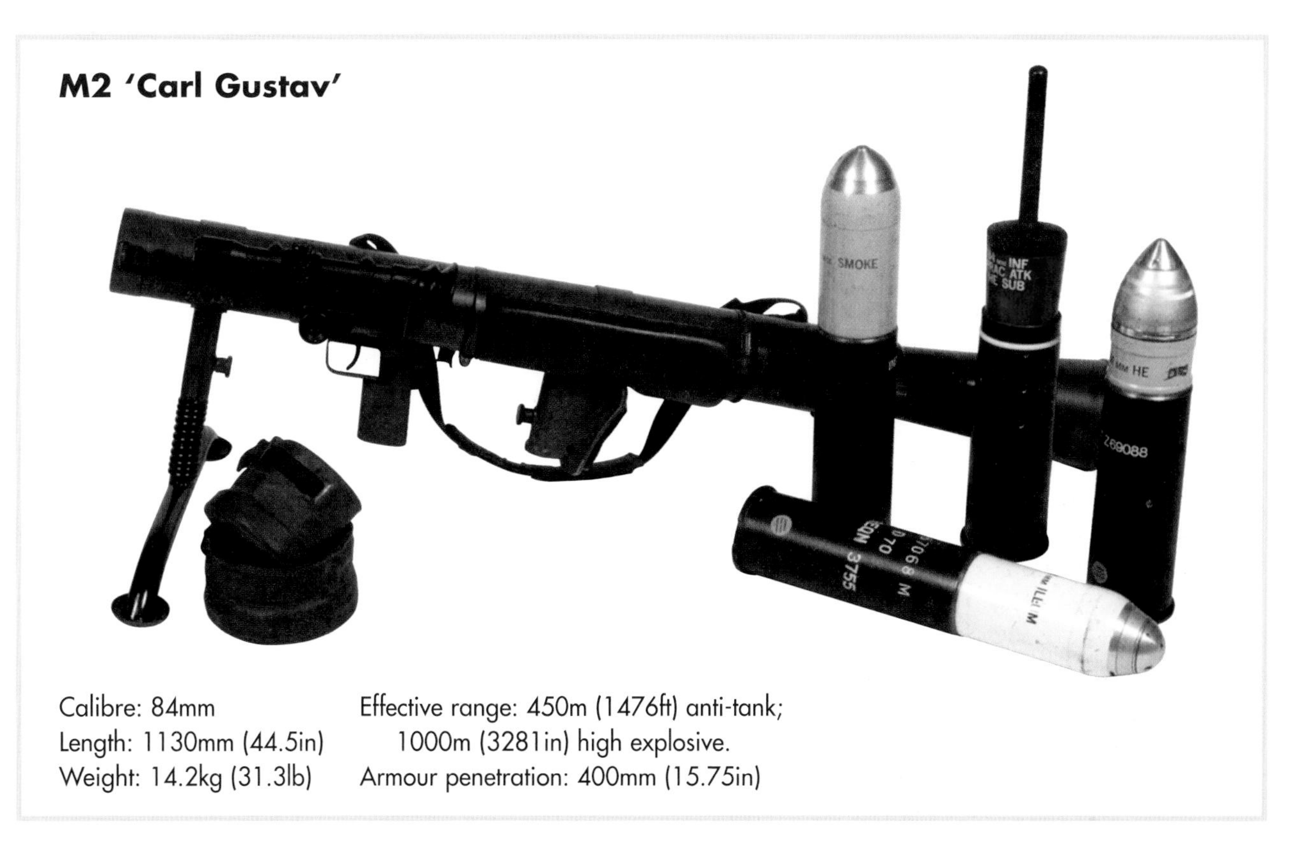

M2 'Carl Gustav'

Calibre: 84mm
Length: 1130mm (44.5in)
Weight: 14.2kg (31.3lb)
Effective range: 450m (1476ft) anti-tank; 1000m (3281in) high explosive.
Armour penetration: 400mm (15.75in)

The reusable launcher, which includes grips and sights, weighs a relatively portable 4.5 kilograms (9.92 pounds); it is the 8.9-kilogram (19.62-pound) round that makes up most of the DARD's mass. Since several rounds must be carried to give a credible anti-tank capability, the user needs support from infantry squadmates who can carry a round each in addition to their own equipment.

Disposable launchers

Disposable, one-shot Light Anti-tank Weapons (LAWs) have the advantage that they are very light and thus can be included in the equipment of any infantry soldier. Of course, they require extra training to be used effectively. Nevertheless, so long as at least one man in a squad has been trained, he can use those carried by his companions and give his unit extra capabilities that might not be otherwise available.

Disposable launchers are, by definition, throwaway items. The round is contained in a cardboard tube, with a minimal flip-up sight and grip assembly. Most have simple cartoon-style instructions on the side, although being able to fire the weapon and being able to hit the target with it may be two very different things.

Left: The British Carl Gustav in action. Weapons of this type not only give infantry the ability to take on tanks but are also useful against bunkers, machine-gun posts and other fortifications. The Carl Gustav is unguided but much easier to carry than a guided missile system.

M72 LAW

Perhaps the most famous of the shoulder-fired disposable LAWs is the M72 LAW. This weapon saw action with American troops in Vietnam and British forces in the Falklands. Early versions of the M72 were rather inaccurate, but improvements to the sight and a more powerful rocket made it effective out to 350 metres (1148 feet). Although the round will go farther than that, perhaps as far as 1000 metres (3281 feet), hitting even a stationary target at such a range is unlikely at best.

The M72 is able to punch through 280mm (11 inches) of steel armour, which was enough in the 1970s but will not defeat a modern tank's armour, especially if it is constructed from advanced composite materials. For this reason the M72 is no longer in use with US or UK forces, although examples turn up in conflicts worldwide. The warhead is quite sufficient to destroy a light vehicle such as an armoured personnel carrier or a reconnaissance vehicle, and LAWs are often used against non-vehicle targets such as bunkers and enemy infantry positions.

Like many such weapons, the M72 LAW has a significant 'backblast' from the rocket motor. It cannot be used from inside a building or vehicle, or with a wall close behind the user, without severe danger to the operator and his companions.

Armbrust 300

The backblast from a LAW makes it a problematical weapon to use under some circumstances and also pinpoints the user for return fire. The German Armbrust ('Crossbow') 300 attempts to solve these problems by using a 'recoilless' configuration.

Newton's laws of motion state that action and reaction are equal and opposite. In practical terms this means that for every bullet that is fired, the gun kicks back the other way; every rocket creates a trail of hot gas behind it. There are ways to reduce 'felt' recoil but physics is a harsh master – if something comes out of the front of a weapon, there must be flash, recoil or something else coming out of the back.

The Armbrust is no exception, but what comes out of the back of the weapon is a shower of plastic flakes that individually have little momentum. This means that the 'danger space' behind an Armbrust is only 1 metre (3.28 feet), and there is no rocket plume or disturbance to give away the firer's position. The Armbrust 300 thus has a very low visible signature and virtually no recoil. Its construction also results in low noise at firing, roughly equivalent to a .22 pistol. Despite this, the weapon delivers a high-explosive warhead out to an effective range of 300 metres (984 feet); this can penetrate 300mm (11.81 inches) of steel armour.

Panzerfaust 3

Calibre: 90, 110 or 125mm overcalibre
Length: 1.35m (4.43ft)
Weight of launcher: 9kg (19.84lb)
Effective range: 500m (1640ft)
Armour penetration: 700mm (27.56in)
Muzzle velocity: 160mps (525fps)

RPG-18 and RPG-22

As ever in the world of armaments, once a weapon has been introduced others will copy or develop the concept. The Soviet armies always considered that the most important system in their arsenal was the anti-tank weapon, and ensured that every unit, of every type, could fight tanks if necessary. One weapon for this purpose, the classic RPG-7, has already been discussed. The RPG-18, however, looks more like a copy of the M72A2 than a development of the RPG-7.

Right: The German Panzerfaust 3 antitank weapon is conceptually quite similar to the original Panzerfaust and the RPG-7, consisting of an overcalibre rocket propelled projectile and a launcher. It can fire anti-bunker rounds as well as antitank projectiles.

Right: The French APILAS LAW strains the bounds of the term 'light' anti-tank weapon, but it does have a warhead that can hurt even a main battle tank.

Hard targets

British forces made effective use of rocket launchers against a wide range of targets during the Falklands conflict.

In May 1982, a team of SAS commandos used M72 LAWs to destroy Argentinian aircraft as they lay in the airfield, while in April 1982 soldiers used a Carl Gustav M2 and several 66mm LAWs to inflict significant damage on an Argentinian corvette.

The RPG-18 consists of a telescoping tube that contains the projectile and acts as the breech and launching tube. Simple flip-up sights allow aiming out to about 200 metres (656 feet) and there are cartoon instructions on the side of the tube.

The weapon fires a 64mm warhead capable of penetrating 375mm (14.76 inches) of armour – ineffective against a modern tank but useful against lighter armour or bunkers. The rocket is fin-stabilized and does not arm until it has travelled 20 metres (65.6 feet) from the launcher. The RPG-18 achieved considerable market success. At the time of the break-up of the Warsaw Pact several member nations were producing this weapon, so it is likely that large numbers still exist even if production has ceased. A 72mm version also exists, having been in production since the mid-1980s under the designation RPG-22.

APILAS 112mm LAW

The French APILAS is a heavyweight disposable LAW firing a 112mm rocket that can penetrate more than 720mm (28.4 inches) of armour. The launcher and rocket together weigh around 9 kilograms (19.84 pounds).

This weapon is unusual not only for its very large warhead but also owing to the light-intensification sight it carries as standard. This raises the unit cost but does make the weapon more effective at night. As well as France, the launcher has been adopted by Finland, Italy and Jordan.

LAW 80

One of the biggest disposable weapon systems ever developed, the British LAW 80 stretches the definition of 'light' anti-tank weapons to its extreme. The weapon's large 94mm warhead is capable of punching through more than 700mm (27.6 inches) of armour, giving it a fighting chance against a main battle tank.

With an effective range of 500 metres (1640 feet), the LAW 80 might outrange the ability of the average soldier to hit the target with it. To overcome this the weapon carries a built-in spotting rifle, which fires tracer rounds to assist in aiming. Weighing 10 kilograms (22 pounds) and stretching 1.5 metres (4.9 feet) when unfolded, this is certainly a monster of a 'light' anti-tank weapon, but it can do the job where lesser weapons may be inadequate. Even the backblast from the LAW 80 is awesome – the danger area behind the launcher as it fires stretches for 20 metres (65 feet).

Tactical uses

Although invented to engage tanks, LAWs are useful general-purpose weapons that can take out bunkers, strongpoints or indeed anything that is vulnerable to a high-explosive warhead. LAWs represent a cost-effective alternative to a close assault on occasions when infantry need to remove a sniper or dug-in machine gun. Their sheer usefulness means that they are used for roles for which they were never designed.

Today, with terrorists becoming increasingly inventive in the ways they attack, considerable credence is given to the 'two guys on a jetski' threat, since such an approach would allow an RPG-7 or similar weapon to be launched at a naval ship at very close range. If this seems far-fetched, a considerable amount of expensive research has gone into finding ways to track and, if necessary, target a jetski using a warship's sensors – something that a few years ago seemed unlikely to be necessary. Similar concern exists over the use of seemingly innocent vehicles to approach a target, at which point a devastating attack can be launched using disposable launchers or LAWs.

Further developments

The disposable launcher concept can also be used to deliver warheads other than anti-tank explosives. Both incendiary and smoke rounds, among others, can be used, giving infantry a measure of effective self-support capability, although at the cost of increased weight and bulk.

Right: A British soldier aims a LAW 80 with the aid of the launcher's integral 9mm spotting rifle, which fires tracer rounds for guidance. Once he has fired, his position will be very obvious due to the weapon's massive backblast.

HAFLA-35L

One variant on the LAW concept is the HAFLA-35L. This is essentially a disposable tube containing a small (35mm) rocket-propelled grenade weapon with a phosphorus incendiary payload rather than high explosive. Intended for use against 'soft' targets such as personnel, the HAFLA has an effective range of 70 metres (230 feet). The HAFLA is light, weighing just 600 grams (1.32 pounds), and can be used by raiding forces to cause cost-effective mayhem without being too much of a burden.

M202A1 Flame Weapon

The changing attitude to launchers is indicated by the adoption of the M202A1 Flame Weapon by US forces as a replacement for backpack flamethrowers. The M202A1 is a four-shot reusable launcher with an effective range of up to 500 metres (1640 feet), far greater than a conventional jet flamethrower. Its 66mm projectiles burst over a radius of 15 metres (49.2 feet) and are reloaded as a 'clip' of four rounds.

Follow-through grenades

The basic concept behind the C90's bunker-busting round, with its breaching warhead and secondary fragmentation grenade, dates back to World War II. The suggestion then was that a shaped charge could be used to blow a hole in a tank's armour large enough for a secondary gas or fragmentation grenade to enter and detonate inside. The thoery was sound but a reliable prototype was never successfully developed.

Tear gas rounds were developed as an alternative to incendiaries for the M202A1, and it is possible that a range of warheads such as smoke, high explosive and, of course, anti-armour rounds could be fielded.

This may be the way all shoulder-fired rocket weapons are headed; a range of warheads for different purposes, even though that would mean carrying a number of different disposable launchers. This means more weight than different projectiles for a single launcher, but it does allow troops to be issued with a mission-tailored load of cheap, disposable support weapons.

RPO Rys

The Russian RPO Rys ('Lynx') is a similar concept to the M202A1: a reusable launcher firing a 122mm napalm round. Like the M202A1, it was introduced to replace backpack flamethrowers, although Rys has itself been replaced in service by Shmel.

RPO-A Shmel

Another Russian invention, the RPO-A Shmel ('Bumblebee') is a disposable 93mm weapon that utilizes an advanced enhanced blast (thermobaric) warhead. Introduced in 1985, Shmel has seen use in Chechnya and Afghanistan, where its area blast effect was shown to be equivalent to a 120mm artillery shell. Incendiary (RPO-Z) and phosphorus/smoke (RPO-D) versions are also available.

The incendiary version of Shmel has replaced Rys in service with the Russian armed forces; it seems that a family of disposable weapons suited the Russian army's needs better than a reusable weapon.

Right: A US soldier in Vietnam aims his M72 LAW. The M72 was, in its day, an excellent weapon. It does not pose a real threat to modern tanks, but remains useful against lighter vehicles and bunkers. Simple, lightweight weapons of this type are unlikely ever to go out of fashion.

C90-CR

It seems that everything today is gaining extra features and capabilities. Weapon systems have followed the trend. Many elegant weapons end up so burdened with technical extras that they become too unreliable or bulky for their intended role. However, this is not always the case. Some extras are useful without being bulky or expensive, and so it is with the Spanish C90-CR disposable anti-tank launcher.

Disposable weapons cannot be fitted with too many bells and whistles before they become too expensive to use, but the C90-CR's extras are just enough to enhance capability without excess cost. The weapon is sighted using a 1.8x optical scope, with tritium dots built in to assist in poor light.

Different versions of the weapon are available, each carrying a different warhead: anti-tank, fragmentation/anti-personnel, smoke/incendiary and a tandem anti-bunker round. The latter uses a breaching warhead to penetrate the bunker, allowing the secondary, fragmentation, warhead to detonate within. The C90 has an effective range of 300 metres (984 feet) against tanks and up to 800 metres (2625 feet) in the anti-personnel role. It is recoilless and has no electrical components.

This family of disposable support weapons may represent the future of the LAW: versatile and with enough capability to be useful without the excessive extras that price many weapons out of the market.

GLOSSARY

Battery – Descriptive term for when a cartridge is in place and the gun is ready for firing.

Bolt – The part of a firearm which usually contains the firing pin or striker and which closes the breech ready for firing.

Blowback – Operating system in which the bolt is not locked to the breech, thus it is consequently pushed back by breech pressure on firing and cycles the gun.

Breech – The rear of the gun barrel.

Breech-block – Another method of closing the breech which generally involves a substantial rectangular block rather than a cylindrical bolt.

Bullpup – Term for when the receiver of a gun is actually set in the butt behind the trigger group, thus allowing for a full length barrel.

Carbine – A shortened rifle for specific assault roles.

Chamber – The section at the end of the barrel which receives and seats the cartridge ready for firing.

Closed Bolt – A mechanical system in which the bolt is closed up to the cartridge before the trigger is pulled. This allows greater stability through reducing the forward motion of parts on firing.

Compensator – A muzzle attachment which controls the direction of gas expanding from the weapon and thus helps to resist muzzle climb or swing during automatic fire.

Delayed Blowback – A delay mechanically imposed on a blowback system to allow pressures in the breech to drop to safe levels before breech opening.

Double action – Relates to pistols which can be fired both by cocking the hammer and then pulling the trigger, and by a single long pull on the trigger which performs both cocking and firing actions.

Flechette – An bolt-like projectile which is smaller than the gun's calibre and requires a sabot to fit it to the barrel. Flechette rounds achieve very high velocities.

Gas Operation – Operating system in which a gun is cycled by gas being bled off from the barrel and used against a piston or the bolt to drive the bolt backwards and cycle the gun for the next round.

GPMG – Abbreviation for General Purpose Machine Gun. A versatile light machine gun intended to perform a range of different roles.

LMG – Abbreviation for Light Machine Gun.

Locking – Describes the various methods by which the bolt or breech block is locked behind the chamber ready for firing.

Long Recoil – A method of recoil operation in which the barrel and bolt recoil for a length greater than that of the entire cartridge, during which extraction and loading are performed.

Muzzle Brake – A muzzle attachment which diverts muzzle blast sideways and thus reduces overall recoil.

Open Bolt – A mechanical system in which the bolt is kept at a distance from the cartridge before the trigger is pulled. This allows for better cooling of the weapon between shots.

PDW – Abbreviation for Personal Defence Weapon. A compact firearm, smaller than a regular assault rifle but more powerful than a pistol, intended as a defensive weapon for personnel whose duties do not normally include small arms combat.

Receiver – The body of the weapon which contains the gun's main operating parts.

Recoil – The rearward force generated by the explosive power of a projectile being fired.

Recoil Operated – Operating system in which the gun is cycled by the recoil-propelled force of both barrel and bolt when the weapon is fired. Both components recoil together for a certain distance before the barrel stops and the bolt continues backwards to perform reloading and rechambering.

SAW – Abbreviation for Squad Automatic Weapon.

Self-loading – Operating system in which one pull of the trigger allows the gun to fires and reload in a single action.

Shaped Charge – An anti-armour charge designed to concentrate the effect of an explosive warhead by focusing a cone of superheated gas on a critical point on the target.

Short Recoil – A compressed version of recoil operation in which the barrel and bolt move back less than the length of the cartridge before the bolt detaches and continues backwards to perform reloading and rechambering.

Calibre conversion chart

The calibre designations of different types of ammunition can be confusing; traditionally, weapons developed in the US are given calibres in inches while those developed in Europe are given calibres in millimetres. The weapons then retain these calibre designations, regardless of who is using the weapon. The tables below give conversions for the 'standard' metric and imperial calibres.

Imperial to Metric		Metric to Imperial	
inches	**mm**	**mm**	**inches**
.22	5.58	4.25	.167
.243	6.17	5.5	.216
.25	6.35	5.6	.22
.257	6.52	6	.236
.276	7.0	6.35	.250
.280	7.11	7.5	.295
.303	7.7	7.62	.300
.308	7.82	7.65	.301
.32	8.13	7.92	.312
.357	9.06	8.0	.314
.375	9.53	8.5	.334
.38	9.65	9.0	.354
.44	11.12	9.3	.366
.45	11.43	10.6	.417
.455	11.55	11.5	.452
.50	12.7	12.0	.472
.577	14.6	15.0	.590

INDEX

Page numbers in *italics* refer to picture captions.